FARMING THE EDGE OF THE SEA

Farming the Edge of the Sea

E. S. Iversen

Fishing News (Books) Ltd.
110 Fleet Street
London, E.C.4

639·2
547,862

Made and printed in Great Britain by
The Garden City Press Limited
Letchworth, Hertfordshire

57h

COVER PICTURE

Oyster farming Australian style. Two-year-old oysters, still attached to their anchor-sticks, are transferred 160 miles south from Port Stephens to George's River in New South Wales. The sticks are nailed to racks and the oysters rapidly grow to maturity. Oysters from this Australian State are famous for their distinctive flavour.

Contents

VI. Evaluation

Fig.

List of Illustrations

Fig.   *page*

Foreword

MORE than half of the surface of planet Earth is buried beneath a mile depth of seawater. The surface of this water receives the major part of the solar radiation reaching the earth and is thus potentially capable of providing a great deal more food than the land itself. It seems appropriate, therefore, that we give serious attention to the possibilities of increasing our exploitation of the living resources of the ocean. At the very least, we should give to this task the amount of finances, scientific manpower and thought that we are currently giving to outer space exploration, a dubious venture that promises relatively little scientific return and no useful resources, but merely the superficial satisfaction of competing for prestige.

In the exploration of inner space we must not be led into the same wild adventures that characterize the outer space effort. Rather, we should continually re-examine the imaginative dreams of large-scale sea farming, fish husbandry and the like, in the light of our advancing knowledge. This does not mean that we should curb our imagination. It means that we must try to reduce the products of imagination to practical workable schemes. Dr. Iversen has done well to produce a book which brings us back to earth.

F. G. WALTON SMITH

Preface

In my work at the University of Miami Institute of Marine Sciences, I receive many inquiries about sea farming. Is sea farming practical? Can I make money at it? Where can I get information on sea farming? How can I prepare myself for such a venture? How much would it cost to get set up in business as a sea farmer? People in all walks of life, most of whom are engaged in businesses totally unrelated to the sea, and corporations interested in product diversification, are asking these questions. My experience with such queries is not unique. The same questions are being asked, with increasing frequency, at the governmental fishery laboratories in the United States and doubtlessly in most countries throughout the world.

This book is an attempt to answer these questions. It is not a handbook, nor a "how-to" book. It reviews important principles of sea farming for anyone who is interested in general works on the sea. More important, it will help those readers who have more specific interests to determine, for instance, what their chances for success in fish farming are after taking into account their qualifications and financial resources. In addition, for more detail, the reader is directed to specialized books and reports. Marine and brackish water algae, mollusks, crustaceans, and fishes presently being cultivated are discussed, including important facts about their life histories, and their suitability for farming is evaluated.

This volume emphasizes farming activities in the developed nations in temperate and subtropical waters of the Northern Hemisphere. Significant differences exist between the temperate and tropical zones in factors affecting sea farming, such as economic conditions, species available for farming, and climate. Increasing food production is important in both the wealthy and the developing nations. In the wealthy nations, demand for more variety in diet develops as wealth increases and as education, incentive, and technical knowledge improve living standards. In poor countries, there is quite a different problem—the production of badly-needed, inexpensive protein food. In these developing countries extensive economical and social studies are required, first, to stimulate a demand for seafood, second, to determine how best to produce it, and finally, how to arrange for its distribution. In the wealthy nations the avenues for distribution already exist, but the application of recent technological advances to supply this demand with an improved product is needed. Too, the demand (which is already high) may be greatly increased by promotion.

Another striking difference between sea farming in temperate and tropical areas is the availability of land and land values. In the wealthy countries there is an ever-increasing demand for salt marshes to be used for housing, industrial development, and recreation; consequently, land values are high. In some regions, land is so expensive that almost any farming scheme involving use of estuarine areas is doomed to failure unless profits are high. In the undeveloped countries, however, where the land value of estuaries is low, ventures in sea farming that produce even small profits can and do succeed.

Discussion is further restricted to estuaries and near-shore waters, as opposed to deep, offshore waters, because it is in these former areas where most sea farming is being practiced and where immediate future potential exists.

I have emphasized the biological aspects of sea farming. I am not an economist, and the general observations on this aspect should be evaluated accordingly.

As an aid to the non-scientist, some of the specialized terms used are defined in the glossary. Conversions from the metric system to the English system are approximate.

Experts have been most helpful by reading portions of this manuscript and offering comments and criticism. Grateful acknowledgment of assistance is made to Mr. William W. Anderson, Dr. John S. Bunt, Dr. Donald P. de Sylva, Mr. James Ellis, Dr. John R. Hendrickson, Dr. Elmer R. Noble, Mr. William M. Stephens, and Mr. David H. Wallace. Dr. de Sylva read a version of the entire manuscript, and Mr. Ellis and Dr. Hendrickson read part; all have suggested helpful improvements in organization, style, and accuracy. Mrs. E. Elizabeth Owen and Mrs. Jean Bradfisch made useful comments on organization and style in versions of the manuscript.

Many others persons, too numerous to mention individually, have gone to considerable inconvenience to provide photographs and information. I am grateful for their cooperation.

To my wife, Jane, who worked diligently throughout the preparation of this book and provided confidence and encouragement, goes my everlasting gratitude.

E. S. I.

Coral Gables, Florida
U.S.A.

I
GENERAL

CHAPTER I

Why Farm the Sea ?

Schemes to farm coastal waters are old. Most records are lost in antiquity, but some show that oysters were raised by the Japanese as early as 2000 B.C. and by the Romans about 100 B.C. In Java, laws to protect milk-fish farmers from fish thieves were established as early as A.D. 1400. Although farming marine and brackish waters is an old, old occupation, it has progressed little over the centuries. Subsistence farming of these waters in the tropics is practiced today almost as it was in the distant past. This is not surprising for in many of these tropical countries most industries change very slowly. The striking two-page illustration overleaf shows the pond development in a Javan estuary.

The striking gap between the extent and techniques of sea farming and modern technology exists in the wealthy countries in the temperate and subtropic latitudes. Marine and brackish-water farming is neglected in the very countries that have the means to do it most successfully, for these countries possess the scientific knowledge and the latest equipment to cut production costs and increase efficiency. There is also great demand in these wealthy countries for the species which can be cultivated, such as oysters, mussels, and shrimp.

Why are there few fish and shellfish farms in the coastal waters of wealthy nations ? The reasons for this limited farming are complex as will become evident in subsequent chapters. In part, development has been retarded by a lack of biological knowledge and because other cheap and abundant sources of fish and land-grown food have been available to feed the growing human populations. This situation is now changing rapidly toward a favorable atmosphere for more extensive sea farming.

Present Seafood Demand

Quite clearly the future role of sea farming depends on the demand for seafood. Housewives in the advanced countries can choose seafood from a variety of frozen and fresh forms. They no longer must buy whole fish that have to be cleaned and scaled; the fish they buy requires little preparation and is attractively packaged (see *Fig. 2*). This revolution in marketing is relatively recent, yet it has had a considerable impact on seafood consumption. In the United States more than half the employed women are married, and a working wife who has little time to prepare meals is interested in shortcuts.

The demand for seafood is increasing markedly due to advertising. Shrimp has been promoted relentlessly in the United States, and the effort has paid off in a greatly increased demand for it. On a per capita basis,

Fig. 1. Vast areas in tropical countries are devoted to brackish water farming. These ponds (tambaks) form a crazy-quilt pattern in an estuary in east Java (next page).

(*W. H. Schuster*)

Fig. 2. Farm-raised fresh water trout are boned, dressed, and wrapped in plastic. Pan-ready fish in attractive packages demand a high price.   (*Snake River Trout Co.*)

consumers are eating about twice as much shrimp today as they were just after World War II.

The wider and more rapid distribution of fishery products due to the better handling methods developed in recent years is also undoubtedly responsible for a greater demand in many countries. Better highways and more efficiently refrigerated carriers are responsible for a fresher and cheaper product to entice families who might never have eaten seafood, or may have had it only occasionally, to eat it regularly.

The evidence that is accumulating from medical research showing that the unsaturated oils present in seafood provide special health benefits makes seafood more attractive to the consumer. The relationship between the amount of serum cholesterol in humans and cardiovascular diseases is still uncertain; of at least six factors related to these diseases, high blood cholesterol is one. The chance of an individual having arteriosclerosis is affected by age, sex, and heredity. Overweight and high blood cholesterol are contributing factors in each case and are the only ones that can be controlled as preventive methods. Seafood, when eaten regularly, serves to reduce the intake of saturated fats.

Research sponsored by the United States National Institute of Health shows that in some shellfish substances called paolins apparently depress tumor growth and also possess antibacterial and antiviral effects. If these health benefits demonstrated in laboratory animals can be confirmed, seafood should be even more attractive to the consumer. Even without such additional benefits, seafood is a nutrition food high in vitamins, minerals, and proteins.

Thus, from many different directions—improved packaging, intensive promotion, and scientific studies into the nutritional value of seafood— has come increased consumption of seafood in recent years.

Future Seafood Demand

All predictions of future population trends forecast rapid increases; in the United States alone the population is expected to be about 250 million people by 1975. With the greater populations there will be, of course, a greater market for food, including seafood. The increase in consumer purchasing power characteristic of wealthier countries increases the demand for seafood. In countries with depressed economies diet is limited, but as income increases, people eat a wider variety of foods, thus encouraging the consumption of seafood. The 1965 figure for fish consumption of about 4·5 kilograms (10 pounds) per capita in the United States is expected to double by 1970.

New means of preserving fish can have a profound effect on per capita fish consumption. Irradiation, a technique which doubles or triples storage life under refrigeration, looks promising. One of these cold pasteurization processes uses cobalt-60 to destroy harmful bacteria, achieving the same result as heat in milk pasteurization. Since fresh fish appeal more to the housewife than fish in other forms, irradiation will provide fresh fish where they were formerly unavailable, as in the mid-continental areas. Additional experimentation is under way to be certain that no harm to man results from eating irradiated fish.

Although the United States buys fish from many foreign countries, it is by no means the greatest fish producer. United States production slipped from second place in 1938 to fifth place in 1963. Since about 1945, the United States has imported increasingly larger quantities of seafood to meet its demand. From 1950 to 1962 domestic foodfish production dropped 24 per cent and the United States population rose about 23 per cent, while in the same period imports of foodfish grew over 100 per cent. Americans are not eating less fish, but more of the fish they eat comes from foreign countries.

The demand for fishery products is growing in nearly all countries in the Northern Hemisphere and will undoubtedly continue to be filled, in part, by imports. Because of this, fish farmers must compete with both domestic and foreign fishermen for a share of the market. Can they do this successfully ? The operation and general trends of both inshore and offshore fisheries, and the attempts at their management through regulation in nearly all countries, show the potential production from these sources and the factors that prevent making low-priced seafood available to the consumer. The future of sea farming, therefore, depends greatly on the future of fisheries.

The Plight of Inshore Fisheries

Many of the difficulties facing the inshore fishermen are imposed on him by unrealistic regulations that improve the position of sea farming by increasing production costs of fish obtained by fishing, and by causing instability of supply. Thus, sea farming is placed on better ground in the competition for a part of the market.

Many fishing vessel skippers miss those "good old days" when fishing was much more lucrative—not that there are fewer fish now, but they say there are so many more boats that it is often a struggle for any one of them to bring home a decent catch.

Of course, those good old days always tend to take on a rosy hue with the passage of years; occasional big catches are remembered, but the pulling up of empty nets is forgotten. However, fishing records demonstrate that catches in many inshore fisheries throughout the world have decreased, while at the same time the number of fishermen and units of gear has increased. Certainly if more fishermen fish on a limited stock of fish, it follows that individual fishermen must get fewer fish for the same effort. *Fig. 3* shows the heavy concentration of fishing craft that occurs in waters fished by European fleets.

The more competitive fishermen respond to reduction in catches by attempting to increase their efficiency. This is evident in the conversion of Gulf of Mexico shrimp boats from a large single net operation to smaller double-net operation, and in the introduction of the power block, a device to retrieve large purse seines used to catch salmon and menhaden more efficiently. The conversion from hook-and-line fishing in the tuna fleet of the eastern Pacific to purse seine fishing is further evidence of the increased competition in today's fisheries. Fishermen who were slow to change their ways in the past must increase their efficiency in order to survive.

When the individual fisherman's catches decrease, a great cry arises from the fishing industry. Government officials attempt to correct the situation by placing regulations or limitations on the fishermen. Many regulations are purposely designed to cause inefficiency. An example of such a regulation is one that prohibits the use of nylon fish nets. For years, gillnets were made of linen and cotton. Then nylon came along. After some initial trials in which fishermen were pleased with the new gear, tests were made in Canada and the United States, and greater efficiency was demonstrated by the nylon gillnet over linen and cotton nets. As a result of this finding, and the concern of possible overfishing, regulations against the use of this netting were put into effect all along the west coast of North America. Such regulations which have as their main purpose the conservation of a species of fish, but using inefficiency as a tool, can do nothing more than raise the price of the produce to the consumer.

Fig. 3. Increasingly, ever bigger fishing fleets have reduced profits to individual fishermen because of stiffer competition for available fish. Picture shows an Icelandic port wholly devoted to catching and processing fish.

(*Brady, Fishing News International*)

These problems, recognized decades ago yet still unsolved, will probably continue to be unsolved for many more years. This places the inshore fisheries in a position of producing a costly product due to a high degree of inefficiency, and makes the marketing of seafood from sea farms more attractive.

Complications in International Fisheries

So far we have considered problems of domestic fisheries only. For those fisheries in which many nations participate, the outlook is also for lower catches and higher prices.

There has been an upsurge in sea farming research recently, even by the traditionally great fishing nations which exploit international waters. The United Kingdom is again attempting to inexpensively mass-rear plaice, sole, and even some mollusks and crustaceans, with a view to increasing their seafood supply. These expensive experiments are going ahead despite the overwhelming failures of American and European fish culturists in the past to supplement commercial marine fish catches on an economic basis. As early as the turn of the century the value of artificial hatching and rearing was questioned, but no scientific evidence bearing on this question became available until the 1950s when man found that his efforts to seed the oceans did not begin to match natural propagation.

Fig. 4. The great fishing nations of the world are modernizing their fleets and are going farther to sea to satisfy their needs for sea food. This is a typical British all-freezer distant water stern trawler costing over $1,500,000.   (*Fishing News*)

Why are English scientists today experimentally rearing plaice to "postage-stamp" size and releasing them into fenced-off bays to be harvested when they have reached marketable size? Part of the reason is because biologists and fisheries administrators who have served on international commissions, some for up to twenty-five years, see little or no hope of arriving at solutions to fishery problems acceptable to all nations or all fishery interests. They believe sea farming is necessary to supplement sea fishing.

Unilateral action has been taken by many nations to protect their own sea fishermen, mostly in the form of declarations of territorial sea areas over which these nations believe they have proprietary jurisdiction. The 1958 and 1960 Conferences on Law of the Sea failed to solve the width of territorial seas and many nations still have not even adopted the Convention agreed upon at these conferences.

The sharp increase in fishing effort through the development of all-freeze trawlers (see *Fig. 4*) by great fishing nations of the world and the need to supply food to the protein-starved peoples in poor countries have, in recent years, posed more complex international problems concerning fisheries than have been known in the past. The entrance into the world fisheries by the newly independent countries has complicated the regulation of high seas fisheries designed to prevent over-fishing of the stocks. International commissions have been set up to study and resolve these problems.

Two older commissions, the International Pacific Salmon Commission and the International Pacific Halibut Commission, have fulfilled part of their stated objectives by increasing biological yields. The success of these two commissions is partly due to several reasons, including these three: only two nations are involved, both with similar cultures and markets (Canada and the United States); fishing is done almost exclusively for a single species of fish (halibut in one case and sockeye salmon in another, although since 1957 pink salmon has been added to the responsibility of the I.P.S.C.); and communication problems are somewhat mitigated by the geographic nearness of the two nations.

Many other international organizations have been notably unsuccessful. The International Commission for the Northwest Atlantic Fisheries involves twelve nations fishing on at least seven species of fish, and little progress has been made towards solutions to the manifold problems which arise.

United States fishery interests were shocked by the 200-mile limit set for territorial waters by Peru, Ecuador, and Chile, yet in the International North Pacific Fisheries Commission the United States is pressing for prohibition of Japanese high-seas fishing of sockeye salmon from mid-Pacific (175 degrees W) to the west coast of North America. Studies on the migration of the Pacific sockeye salmon being exploited have suggested that the majority of this stock occurring in the northeastern half of the Pacific Ocean originated from North American streams and will return to spawn there.

In time, nations fishing the open sea may cooperate to increase the stocks of commercial marine animals by restricting fishing effort. However, the past record does not provide hope for cooperation any time soon, but implies that nations, instead of attempting to reach an international settlement, will attempt to out-fish each other. This only increases the rate of decline of stocks subject to the effects of heavy fishing.

Whaling serves as an excellent example of poor international conservation. Whales in the Northern Hemisphere were heavily overfished as early as 1900. Thirty years later, modern gear brought the supply of whales in the Southern Hemisphere to the danger point. An International Whaling Convention was signed in 1931 in an effort to halt the decline in whale stocks. By 1964 the Convention agreed that the blue whale should not be fished at all since it was near extinction, yet the member nations, with their special interests, continued to fish this whale. This Convention failed dismally in its objectives. Attempts to manage this valuable resource probably will not come about, if ever, until the whales are at a dangerously low level, so low that it is unprofitable to fish even the most undesirable species of whale. If effective regulations are agreed upon, recovery in the whale fisheries will be slow because whales grow slowly and have a low reproductive potential.

Problems which affect each country differently can arise in international fisheries because of the diverse gear, ships, and market requirements of individual nations. Experience shows that the large fishing nations of the world find it difficult or more often, fail completely, to reach agreements on their differences which are acceptable to all concerned. Because wise use is not being made of these resources the possibility and eventuality of sea farming production to supplement reduced fish catches, is worthy of careful consideration.

Dr. J. Shelbourne, Fisheries Laboratory, Lowestoft, England, in discussing the future of artificial propagation of marine fish, points out that although nations still rely on wild stocks for supplies, there is growing

Fig. 5. Although many species of fish form large schools, the vastness of the oceans requires that considerable time be spent searching for them.
(United States Bureau of Commercial Fisheries)

awareness of their inadequacies; further, he believes that these inadequacies will lead to farming and domestication of more sea fishes on an industrial scale. This applies even to the great fishing nations.

One factor that adds greatly to the price of fishes caught in the offshore fisheries is the time spent searching for fish schools. It is frequently the major part of a fishing trip. In the United States, as long ago as the 1920s, marine biologists and the fishing industry began to use aircraft as a way to increase production because of its special advantages over conventional searching by vessels. The pilot-observer can scan large areas quickly, can locate schools at greater depths, and can provide accurate information on their movements. Detection from the air is limited to fishes that form large schools close to the surface, for example, menhaden off the United States Atlantic coast and the Gulf of Mexico, and tuna and salmon off the Pacific coast. It is a successful, though costly, practice. *Fig. 5* shows a school of menhaden being seine-netted after aerial location.

In a recent attempt to find a cheaper method for searching than the conventional aircraft or helicopters, the United States Bureau of Commercial Fisheries experimented with a hot-air balloon. The balloon costs about $4,000 and can carry two men aloft in winds up to about twelve knots. The balloons are easily stored aboard vessels and by improvement they may become useful in spotting fish.

SONAR (SOund Navigation And Ranging), first used by the United States Navy during World War II to detect submarines, is another device which helps fishermen to find fish. Since about 1950 fishing skippers have been able to watch Sonar screens to determine the distance and direction a fish school is from their vessels.

Unfortunately, these devices, too, are very expensive to buy and maintain and add to the cost of fish produced. This in turn allows sea farmers a better opportunity to compete for a share of the market.

Advantages and Feasibility of Sea Farming

One principal advantage to farming fish is that it is possible to stabilize supply. To function efficiently, any industry requires a continuous supply of raw material. Interruptions in the flow of raw material are costly. The supply of fish frequently is one of glut or scarcity because of natural fluctuations in stocks of fish. In Alaska, salmon, for example, usually migrate into the fishing areas near the coast in runs that may last only a few weeks at a time. Man-power and equipment to harvest this run must be mustered and ready to go at the start of the run. When the run is over, there are idle machines and unemployment for many people until the next run; fishermen and cannery workers must find other employment for the remainder of the year or go on relief.

On the other hand, in fish farms accurate assessments of the stock size on hand can usually be made and the stock can be harvested as needed. The fish harvested from farms can remain fresh up to shortly before they reach the consumer and need not be iced or frozen for long periods as is the case in some fisheries. A considerable improvement in quality is possible. European and American oysters and clams grown on farms are of better quality and bring higher prices than those fished on public grounds. For example, the average price per pound of oysters fished on public grounds in New England for the period of 1950–63 was about $0.43, while the price for those reared on private farms was about $0.48.

Successful Trout Farms

Success of fresh water trout farming provides a good example of successfully overcoming high production costs (principally costs of food and labor) associated with fish farming by developing a high quality product (*Fig. 6*). Trout are being successfully raised commercially in France, Scandinavia, the United States, and Japan. In France there are reported to be over 200 farms, some of which receive government subsidies. Denmark, one of the world's leading producers of trout, has more than 500 trout farms. These farms receive no government subsidy. They have a form of cooperative which supports biologists who are on call to help solve disease and other problems when needed. Sea fish provide an inexpensive, plentiful supply of food for the trout. In the United States commercial trout farms include direct selling of the fish as food, farms where sport fishermen pay to fish, and marketing eggs and fingerlings. In Japan, trout reared using silkworm pupae, are exported to other countries. Over 990 metric tons (1,000 tons) of Japanese trout were sold in the United States alone during 1962. Where Japanese carp has dropped in importance since World War II, trout has increased due to the greater demand in the American market, and has spurred the development of pelleted feeds.

Some Predictions

Although seafood is only a fraction of total food consumed, demand for seafood in wealthy countries can be expected to rise because the human

Fig. 6. This successful fresh water trout farm markets a high quality product. Through large tanks in the foreground, water is changed every 20 minutes. Each tank produces an average of 150,000 pounds of trout per year.

(*Snake River Trout Co.*)

population is increasing. Effective sales promotion and new handling and marketing techniques, coupled with higher standards of living, can also be expected to increase the per head consumption of seafood. The sea can produce required seafood for years to come, especially if less desirable species can be marketed. The fishing industries in many countries are in a bad position and are heading for darker days of reduced harvests. This subsequently increases the price to consumers. The local limitations on fishing that masquerade as conservation must be replaced with legislation to assist the efficient fishermen, but this probably will not be solved soon. After all, over the many decades during which regulations have been imposed, few have been helpful toward producing greater yields more cheaply. It will be expected that seafood prices will remain high, and that seafood production by the wealthy nations will decrease and be supplemented in many cases by imports.

It appears then that the stage is set for larger scale sea farming by well informed businessmen who can overcome the difficulties facing the industry today.

CHAPTER 2

Sea Farming, Present and Future

The most important groups of animals to sea farmers are mollusks (clams, oysters, and mussels), crustaceans (shrimps, crabs, and lobsters), and fishes. When we think of fishes, we think of the elongated, scaly vertebrates that breathe by means of gills (finfish), but in this book the word "fish" will be used to represent any or all of these various aquatic animals. Mollusks, crustaceans, or finfishes will be specified when they are discussed separately.

The term brackish water also requires definition. It occurs at the edge of the sea at the transition zone between fresh and salt water; it is a mixture of sea water and fresh water, hence its salt content is below that of sea water. In the open sea, every 1,000 parts of sea water contain about 30 parts of salts. Under certain conditions of confinement or restriction, sea water will, through evaporation and a lack of exchange, reach salt concentrations or salinities much greater than normal sea water. Similarly, rainfall or excessive run-off from land can reduce the salinity of a restricted area.

The words "culture," "rear," and "raise" that appear in the literature on sea farming are defined differently by almost all authors, who distinguish among them to suit their own needs. These words will be used interchangeably in this book to mean the providing of good conditions for growth and existence of marine and brackish water plants and animals. Likewise, the words "mariculture," "sea farming," "fish culture," "aquaculture," and "aquiculture" are similar in meaning. Mariculture and sea farming generally denote raising organisms in marine environments, while fish culture, aquaculture, and aquiculture are broader terms denoting the raising of organisms in water, whether it is sea water or fresh water. As between mariculture and sea farming, the latter has the advantage of being a more popular and more easily understood term.

Dr. C. F. Hickling, an expert on fish culture, defines fish culture in terms of increasing fish production, by whatever methods, above what can be produced naturally. My definition of sea farming is "a means to promote or improve growth, and hence production, of marine and brackish water plants and animals for commercial use by protection and nurture on areas **leased or owned**." The concepts of sea fishing and sea farming overlap somewhat, but I believe there is an important difference which should be established. Both occupations involve the harvesting of living resources of the sea, but most farming involves care or cultivation of stocks under private ownership, whereas fisheries are common property resources. The concepts of husbandry and management apply both to farming of fishes and commercial fishing. However, fisheries may be managed by governments in order to produce the greatest yields year after year. When fishery biologists have adequate information on the biology of commercial species and the fisheries for them, they recommend regulations to make the wisest use of the resources.

Management of commercial fisheries entails some regulation, rearing (in government-sponsored hatchery programs), and habitat alteration, but harvesting from the fisheries is essentially accomplished by searching for, and capturing, on **public** areas, large enough concentrations of wild fish to sell for profit, in competition with other fishermen of the same or of a different nationality. To facilitate fish harvest, in some parts of the world fishermen anchor rafts or provide other types of artificial habitats to try to concentrate commercial species of fishes into a small area. The fishermen provide no care to the fish, but merely try to encourage fish which normally do not form large schools to accumulate in one place to permit economical harvesting.

Sea farming, on the other hand, involves rearing fish with some care (but not necessarily always), on leased or owned lands. The stock may be reared from eggs to marketable sizes, or collected as "young" and reared to marketable sizes. In other cases, they may be reared for part of their lives

Fig. 7. Harvesting can be done easily at an opportune time on fish farms.
(*Snake River Trout Co.*)

(as is done with seed oysters, seed clams, and juvenile milkfish) and sold to a farmer who then raises them to marketable sizes. The stocks may be protected as far as possible from predators, from disease, and from other species which compete for food and space. They are usually fed at least during some part of their holding period, or are placed in a location where they will receive sufficient natural food. Stocks may also be transplanted from poor growing areas to better growing areas, as is done with oysters. It should be understood that sea farming implies that, rather than to search for the fruits of the sea, man tries to alter natural processes for larger total production per unit area, and to simplify harvesting—as is being done on the fish farm shown in *Fig. 7*.

The rearing and release of young fish into open bodies of water to supplement catches of commercial fisheries is called sea farming by some people. Since the early 1900s there has been almost a total failure of national hatcheries in several countries to raise and release sufficient numbers of fish into the sea to substantially increase the commercial catch on an economic basis. To approach an economically feasible level, fish must be reared at a cost below what the fisherman is paid at the dock for his catch. One of the most important faults in the idea that man can add large numbers of fish to the sea to increase commercial catches (the slogan in the heyday of hatcheries was to "improve on nature") lies in the extremely high natural mortality suffered by fish in nature—occasionally as high as 99 per cent from egg to adult. A second fault is that low-cost, mass-rearing techniques have never been developed. If inexpensive rearing techniques can be invented which allow the production of prodigious numbers of young, and which, through artificial selection, reduce mortality, hatcheries may yet supplement commercial fishermen's catches.

Table 1

COMPARISON OF ACTIVITIES OF COMMERCIAL SEA FISHERMEN
AND SEA FARMERS

Activity	Fisherman	Farmer
Obtaining stock	Relies almost completely on natural propagation, in public areas.	May obtain adults and spawn them artificially, or collects young to rear on private areas (leased or owned).
Care of stock	Provides no care	Generally provides restricted body of water, dikes, and sluice gates. Controls quality and quantity of water. Provides food and controls competition, disease, and predation.
Production increase	Relies on governmental regulations. More efficient fishing gear. Possible contribution from hatchery-reared stocks.	Increases growth and survival through feeding, artificial selection, and protection from disease, predators, and competitors.
Harvesting	Relies on searching or some means of accumulating in public areas. Carried out by any licensed or otherwise qualified fishermen, during open seasons, using legal gear, when fish schools are available.	As needed, draining, nets, or otherwise, by owner, lessee, or his employees, on private areas (leased or owned). Can be done at the most suitable economic time.

Hatchery-reared fish have supplemented sportfishermen's catches, and still do, and have even been used to start fisheries in areas where they did not previously exist. In the final analysis, government rearing of commerical species of fish constitutes a "subsidy" to the fishing industry. This sort of subsidy is justified because, if large numbers of hatchery-reared fish are caught, the end product is a stronger economy and increased protein production.

Successful sea farmers greatly reduce fish mortality by providing their stock with protection from predators and freedom from competition, by preventing disease, and by supplying ample food to insure rapid growth (Table 1).

Important Sea Farming Areas

There are many areas in temperate waters where marine and brackish-water fish farming is a reality. A short survey of some of the more important of these sea-farming areas will bring into focus the extent of the practice and will illustrate that the practice is important and widespread in these waters. More detail is included in later sections where the more important species are discussed.

In the rich *rias* or river mouths around Arosa and Vigo in northwestern Spain, mussels and oysters are farmed. There, growth of oysters in cages is rapid and continuous throughout the year. Mussels are reared on ropes hanging vertically from wooden supports that radiate from rafts (*Fig. 8*). This technique produces large yields from relatively small areas by affording ample food as well as protection from bottom-dwelling predators.

The mussel is highly esteemed in France. The use of private lands to grow mussels, oysters, and clams, and shellfish purification methods used to overcome pollution effects are widespread there. Today, more than 400 to 500 million oysters are raised annually in the Arcachon and Anse de l'Aiguillon regions in France, making it the greatest center of oyster culture in the world—*Fig. 9* shows one aspect of the methods used.

Fig. 8. Mussels suspended from ropes on these rafts in the Bay of Vigo, Spain, grow rapidly and are safe from bottom predators.   (*B. Andreu*)

Fig. 9. Young drifting stages of oysters settle on limed tiles in this intertidal area at Arcachon, France.   (*H. A. Cole*)

The alluvial deposits which rivers bring to estuaries enrich many areas in the Po Delta of Italy along the Adriatic Sea. A variety of marine fish are farmed in fenced-in ponds (*villa da pesca*); in the Po region alone over 8,910 hectares (22,000 acres) are farmed by primitive, yet productive, methods.

The shellfish farms of Holland are highly developed. The Dutch pioneered the practice of hanging cultures to avoid bottom-dwelling predators and thus increase production. The Waddensea, sheltered from the North Sea by a line of islands, has been the site of intensive mussel culture since 1950. Prior to this, the Dutch fish and shellfish catch was about 16,650 metric tons (18,350 tons) including 4,950 metric tons (5,500 tons) of mussels. In 1961, 69,300 metric tons (76,400 tons) of mussels were raised, whereas the fish catch had not changed significantly. Mussels are raised on only about 5 per cent of the available area, hence considerable future expansion is still possible.

Nine species of shrimp and five species of fish are cultivated commercially in India's brackish and marine waters. Although supplemental feeding is not used, in some areas pond waters are fertilized. Yields vary greatly, depending on the type of subsoil and the range of tides. The most productive areas yield over 454 kilograms (1,000 pounds) per 0·4 hectare (acre) in about six months.

In Korea, cultured oysters, cockles, and sea mussels have been important since the government began encouraging shellfish culture in 1958. Oyster production there almost doubled in 1958–60, rising from about 600 metric tons (660 tons) to more than 11,000 metric tons (12,100 tons) annually.

A fisheries experimental station started in the Philippines in 1934 has helped the milkfish farmers to increase their production. This industry became worth about 88 million U.S. dollars in ten years. Only a few decades ago there was a paucity of scientific information on this important species, but although more is known now, much remains to be

Fig. 10. Seed stock for this Pacific oyster farm in Puget Sound, Washington, is shipped from Japan.   (*E. N. Steele*)

done. The cultivation of sugpo, the jumbo tiger shrimp in the Philippines, either in pure culture or in combination with milkfish, is lucrative.

Japan, in a dedicated effort to feed her populace, has vast areas under marine cultivation. Shrimps, crabs, lobsters, fishes, and even octopuses and squids are raised. In 1961, for example, 119,700 metric tons (133,000 tons) of red algae, wet weight, 20,700 metric tons (23,000 tons) of oysters, and 3,500 metric tons (3,900 tons) of fish were produced by cultivation. Some species are reared from eggs to marketable sizes while others are captured when they are partly grown and so need to be held for only short periods.

In the United States, the State of Washington produces over 80 per cent of the Pacific Coast oysters. This production is based almost entirely on the farming of the Pacific oyster, a species which requires imported seed from Japan (*Fig. 10*). Brackish-water ponds are used to raise a dozen or more species of fishes in Hawaii. The most important of these is mullet. On the eastern coast of the United States and Canada, the American oyster and the hard clam are raised on private lands.

Research and the Future of Sea Farming

Lack of information on the biology of species being farmed, or those suitable for farming, has held back more extensive sea farming operations. Each year more knowledge is gained on the biology of such species, knowledge that can vitally affect production. Since World War II we have learned much about important aspects of the oyster's life cycle, their diseases, and the extent of predation upon them. More is known now about the biology of important fishes such as mullet, plaice, and milkfish. Oysters and clams have been reared successfully in hatcheries; in Japan, shrimp have been raised from eggs to adults; in the United States several species of commercial shrimp have been reared, under laboratory conditions, from eggs to adults. We can expect that numerous gains will accrue from present and future research which will improve the position of sea farming.

At Lowestoft and Port Erin (Isle of Man), England, scientists are mass-rearing young plaice. As techniques are improved they anticipate that these artificially reared plaice can be released into the sea in vast numbers to grow and can be harvested within about two years. Engineers are seeking ways to fence in plaice which normally move into deep offshore waters as they grow older. Electricity, ultrasonics, and nets are being considered as fences. Mollusks and several fish species are also being reared at the Government Laboratory at Conway, Wales, with the use of heated water discharged as a waste (coolant) from power plants.

Two major problems face oyster farmers who plant seed on the bottom. One is the high mortality caused by the numerous predatory bottom-dwelling animals that prey on oysters; the other is that some areas, though rich in oyster food, have bottoms covered with silt which shifts and smothers the oysters. These problems can be overcome by raft culture, a technique that has proved successful in Europe and Japan, where it is still under study. At the United States Bureau of Commercial Fisheries Laboratory at Oxford, Maryland, extensive work on culture of suspended oysters is being carried out.

Dr. V. Loosanoff and his co-workers pioneered in hatchery raising of clams and oysters at the United States Bureau of Commercial Fisheries Laboratory at Milford, Connecticut, and have made outstanding progress on shellfish predator control. In some experiments they fed dried algae to larval shellfish and found it greatly simplified rearing species through high mortality periods of their life cycles.

At the University of Washington College of Fisheries, Dr. L. R. Donaldson has produced, by selective breeding, salmon stocks that are resistant to high temperatures and diseases, that mature earlier, and that have a higher survival rate than non-selected stocks. This encouraging success, and the salmon's habit of returning to natal streams, stimulates thinking about the sea as a pasture into which masses of selectively bred fish can be released as young, to feed and grow in the sea and then to return to their home ponds to be harvested.

Of great importance for fish farmers employing near-coast or estuarine areas is knowledge of the effects of pollution by pesticides on estuarine animals. Dr. P. Butler, Florida Shellfish Laboratory of the United States Bureau of Commercial Fisheries, has investigated the effects on growth, nutrition, and reproduction of shellfish when they are exposed to minute concentrations of pesticides. Even at extremely low concentrations shellfish are killed by these poisons.

Dr. G. R. Lunz, State Laboratory of South Carolina, for many years has advocated increased fish farming in the United States. In his farming experiments, he followed the east Asian approach of allowing larval shrimp

Fig. 11. Unusual "personnel" may someday aid offshore sea farmers in rounding up fish. This 7-foot porpoise did chores for divers working at 200 feet.   (*United States Navy*)

to drift into ponds from the sea and rearing them there to marketable sizes. He attempted to determine the feasibility of stocking ponds by this method. At the time of his experiments no one had raised commercial penaeid shrimp from eggs to adults in United States. He is confident of the value of shrimp and oyster farming despite the many problems such as predatory fish being introduced into his ponds along with the larval shrimp. Development of shrimp farming in the United States shows promise because it is possible now to rear shrimp from eggs to adults. This knowledge, plus recent studies on temperature and salinity effects on larval shrimp growth, calls for complete evaluation of the feasibility of shrimp farming.

Future of Offshore Farming

Possible future methods for increasing the production of the sea by farming are numerous. The future of sea farming has received attention from the popular press and even from scientists. It envisions, for instance, fish and whales raised in large enclosures and herded about by divers who are assisted by trained porpoises (*Fig. 11*), or countless acres of algae being cared for by undersea farmers. In other schemes, means of churning up the tons of natural chemical elements lying on the oceans' bottoms are being considered. Today these methods may seem impractical or visionary, but a few years ago who would have thought space travel possible?

The myriad, microscopic, drifting organisms called plankton have come in for their share of attention by fishermen and fish farmers. Because of their vast numbers, and because they are low on the food web (chain), these organisms appear to have considerable potential for farming. Plankton has a rather high protein, fat, and carbohydrate content. The protein in some plankton animals, such as copepods, for example, may be as high as 77 per cent, and the fat content about 20 per cent. In some of the phytoplankters (tiny drifting plants) the fat content may be about 10 per cent. There are many accounts by people who have eaten plankton and found it nourishing, albeit not tasty. Some forms are even poisonous.

Unfortunately, the problems of finding and harvesting plankton in commercial quantities are many and formidable. Although plankton is consistently dense in the Arctic and Antarctic, and in areas of upwelling (where cold, nutrient-rich waters rise to the surface), it is unevenly distributed in most other areas. Plankton-eating fishes are very efficient in harvesting plankton in the open sea, but if man is to harvest it he must devise a means which is cheap and efficient. The cost of pumping large quantities of water to concentrate and strain out the plankton organisms is extremely high.

The suggestion has been made many times that it might be feasible to farm marine plankton in brackish lagoons and ponds, but little is known about the ecology and physiology of the many plants and animals in the plankton. Before plankton can be raised as food on an economical basis, we need to learn much more about the biology of the various organisms. Of course, in many cases, the fish farmer may raise plankton to feed his fish or shellfish because the ultimate product he raises has a high market value. He could not hope to get the production or the profit if he tried to market the plankton. In later chapters we will talk about raising plankton to feed fish and shellfish and arranging the ponds so that natural growth of plankton can enter the pond and be available to the impounded species.

Experiments using bubble or electric fences have been conducted to restrain fish in bays and fiords or areas of the sea on the continental shelves, fencing them in just as on land farms. Air-bubble screens have been experimented with in the United States and were found to be successful for guiding menhaden and herring into traps. Since some fishes are reluctant to pass through air-bubble screens, their use for fencing fish in semi-enclosed bays, and even in the open sea, has been suggested. The method is relatively simple. Flexible polyethylene tubing with many tiny openings and weighted to make it sink, is attached to an air compressor on shore, boat, or raft. The compressor runs continuously, causing a steady stream of bubbles to rise, forming the screen. Unfortunately, these screens are not fool-proof. When the water is cloudy, for example, the screen is less visible, and the fish may pass through it. Electric fences operate on the

Fig. 12. Sea farmers living in underwater chambers such as this experimental one may work someday in offshore waters. Presently, sea farming is practical only in estuaries and near shore waters.   (*United States Navy*)

principal that an alternating current electric field will repel fish. However, the outlook for electric fences is not promising because of the high voltage requirements and the rapid dissipation of current strength in sea water.

There are several requirements for successful offshore fish farming, some unique to this type of farming, others necessary for any type of fish farming. These include establishment of ownership of the farm or stock and prevention of theft of stock, development of suitable underwater devices to permit man to work for extended periods in the sea, and development of underwater cages, fences, or accumulators to attract fish, provide food for them, and hold them until they are suitable for harvest. It is conceivable that with better underwater swimming devices and underwater chambers, deep water fish farms will approach reality (*Fig. 12* may be showing the way).

New, ingenious chambers are being designed that permit undersea activities that were formerly considered impossible. One such device, invented by Edwin A. Link (who achieved fame in World War II with his aviation training device called the Link Trainer), enables divers to remain underwater for extended periods of time at a presently proved depth of 130 meters (430 feet). The inventor claims that with perfection of equipment it will be possible for man to withstand depths of 305 meters (1,000

Fig. 13. As man increases his activities in "inner space" his knowledge of the feasibility of farming there will increase.
(*United States Navy*)

feet). A significant feature of this invention is that the diver is able to re-main down for days and thus requires decompression only once upon his return to the surface.

Captain Jacques-Yves Cousteau designed an undersea shelter in which French aquanauts spent a month submerged in the Red Sea. Similar ex-periments have been carried out by the United States Navy in the *Sealab* experiments. Navy tests off Bermuda and California probed the problems associated with man's spending extended periods of time under the sea, a prerequisite for increasing our knowledge of it (*Fig. 13*).

This progress in undersea exploration, which began in the 1950s, will provide data which may greatly aid future sea farming. More than two dozen manned submersibles had been designed or constructed by 1967. These undersea craft will greatly enhance man's knowledge of the biology of species on the continental shelf, and, in turn, provide evidence to decide if farming this area is practical.

Perhaps in the future exploitation of the sea the personable porpoises or other trained marine animals might play important roles. They could be used to search for fish schools and to herd them into nets or enclosed areas, just as sheep dogs do. They might even be trained to notify fisher-men of the whereabouts of the schools so they can proceed to the spot and harvest them. Trained porpoises have already been released in the open sea to work for man. For instance, off California in 1965, a porpoise delivered tools and other necessities to *Sealab* aquanauts, thus demonstrating the feasibility of using marine animals for man's benefit.

In addition to trying to develop diving gear for man, experiments are under way to see if man can breathe dissolved gases unaided. Since submerged dogs, hamsters, and mice have been found able to extract oxygen from sea water and remain alive, the question arises whether it is possible for man to accomplish this feat. The freedom of action and the lack of bulky gear would make the work of a diver on deep-water fish farms much easier.

Artificial Reefs

If we ignore many of the technical difficulties of ownership or assume that they can be overcome, we can peer into the future at the role the sea will play in our lives and envision "sea farming reefs" on the continental shelf. These reefs will consist of fish apartments such as the Japanese government is using, to which fish are attracted and around which they grow and breed. Fish are attracted by submerged structures and will remain in the vicinity of them. Divers, even in the days of the old diving suits with "hard hats," knew that accumulations of fish were to be found around reefs and sunken vessels, but not on open sandy bottoms. The reason for this phenomenon is still unknown. In some cases they may be attracted by the food they obtain from the attached plants and animals, or in other cases they may remain in such areas for protection. Scientists call this attraction to a submerged object "thigmotropism," which they define as the desire of an animal to be close to a solid object.

Whatever the reason for this attraction, more fish occur near objects than in nearby similar areas without objects. Even today along the east coast of the United States some sportsmen seek to prevent salvage of wrecked vessels because fishing near sunken vessels has provided good catches. The offshore oil-drilling rigs in California and in the Gulf of Mexico have also become points of interest to sportfishermen who know that they have a better chance of making good catches there than over areas that have no solid objects.

The first artificial reefs for fishing in the United States were started off New Jersey during the 1930s. Since about 1950, at least twelve coastal states in the United States have made use of fishes' desire to be close to large, solid objects and have constructed artificial reefs to improve catches of sport fish with varying success. They have used car bodies, trolley cars, stones, rubble, concrete, pipe, and especially formed fish "apartments" (*Fig. 14*). In spite of their ability to attract fish, reefs of metal scrap, such as automobiles and trolley cars, have corroded rapidly. After a few years in the sea there is nothing left of the metal, and if there is any wood in the bod:es, as was the case in the street cars used off the coast of California, boring mollusks riddle it. Concrete pipe and stone rubble make space available for much longer periods than previously tried materials, but, unfortunately, it is difficult to pile them high enough off the bottom of the

Fig. 14. Submerged streetcars off the California coast proved to be expensive fish-attracting reefs.   (*California Department of Fish & Game, C. H. Turner*)

sea to make good reefs. The preformed concrete apartments that have been used in Japan and California are expensive, but by using them fairly good reefs can be developed.

As a result of the lack of careful measurements of productivity in areas where artificial reefs were placed, knowledge is limited on how much more productive an area can become through their use. However, there are two studies which demonstrate the value in terms of increased production of fish as a result of placing objects in the water; one was done off the coast of California, the other in the Virgin Islands.

Automobile and streetcar bodies were used to attract fish off the California coast in an area where trawling demonstrated few fish to be present (*Fig. 15*). Subsequent to placing the reef, diver-biologists on periodic visits watched the numbers of fish increase sharply over a two and a half year period. Measurements by individual visits of this sort provide what ecologists call "standing crop estimates," or, in other words, estimates at a particular time. At the California artificial reef, scientists counted as many as 1,500 kelp bass averaging 28 centimeters (11 inches) long, as many as 2,000 sand bass about the same length, and some 5,000 white seaperch of about 15 centimeters (6 inches), just to name a few. The quantity of fish present clearly demonstrated that the reef was productive.

In the Virgin Islands, Dr. John R. Randall made an artificial reef of stone blocks off St. Thomas and compared the production on it with the production around the natural reefs. Although he tried to duplicate the environmental conditions of natural reefs, he felt that his reef may have been better located than a natural reef. After about one year he collected all the fishes in the area, which amounted to about 1·7 kilograms (3·8 pounds) of fish per square meter (yard) of artificial reef. At two other natural reefs off the Virgin Islands he obtained only about 159 grams

Fig. 15. Pile perch are shown here swimming between submerged streetcars. Although fishes moved into these habitats, the experiment was not successful because of the great expense and because the streetcar bodies deteriorated rapidly.
(California Dept. of Fish and Game, C. H. Turner)

(0·29 pounds) of fish per square meter (yard) of reef. Hence, the artificial reef was about eleven times as productive as the natural reef.

So many environmental variables affect production around a reef that it is nearly impossible to consider them all and the roles they play in reef ecology. This complex environment is difficult to study. But despite the experimental complications, mounting evidence suggests that if properly designed reefs are placed in suitable areas, taking into consideration currents, bottom types, and adjacent reefs, production of fish can be greatly increased.

Costs of constructing artificial reefs are high because, in addition to the cost of individual shelters (as high as $75 each), the materials must be transported to a loading area, then placed aboard a vessel and moved to the dumping site. The reefs should preferably be cabled in place by divers so that they do not scatter or roll away. The use of large barges, cranes, and tugs quickly adds up to a substantial expense, and once a reef is placed, navigational buoys are required to mark the area. The many costs associated with the installation and maintenance of these buoys further increase the cost of an artificial reef. *Fig. 16* shows one type of shelter favored by fish.

In 1959, the Texas Parks and Wildlife Department constructed an artificial reef consisting of 600 automobile bodies near Freeport, Texas. This reef cost $17,000 and disappeared within four years. The cables holding the car bodies together corroded, and currents swept away those auto bodies that did not sink into the mud bottom. During 1962 and 1963, biologists used 91 and 122 centimeters (3 and 4 foot) diameter reinforced

Fig. 16. Fish seem to prefer these long-lasting, expensive
concrete fish shelters more than old auto bodies.
        (California Dept. of Fish and Game, C. H. Turner)

concrete pipe to construct new reefs. This time the price was $31,000 for
an area off the Texas coast covering 30 by 30 meters (100 by 100 feet). In-
spection by divers showed that the large pipes were not sinking into the
bottom, and sampling by hook-and-line showed that fish were in the area.
However, marine biologists are skeptical of the value of reefs because of
the high costs of placing them and of the subsequent costly maintenance
of navigational buoys.

At the present time, artificial reefs are essentially a tool of the sport and
commercial fisheries management program, and a poorly understood tool
at that. So little is known about the success of these reefs from reliable
before-and-after observations that no recommendations can be made as
to their importance to fish farming. They may well have an important
role in future sportfishing, and even in fish farming, as many suggest.

The Future

Over the centuries sea farming has developed by trial and error. The
successful farmers passed their knowledge on to their sons. Sea farming is
most practiced in tropical countries; in Java, for example, over 60 per
cent of the fish eaten come from ponds which cover hundreds of square
miles (*Fig. 17* shows a typical "tambak"). A puzzling situation to the
many individuals who are interested in the sea is the gap between how
little sea farming is presently practiced in wealthy countries in the temperate latitudes, and the potential which exists.

Rapid strides in science and technology, and an increased food demand
from growing human populations, cause the status of sea farming in
wealthy countries to take on new meaning.

Fig. 17. In Java, the majority of food fish comes from brackish fish ponds such as these tambaks. (*W. H. Schuster*)

The best and most immediately promising locations for sea farming are in the fertile bays, estuaries, and intertidal zones that man has ready access to, and wherein his stock can be enclosed and protected.

The increased interest in the sea and near-shore areas has placed sea farming in an exciting position. Cautious scientists look for much more extensive temperate water fish farming in two or three decades, others believe this can be realized much sooner. Production from sea farms, even if increased substantially, will not greatly affect production from sea fisheries; it will be a fraction of that produced by fishing.

II
PROCEDURES

CHAPTER 3

Utilizing Productive Areas

The Estuary

It is hard to define what estuaries are. If you were to ask twenty biologists to define an estuary, you would receive twenty different responses. However, each biologist would stress the fact that an estuary is very complex, more so than either a fresh water or a sea water environment, because it is a transition zone between the two. One definition that is occasionally given simply says that estuaries are places where rivers flow into the sea and generally are in bays or semi-enclosed areas. Many situations fit this category, so that for our purposes this definition should serve.

One of the most prominent characteristics of the estuary is the dynamic nature of the processes taking place. For example, the temperature, salinity, and pH (acid-alkalinity balance), change markedly and quickly. In a long, narrow estuary there are significant changes in its physical and chemical characteristics from one end to the other. At the end of the estuary fed by fresh water, the salinity is low and the temperature is nearly like that of the supply; on the seaward end, the physical and chemical characteristics of the estuary are more nearly like the sea. The fauna that live there will also vary throughout the estuary, and in some cases the difference can be quite pronounced, especially where there is a long estuary with a high out-flow of fresh water. In some areas, estuaries which receive little fresh water may have salinities so high that only a few species can survive.

Another important characteristic of estuaries, and one which makes them of considerable importance to fish farmers, is their extremely high productivity. Just as it is difficult to obtain a clear-cut definition of estuaries, it is difficult to obtain accurate figures on how much more productive estuaries are than either the surrounding sea, the upland areas, or the fresh water. Many attempts have been made to measure estuarine productivity, but even the methods used in measurements have not been standardized and are not applicable in all areas. Notwithstanding these difficulties, estuaries and tidal marshes are regarded by scientists as among the most fertile natural areas in the world; rates as high as twenty times as productive as the open sea, and seven times as productive as the "average" wheat field are frequently given.

High fertility of brackish waters does not mean that everything produced is usable by humans, but rather that the weight of all organisms produced per unit of ground per year is greater than elsewhere.

Life in estuaries is tenuous. Their inhabitants do not obtain this added benefit of abundant food, phosphorus, and nitrogen, without sacrifices.

The animals that live there are uniquely adapted to withstand wide and rapid fluctuations of physical and chemical factors.

If floods occur in rivers feeding into estuaries, the salinity of these areas can drop sharply and stay low for a sufficiently long time to cause a high mortality of many animals, especially the sessile ones. Dr. P. Butler, of the U.S. Bureau of Commercial Fisheries, reported that a good example of this kind of damage was in the western end of the Mississippi Sound, near the mouth of the Mississippi River, where salinity was so reduced by fresh water that disastrous mortality to oysters resulted. It can be expected that in any area of an estuary that is to be used for raising fish for man, conditions can become so extreme that the stock may be killed. Estuaries also allow many species to escape from predators or parasites. Certain fishes and shellfishes can survive in lower salinities than can their enemies. Continued low salinity prevailing for long periods will kill starfish which prey on shellfish, and it may prevent the spread of some shellfish diseases, such as fungus in oysters because the fungus cannot survive at low salinities.

The biology of the estuary is controlled to a great extent by its bottom. Whereas in the open sea the characteristics of the water are very important in determining the productivity and species present, and the bottom is relatively unimportant, in the estuary fish are in close contact with the bottom or bottom inhabitants. The shallower the estuary, the more important the role of the bottom becomes. Muddy bottoms are alive with microbes, algae, and higher animals, which, by complex reactions, release nitrogen, phosphorus, and other vital plant foods. This production is much lower on sandy bottoms. *Fig. 18* illustrates the richness of intertidal zones.

The mechanism of enrichment in estuaries by fresh water may be different among areas. In most regions, the enriched drainage from the land may be carried into the estuaries and cause high productivity. However, Dr. E. P. Odum, of the University of Georgia, points out that the out-flowing fresh water helps to stir up or "cycle" nutrient substances on the bottoms of estuaries, thereby causing high production.

Knowledge of the chemical and physical constituents of the oceans is limited because it is difficult and expensive to get data from the sea. But our understanding of these growth-stimulating processes that take place in estuaries is a great deal more limited.

The principal elements that photosynthetic plants such as algae and sea grasses need for growth are carbon, hydrogen, sulphur, nitrogen, and phosphorus. Hydrogen and oxygen are everywhere, and carbon is derived from carbon dioxide. Sulphur is dissolved in sea water in its oxidized form and is subject to rapid oxidation. It is dominant in the environment because of the sulphur bacteria in mud. Nitrogen is a controlling factor in estuarine productivity, but we do not know how much is needed to keep a good chemical balance, nor how much of it bacteria and algae need.

Any impoundment in an estuarine area causes its characteristics to change greatly. For example, just as the amount of suspended material carried by water will settle in a pond where velocity is reduced, so it does

Fig. 18. The abundance of plants and animals living in intertidal zones such as this one in Maine is controlled largely by the bottom type.   (*Ivan Flye*)

when streams laden with this material empty into an estuary. The amount of exchange of fresh water with salt water can be greatly reduced by impounding parts of estuaries, especially since the screens or gates used are of very fine mesh to exclude the young of predatory fish. These fine screens become quickly clogged with algae and floating debris and reduce the water exchange.

The construction of ponds in estuarine areas requires that the best use be made of the tidal flow since, unlike the fresh water farm, the exchange of water in the ponds usually cannot be accomplished by a source such as a stream or river alone, but rather depends mainly on the exchange by the tide to flush waste products from the pond and bring in food and dissolved oxygen from the sea, and to cycle nutrients. How the tides do this work is shown in *Fig. 19.*

Pond Location and Stock Supply

The location of sea ponds depends partially on the method to be used to obtain the young organisms for cultivation. Animals suitable for sea

Fig. 19. Tidal flushing exchanges the sea water in these Hawaiian mullet farms—
an aerial view.   (*Bernice P. Bishop Museum*)

farming include those species which can be raised from egg to adult in
captivity and those of which the young must be obtained from natural
reproduction in the sea.

Some important general considerations must be covered before going
into the rudimentary methods of farming marine fishes and shellfishes.
First, there is the matter of a "critical" period which occurs early in the
lives of these animals. This period is one of high mortality, when the very
young fish, having consumed all available yolk from their egg, must begin
feeding on food from the sea. This is a substantial physiological adjustment
for any organism and, under natural conditions, many die at this time. In
addition to this loss, if suitable food is not readily available as soon as they
need it, wholesale lots of young which have survived the critical change
will die.

A sea farmer who raises fish from eggs can expect very high mortality at
some time during their larval development. He should learn when this
happens on the species he wants to rear and how severe it can be. On the
other hand, if he obtains the fish or shellfish after they have passed through
these critical stages, mortality will be lower.

It is inadvisable for the fish farmer to depend on a single species for his total income. If more than one species can live together without reducing the production of any single species (they may, in fact, increase production), or if the monetary return is greater, he should farm more than one. This is good business because natural fluctuations in requirements for a single species make good and bad crop-years.

Obtaining Stock from the Sea

In many farms young are obtained from the sea, impounded, and raised to marketable size. Ponds used in this procedure have gates constructed to allow young fish or shellfish to enter the ponds with the inflowing tidal current. The sea farmer must be able to identify the young stages of the species he seeks to rear and must have a good understanding of their requirements. He must know when they migrate in greatest numbers, and he must understand the currents, for it is these which carry large numbers of the young stages into his ponds. Understanding the current system and tides which will bring the young, delicate animals into the impoundment is of utmost importance for a successful operation.

Other sea farmers collect stocks from the sea (*Fig. 20*) or buy from fishermen who collect them, then place them in impoundments or on a prepared bottom (as is done with oysters). Pond location is not as critical in this procedure as when tidal currents bring in stock. The method avoids the high mortality which accompanies the critical period. It is often difficult for the rapidly-developing young to locate the proper size and kind of food and begin feeding in nature, and it is even more difficult for man to provide proper conditions and food for confined animals. We will

Fig. 20. Pompano have not been bred in captivity, so these farmers must collect seed stock along the beach.

(*E. S. Iversen*)

have more to say on the difficulty of feeding larval stages in the next chapter.

In the second procedure—that of putting the young into ponds which are screened off from the sea and do not require currents to carry the young into them—the danger of predators entering is extremely small, but not entirely unlikely. The sea farmer places in the pond only the species that he wants to raise, not everything that is drifting in the sea. Elimination of undesirable predators or competitors is usually required from time to time even if adequate screening of water intake is installed. A simple method used is shown in *Fig. 21*.

When the farmer's supply of fish for a pond is obtained by either of these ways, the stock supply varies greatly, due to natural fluctuations. This variability can cause considerable loss of income (Table 2).

Table 2

ADVANTAGES AND DISADVANTAGES OF METHODS OF OBTAINING
BROOD STOCK

| | Spawned naturally in the sea | | Spawned artificially in captivity |
	Carried by currents	Collected by fishing	
Numbers of:			
Parasites	High	Low	High (in young stock)
Competitors	High	Low	Low
Predators	High	Low	Low
Mortality of stock	Low. Past "critical" stage	Low. Past "critical" stage	High. Before "critical" stage
Cost of stocking	Low	High	Low to moderate
Supply of stock	Variable. Depends on success of natural spawning and suitable currents	Variable. Depends on success of natural spawning and suitable currents	Stable. Depends on few spawners and proper care. Can be very stable if spawning takes place in impoundment
Representative groups	Shrimp, oyster	Mullet, milkfish	Shrimp

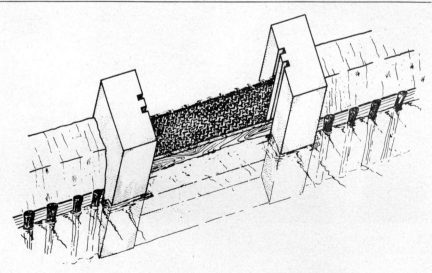

Fig. 21. Sluice gate drawboard and screen allow exchange of water between farm ponds and the sea. Young of predators and competitors can enter ponds through the holes in the screens. *(From D. Allen, 1963)*

One important problem that arises when ponds are stocked by allowing the young to drift in is that undesirable species, the predators, competitors, and parasites, also drift freely in the sea and can drift into ponds along with the desirable species. Those predators which grow large, if not removed, eat many of the desirable animals. Competitor fish can consume more available food than the desirable species. The parasites and predators can attack the young of a farmer's stock and cause high mortality, or reduce growth of the stock of fish. To sort through all the animals in the ponds is laborious and expensive.

Raising from Egg to Adult

The second general method of obtaining young involves that group of fishes and shellfishes which can be reared all the way from egg to marketable size in impounded waters. In this procedure, it is necessary to confine ripe adults in tanks or ponds to spawn either naturally or be spawned artificially (*Fig. 22*).

The farmer who is able to raise fish and shellfish from the egg through to large sizes ensures a steady supply of young. Whereas in the previous system the young stages must be fished for, or are allowed to drift into the ponds, in this system the capture of a relatively few mature adults can provide large numbers of young which can supply a good-sized stable stock for the sea farmer to raise for market.

Fig. 22. Shrimp spawn in these tile-lined tanks at Dr. Fujinaga's hatchery at Takamatsu, Japan. (*C. P. Idyll*)

By selecting a time close to the natural spawning time, it is usually easy to obtain both sexes (or only a female, as in shrimp) in spawning condition. The difficulties inherent in this system are many. A proper holding arrangement must be provided for the delicate young stages. They must be provided with abundant clean water, whether open or closed circulation is used. They must be carefully fed. If food is not readily available to them, or if it is not of the right size for them to ingest, extremely high mortality can occur, for their food requirements are rigid. In nature, and in fish farms, the success of a brood may depend on how nearly these requirements are met.

The cost of raising fish from eggs to marketable sizes may be higher than if the animals are collected after they have passed through the delicate larval stages. Thus, the total cost may be quite high for mass-rearing the total stock of animals held because of the labor involved in preparing proper food and cleaning the holding tanks for the very small animals, but the cost for individual fish or shellfish will probably be substantially lower

Fig. 23. Young trout live in fresh water supplied from a river at this trout farm in Tasmania. The trout spend a portion of their lives in brackish water where they grow fast.
(*Australian News and Information Bureau*)

than fishing for the young stages in the sea or monitoring these animals as they come into the ponds, as in the first technique suggested.

One of the most important advantages to raising stock from eggs is that the fish farmer can more easily exclude many predators, competitors, and parasites from his pond. Also, when young are raised through the critical larval stages, they have a greatly reduced chance of getting diseases from adults of the species. When the breeding adults are kept in the same tanks or ponds with the young for extended periods, ectoparasites carried by the parent can easily be passed to the young. This is especially true of some of the protozoans and monogenetic trematodes. They are excluded in the case where the eggs are raised in the tanks separate from breeding stock.

Pond Construction

Nursery and rearing ponds for milkfish in the Philippines comprise about 0·4 to 1·6 hectares (1 to 4 acres). The largest rearing ponds may reach about 400 hectares (1,000 acres).

In general, the most desirable location for fish ponds is along tidal flats near streams to insure that a supply of fresh water (*Fig. 23*) will keep the ponds brackish. Tidal flats are the most common location for milkfish farms because they require no excavation or filling to prepare them for farming; ponds are formed by placing dikes around the desired areas. Tidal flats with clay bottoms are preferred for pond construction because clay retains water and is good for building dikes. Sand or rock subsoils are impractical. In the Philippines, if there is insufficient clay or mud for making dikes in the selected location, small dugout canoes are used to transport the clay to the pond. Pond bottoms must be higher than mean low tide for good drainage, predator removal, and harvest of the stock. Simple methods of construction are suggested by *Fig. 24*.

Pond construction can be divided into several general types. The type requiring the most labor and cost involves completely enclosing a portion of a tide flat. The dikes in these ponds have to be strong, especially if there is any wave action against them. Bays or lagoons which are partially enclosed by natural shores and possess suitable characteristics for farming can be made usable by relatively short artificial dikes. Probably most brackish water ponds are constructed this way. The least expensive is that type of construction where short fences or gates enclose narrow exits from a lagoon or estuary.

Dikes are formed in layers, and each layer must dry before the next is added. Dikes are built to various heights depending on the tidal variation. The ponds are designed to slope toward an outlet. Larger ponds may have several channels to speed drainage.

Mangroves are often planted along the dikes to prevent erosion from wind and waves (*Fig. 25*), but farm ponds constructed in mangrove areas on tide flats must be cleared of the trees. Although it is expensive to clear an area of these trees and stumps, the hardwood is valuable as firewood and the mangrove bark is occasionally used to treat fishing nets.

Fig. 24. In tropical countries, small dugout canoes are used to carry building
materials for brackish water pond construction.   (*W. H. Schuster*)

Water depth in ponds should be about 61 centimeters (2 feet). The water
in shallower ponds can become hot and occasionally will cause high fish
mortality. In the tropics, fish farmers place palm fronds in the dikes around
shallow nursery ponds to afford shade. Deep ponds will not allow light to
reach the bottom, and plants which serve as food will not grow. Many
farmers provide a small area of deeper water in ponds as a holding pond
for fish during draining.

Concrete, wood, or stone sluice gates (*Fig. 26*) control the entrance and
exit of water in the ponds. Screens of split bamboo are placed across the
gate openings to prevent the escape of milkfish and the entrance of peda-
tors and other undesirable fish.

Artificial ponds, constructed of concrete or plastic, are expensive and
may not yield as good fish growth as in the cheaper dirt ponds. Of course,
the feeding habits of the species raised is an important consideration here.
If they are strict carnivores, dirt bottoms are not as important. But, in
general, the many small organisms such as algae and invertebrates may be
very important in supplementing food production for the fish. At the

Fig. 25. Mangrove roots reduce erosion of dikes in Java tambaks.

(*W. H. Schuster*)

same time, the environment in dirt ponds or estuaries may be much more favorable to disease organisms than in the artificial ponds.

Farming Mollusks off the Bottom

Raft culture is an old technique that increases mussel and oyster production. Rafting was used in France as early as 1863. Any species which have the ability to attach to objects, either with a cement gland (as in oysters) or by a byssus (as in mussels) can be raft-cultured. The principal advantage of using the raft technique is that it permits utilization of estuaries and bays which have large amounts of suitable plankton in the water, but in which the bottoms are not suitable for growing these mollusks. Undesirable bottom is, for example, composed of loose sand or heavy mud on which the mussel seed or oyster seed cannot grow because it will be smothered. Thus by placing any kind of raft or floating device in the water with places for attachment, such as clean shell, it is possible to utilize areas which could not otherwise be used. The forerunner of the rafting method probably comes from early techniques of placing twigs on the bottom or making twig fences on which mussels could attach.

Another advantage of rafting is that in some situations mortalities due to storms or other unfavorable conditions can be avoided. If a violent storm approaches an area, rafts, with the oysters or mussels hanging below, can be towed to a protected area, whereas those planted on shallow bottoms may receive the full force of the storm. Oysters or mussels on rafts are

Fig. 26. Water Pressure against this clapper mechanism stoppers this culvert when the tide drops.   (*P. J. Warren*)

always submerged, hence they are not exposed to extremes in temperatures. Those on the bottom in the upper part of the intertidal zone during low tide may be exposed to high temperatures during summer. In winter, those same oysters may be exposed to extremely cold temperatures, in fact, close to freezing at some latitudes. During the growing season one can expect a loss of growth when the tide is out because the oysters will cease feeding. This is not so in the case of raft-grown oysters because they are always submerged; therefore, maximum use is made of the growing season, no matter how short it may be.

The ease of harvesting rafted mollusks is worthy of consideration. It is easier to pull up strings of oysters or mussels into a boat than to dredge them from the bottom or to walk along during low tide (in intertidal areas) and pick them up.

Raft culture for raising mollusks (*Fig. 27*) is considerably more expensive than simply planting oysters on the bottom. The materials to make rafts, plus the great deal of labor involved, substantially increases production costs. The cost of logs, plus some means of preventing their deterioration by boring animals, and corrosion of any metal involved in the raft's construction, can be considerable. Unfortunately, rafts generally do not last long. Copper paint may have to be applied to the raft to slow

Fig. 27. Inspecting these two-year-old oysters on trays is easily done by punt in a New South Wales farm. (*Australian News and Information Bureau*)

its deterioration. In Washington State, oyster rafts measuring 7 by 110 meters (24 by 360 feet) are constructed of styrofoam. This technique presumably cuts down the degree of deterioration which would surely result if logs were used. However, in heavy seas styrofoam is unsuitable. Where there is floating ice, it may cut the strings of oysters free from the raft and destroy the raft as well. In certain circumstances, loss due to storms may be considerable, even to rafts, if they cannot be stored during foul weather.

Another advantage of rafting is that, in nearly all cases, the growth of rafted mollusks is much faster than for those growing on the bottom. William Shaw, of the U.S. Bureau of Commercial Fisheries, found one difficulty with the rafted oysters he grew in Cape Cod: although the oysters grew much faster attached to strings beneath the rafts, the shells were thin and fragile. He found it necessary to place the oysters on the bottom to thicken their shells. After one year on the bottom, the shells thickened approximately threefold. The slower growth rate and more available carbonates associated with a bottom-dwelling existence perhaps allow the animals to accumulate more calcium carbonate on their shells.

Shaw compared the gross profit on his raft-raised oysters (selling price minus cost price) with the gross profit made by oystermen who transplanted Long Island oysters to Cape Cod to fatten them during the summer. The raft-grown oysters took two years to grow and earned a gross profit of about $3·75 a bushel, whereas the oystermen received $4·50 a bushel. On a large scale, the profit earned from the raft-cultured oysters would be considerably greater than transplants because the per-unit labor and material would be cheaper.

A disadvantage of rafts or markers is that they can be hazardous to navigation.

Open Areas for Mollusks

Oysters and clams are also reared in areas which do not have walls or dikes. These sites must be carefully selected to ensure that the proper conditions for good growth exist there before an extensive effort is applied to improve them.

Most of the steps in farming oysters are outlined in that chapter and for the most part consist of removing predators such as starfish and old shell which contains predators' eggs, and making certain that adequate cultivation of the oysters makes maximum use of the area. In Washington State dams are sometimes placed on the low side of the oyster-growing flats to retain water when the tide goes out. Since the oysters are bathed around the clock rather than only on high tides, they grow more rapidly and suffer less from temperature, salinity, and nutrient changes than oysters which are grown on tide flats which go dry during low tides.

Clam beaches with soil that allows young clams to settle can sometimes be improved greatly by adding soil to the normal bottom when the young clams are settling. This procedure, used to advantage in Japan, produces a

Fig. 28. Successful sea farming requires ownership or leases of large intertidal or near shore areas. (*Australian News and Information Bureau*)

high set of young clams because it prevents the currents from sweeping them away before they can burrow into the bottom.

Site Ownership

The laws affecting owning and leasing of submerged lands are generally at the local government level. In the United States, title to submerged lands remains with the states.

An international agreement, the "Convention of the Continental Shelf of June, 1964," deals with the use of the continental shelf out to about 100 fathoms. Coastal states have control over the resources of the area bounding their shores, including sedentary species. This jurisdiction includes fishing and farming.

The establishment of impounded areas above the high water mark requires leasing or purchasing either from private owners or from state governments. *Fig. 28* shows how areas are marked off.

In the United States, considerable variation exists in the leasing and sale procedures among states, from as low as $0.25 per acre on a twenty-year lease (Georgia), to $50 initial costs, plus $1 per acre per year (California). The more progressive states, such as New York, are encouraging a high

Fig. 29. In some sea farms with open circulation systems, settling tanks may be required such as these 4,500-gallon insulated fiberglass basins.   (*Carolina Fiberglass Products Co.*)

rental system, through laws. High rentals have been the rule in Europe for years, and they obligate the lessee to efficiently manage his leased area, whereas low-priced leases encourage harvesting the standing (wild) crop, then abandoning the lease when the stock is depleted. Any procedure that tends to stabilize ownership and requires an investment in the land encourages greater production of higher quality fish.

For up-to-date, accurate information on leasing or buying submerged lands, state or national conservation departments should be contacted.

Tanks and Aquaria for Rearing Young

Two supply systems can be used to provide tanks and aquaria with water, the closed system in which water is recirculated, and the open system in which water is continually pumped in and then discharged. Each system has merit.

In the closed system the bio-chemical characteristics of sea water change. It is important to realize that water from the open sea is stable. Usually sea water has a constant temperature and pH. However, as soon as sea water is removed from the sea, bacteria increase, and a chain reaction starts.

Fig. 30. Sea water systems, pipes, tanks and fittings should be chemically inert. Some metals are toxic to marine plants and animals. (*Carolina Fiberglass Products Co.*)

Increase (or decrease) in the number of bacteria in sea water can cause the water to become toxic to organisms.

Abundant changes in bacteria can alter the carbon dioxide, the pH, or, in some cases, can even produce poisonous methane. Some aquarists store sea water for the tanks for six weeks or more in the dark to reduce bacteria, others used very fine filters or antibiotic ultra-violet lights to kill the bacteria. After long recirculation of sea water, the pH becomes permanently lowered. Nitrates accumulate, and ammonia produced by the fish and the bacterial breakdown of the plants and animals increases in the recirculating water. For example, many organic substances in sea water, such as enzymes, vitamins, pigments, amino acids, antibiotics, and toxins, are important to some animals, but disappear from the water in the closed system. The closed system prevents a certain amount of fouling of the water because it can be filtered before it is used, and organisms will not be brought into the system. Likewise, many of the disease organisms can be prevented from coming into the water by filtering and re-using the filtered water repeatedly.

The open system, on the other hand, requires clean water to be drawn

Fig. 31. In Hunterston, Scotland, warm waste water from a nuclear power plant is used to experimentally raise plaice, sole, and oysters.   (*White Fish Authority*)

in from the sea continually. The incoming sea water allows fouling organisms to enter and settle in the pipes. This can be reduced by a dual pipe system which allows one system to be closed off and fresh water pumped in for a period to kill off the fouling organisms while the companion system is being used (see *Fig. 29*).

The open system can provide good water only if the intake can be placed in an area where no silt or sand can cause a sedimentation problem in the tanks and aquaria. To overcome this difficulty, salt water wells are driven into sandy areas inshore to provide a steady water supply which can be filtered, and which usually does not have silt or fouling problems. Wells are not completely foolproof, however. Some of the wells dug by the U.S. Fish and Wildlife Services laboratories at New Jersey and Hawaii produced water unfit to hold animals. In New Jersey, the hydrogen sulfide in the water had to be extracted, and in Hawaii the water pumped was nearly oxygen-free and had to be aerated before fish could live in it.

The materials used in sea water systems must be chemically inert (see *Fig. 30*). This means that metals, especially copper, should not be used in the system's construction. Fresh water fish are affected by free metal ions in concentrations as low as a few parts per million. These ions are slightly less toxic in salt water. However, some animals, especially crustaceans, tend to accumulate the free ions from these metals and will be killed if they are exposed to the ions for a long period of time. Marine fish have been found to be sensitive to concentrations of copper at less than 0·20 parts per million. The use of plastic piping and fixtures to prevent mortality is recommended.

Detergents are lethal to aquatic organisms and should never be used to clean tanks or aquaria.

Power Plant Farms

More and more power plants are required to supply the needs of human populations. Waste water released by these plants may play an important role in sea farming. Since the coolant water released from them is generally hotter than the surrounding water, running it into ponds in northern climates can produce year-around summer conditions.

Waste water from power-generating plants can be used to increase production of the minute algal plants that serve as a food source for pond animals (*Fig. 31* shows one such installation in Scotland). Whereas in the open sea sufficient carbon dioxide is usually present to meet the requirements of phytoplankton, in concentrated, fertilized cultures phytoplankton production may be limited by a shortage of this gas. One of the waste products of power plants is flue gas containing a high concentration of carbon dioxide. In Dorset, England, flue gas containing up to 15 per cent carbon dioxide bubbled through sea water, supplied enough of this gas for diatoms to carry on photosynthesis. Centrifuging removes diatoms from the culture which can be fed to clams, shrimps, and plankton-feeding fishes.

Chapter 4

Foods, Feeding, and Fertilizers

The different groups of marine animals raised in sea farms—mollusks, crustaceans, and finfish—consume many different foods. Even within these groups there is considerable variation in feeding: some species are plankton feeders all their lives, while others consume plankton only during their early life. As adults, some crustaceans and finfish eat plants only (herbivores), others flesh only (carnivores), and still others eat both plants and flesh (omnivores).

As finfish grow, they eat more and sometimes quite different food than when they were young adults. Fish farmers must supply the proper food or fertilizer to stimulate growth of food for herbivores, or move the fish to ponds or areas where food is abundant to produce rapid growth. Because sea farmers can control the amount and type of food available to their stock, they are able to encourage rapid growth and thereby achieve early and profitable harvests.

Plankton Feeders

The young of many species feed on plankton. Hence, if the sea farmer is raising the very young stages of his stock, he must also mass-rear plankton to feed them.

Pure cultures of algae, yeasts, or tiny animals which may be suitable for feeding are often difficult to obtain and keep alive. Temperature, light conditions, and nutrients for the cultures must be controlled closely to produce large numbers of the desirable microscopic organisms for feeding.

At the U.S. Fish and Wildlife Service laboratory in Milford, Connecticut, species of marine algae were mass-cultured in tanks of natural sea water (*Fig. 32*). Often some undesirable organisms passed through the filters into their culture tanks and replaced the desired culture. To eliminate this, scientists used an artificial salt water medium. They had success with a commercial mix that can be dissolved in tap or distilled water and to which they added nitrogen and vitamins. They raised cultures in large outdoor 280-liter (74 gallon) tanks constructed of fiberglass, using the artificial salt water mix. The culture tanks, covered with plastic sheeting, were placed inside larger cooling tanks filled with circulating sea water from the nearby harbor. An air pump aerated and stirred the tanks.

In experiments in England, success in rearing the small diatom, *Phaeodactylum tricornutum*, was achieved in concrete tanks of about 1,000 liters (264 gallons) using fertilized sea water. The water used was the coolant from an electric generating plant and contained considerable carbon dioxide, an important requirement for the growth and reproduction of tiny

Fig. 32. Marine algae is mass-cultured in carboys for feeding to larval oysters at Milford, Connecticut laboratory of the United States Bureau of Commercial Fisheries.   (*E. S. Iversen*)

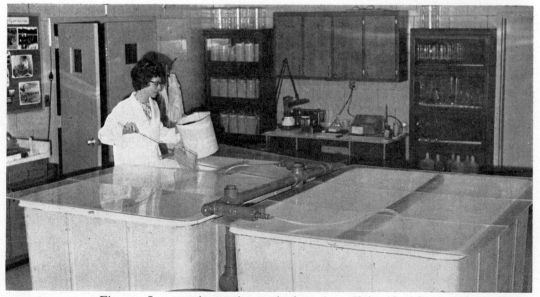

Fig. 33. Large tanks may be required to raise sufficient feed for stock fishes. Fiberglass tanks are used in experimental rearing.   (*Carolina Fiberglass Products Co.*)

plants. In the course of this work the experimenters had trouble regulating the environment in the 1,000-liter tanks (264 gallons). They replaced the large tanks with 15-liter (4 gallon) glass carboys and found they could maintain a relatively large volume of plants in them. If the cultures became contaminated with undesirable species, or died off in individual carboys, there would be less loss.

Fiberglass was also found to be a satisfactory material for construction of culture tanks (*Fig. 33*). Although one generally thinks of plastics as being non-toxic to organisms, it is advisable to test materials before setting culture tanks. Each tank should be rinsed thoroughly before use. If the fertilizers and food required for the species cultured are available, and if each culture is heavily inoculated, there is little chance for contamination in these small tanks.

The brine shrimp (*Artemia salina*) is a small crustacean that is very useful as food for young stages of fishes. The eggs of the brine shrimp must be dried before they will hatch. This aspect of their life history is valuable to the fish farmer, for the eggs can be purchased at all seasons of the year, and, if stored in a cool, dry place, will live for several years. The eggs float on the surface of the water and will hatch within about forty-eight

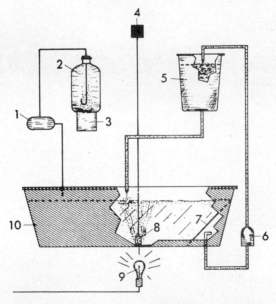

1 METERING PUMP	6 PUMP
2 DIATOM CULTURE	7 PLANKTON SCREEN
3 MAGNETIC STIRRER	8 AIR STONE
4 AIR PUMP	9 LIGHT
5 CRUSHED OYSTER SHELL FILTER	10 100-LITER FIBERGLASS AQUARIUM

Fig. 34. Arrangement for mass culture of shrimp larvae used at the United States Bureau of Commercial Fisheries Laboratory in Galveston, Texas.
(*United States Bureau of Commercial Fisheries*)

hours if maintained at a temperature of about 24 degrees centigrade (75 degrees Fahrenheit). In lieu of sea water a solution can be made of about two teaspoonfuls of common table salt to about one liter (quart) of water in which to incubate the eggs. The naupliar stages which hatch can be caught in the culture medium with a very fine-mesh cloth and transferred to containers for feeding to fish. Yeast and one-celled algae can be used to feed the young brine shrimp if it is desirable to raise them to adults and thus maintain a permanent supply of eggs.

Cultures of several single-celled algae and marine yeasts have been used to feed larval pink shrimp (*Fig. 34* shows one system). The advantage of culturing and feeding several different kinds of food is that it makes available different-sized organisms to the larval fishes and shellfishes so that they can locate and capture whichever food is most suitable for their needs. Larval fishes and shellfishes will starve in a pond of plankton too large or too active for them to ingest.

Several different foods have been used in the plaice-rearing experiments in Britain. Even naupliar stages of the brine shrimp are too large for the very young plaice, so that at first they are fed naupliar stages of barnacles. Five-day-old fish are fed a mixture of barnacle larvae and brine shrimp

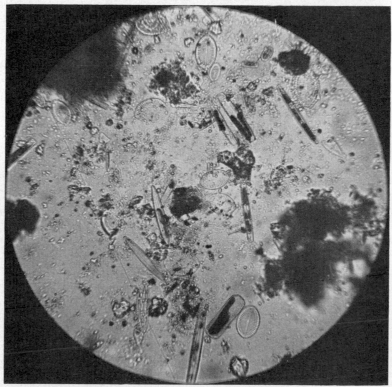

Fig. 35. Adequate plankton organisms and bottom vegetation such as is shown in this photomicrograph must be present in sea farms to serve as food for mollusks.   (*B. Havinga*)

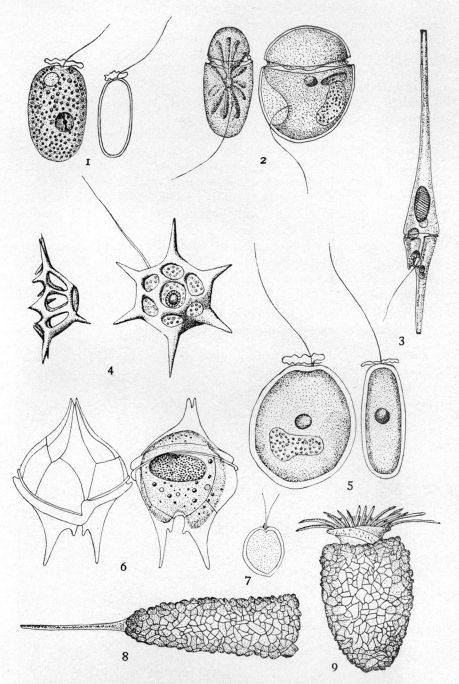

Fig. 36. Minute, variously shaped protozoans constitute food of mussels.
(*United States Bureau of Commercial Fisheries*)

larvae, and as they get older, the proportion of brine shrimp larvae is increased until pure brine shrimp larvae is being fed. After the larval plaice metamorphose, they are able to feed on larger food such as a marine worm (related to the common earthworm) which is cultured in damp peat and nourished with pre-cooked meal.

Impounded plankton feeders, such as oysters and clams, should be able to derive their food from the water which enters the ponds, but if the water exchange in the ponds is too slow it may bring insufficient food to the impounded animals and reduced production will result. *Fig. 35* shows the type of food needed and *Fig. 36* illustrates the protozoans of which mussels are fond.

Dried food which can be stored without refrigeration and fed to larval shellfish avoids the difficulties of rearing live culture for feeding. In attempts to dry algae for food at the Milford laboratory, living cultures of algae were centrifuged and freeze-dried. It was found that the dried algae would readily become re-suspended in sea water simply by shaking it vigorously. Several different species of unicellular algae were dried and found to be useful for feeding.

There are problems in using dried foods for early stages of clams and oyster larvae, but dried foods seem to have considerable potential in farming the larger stages of mollusks. Larval hard clams, fed dried unicellular algae, were raised to a stage where they metamorphosed into juveniles. They grew almost as well as if they had been fed on the best live food obtainable. On the other hand, the experimenters found that dried algae is unsuitable for raising oysters. Satisfactory dried foods have not been found for many finfish so it is still necessary to prepare culture media to feed to the small animals which in turn will be used for fish food.

Plant Feeders

Milkfish and tilapia are good examples of plant feeders. Providing feed for these species simply involves making proper conditions for the algae to grow; a dried out pond facilitates the growth of algae when it is refilled (*Fig. 37*). The procedures used in milkfish raising in the Philippines are outlined in Chapter 10. Plankton and higher plants both remain alive in ponds and are available as constant food supplies. They usually require no supplemental foods, consequently, these species which feed on plankton and higher plants (feed low on the food web) are less expensive to raise.

Flesh Feeders

Carnivores are generally quite costly to raise, for it is necessary to find a reliable source of food, refrigerate it, and feed certain amounts at regular intervals. Unlike the case with herbivores, a serious problem may develop if they are overfed because uneaten food deteriorates and fouls the water. In *Fig. 38* scrap fish is being fed to pompano.

The diet of shrimps varies geographically and with species. In Japan, algae and yeasts are fed to larval shrimps. After they become adults their food is ground-up clams spread over the water. In the Philippines,

Fig. 37. Draining and drying brackish water ponds kills predatory organisms and is believed to produce a good growth of algae when refilled.   (*W. H. Schuster*)

Fig. 38. The common pompano farmed near St. Augustine, Florida, grows rapidly when fed "scrap fish" from shrimp trawlers.   (*E. S. Iversen*)

detritus, algae, and dead or decaying fish are eaten by the sugpo shrimp. In farm ponds in India, adult shrimps are fed rice, bran, oysters, and sardines.

Artificial Fertilization of Ponds

The value of fertilizing brackish water or enclosed sea water to increase the yield of plankton as food for fish has not been well-defined. Considerable variation in results has been obtained from using fertilizers to increase production. In some studies no chemical analysis of the water were made before fertilizing to determine what plant nutrients were lacking and hence what type of fertilizer was required. When inorganic fertilizers are used, the large amounts added, in some cases, do not produce the expected blooms of plant plankton. In one experiment in Britain enormous quantities of phosphate were added to a small, brackish basin to supply needed nutrients, but phytoplankton production did not increase as sharply as was expected. Apparently most of the phosphate was adsorbed at the surface of the mud and therefore was not available to be assimilated by the phytoplankton. Also, some phytoplankton organisms have narrow phosphate tolerances.

In Scotland, inorganic fertilizer was unsuccessful in increasing plankton production. The inorganic phosphorus tended to increase the phytoplankton, but this increased the pH of the water (made it more alkaline) so much that the zooplankton desired as fish food, could not live.

Malcolm Johnson, while at Marineland Aquarium, fertilized ponds in Florida with an inorganic fertilizer containing 7 parts nitrogen, and 9 parts phosphoric acid at the rate of 91 kilograms (200 pounds) per 0·4 hectare (acre) found that in one fertilized pond only 18 kilograms (40 pounds) more mullet and in another, only 55 kilograms (122 pounds) more mullet per 0·4 hectare (acre), were obtained than in an unfertilized pond. The cost of the fertilizers in this case was much more than the value of the additional mullet produced.

Heavy fertilization may cause the rapid growth of filamentous algae and water weeds which can cause considerable difficulty if the fish in the ponds do not eat these plants. If the growth of weeds is checked by the lack of some of the nutrients which are supplied by commercial fertilizers added to the water, it is possible to get a rapid and dense bloom of undesired plants which can choke the entire pond.

Organic Versus Inorganic Fertilizers

In many areas of the world, human or farm animal wastes are poured directly into the brackish-water impoundments, causing substantial algal growth. This method of fertilization is highly unsanitary and can spread disease among humans. It is not practiced in the more advanced countries; fish farmers there use inorganic fertilizers, which, in addition to being less objectionable, do not transmit diseases dangerous to man. Besides being cleaner and easier to apply, inorganic fertilizers have the additional advantage of containing more accurately known amounts of fertilizing elements so that less poundage is required to obtain the same amounts of fertilizing elements. Inorganic fertilizers should be broadcast evenly over the pond surface. On the other hand, broadcasting organic fertilizers can cause an oxygen depletion and death of fish, especially at higher water temperatures. It is best to place organic fertilizer in small heaps on the pond bottoms, or in perforated containers spaced about 6 meters (20 feet) apart.

The cost of using inorganic fertilizers in brackish bays is too high to be practical. However, if more studies are done under controlled conditions to determine the effects of different fertilizers, perhaps it will be possible to learn to enrich such areas economically to obtain greater plankton production and, in turn, high fish production. Dr. E. J. Ferguson Wood, of the University of Miami, Institute of Marine Sciences, states (1956), "When we consider the limitations of our knowledge, it is obvious that the random fertilization of estuaries and lagoons to produce fish is likely to prove costly and wasteful, so that a thorough fundamental knowledge of the processes involved is essential to economic husbandry."

Feeds

Hatcheries in the United States' Pacific Northwest in the past fed fish frozen animal scraps, or fish scraps. These scraps had to be thawed, ground, and mixed. Ground-up meat disintegrates rapidly and scatters when placed in ponds. If these ground foods are not thoroughly mixed, the diets of fish will be unbalanced and cause variation in growth rates. In recent years, pelleted foods for feeding to trout and salmon have become popular. The dry pellet is much easier to handle and eliminates most of the steps required in preparation of fresh foods. Some experiments in which fish were fed "Oregon" pellets (developed by the State of Oregon Fish Commission) resulted in more uniform size of individual fish. The pelleted food need not be mixed; it can be eaten as compounded. There is little loss of food because the pellets stay together and can be easily found by the fish. This results in higher food utilization and less water pollution, and may prevent the growth of undesirable weeds. The pellets require less storage space and are generally cheaper than other food. Too, fish tend to contract less disease from pellets than from ground fish because the latter may contain live stages of parasites (see Chapter 14). Such pellets have a high moisture content (about 35 per cent of total weight) and contain raw ingredients so that they must be refrigerated, which is somewhat of a disadvantage.

Oregon pellets consist of a mixture of wet fish and dry meal to which supplements, such as oil and vitamins, are added. Table 3 illustrates the percentage composition of these pellets.

Good results were obtained in feeding experiments with these moist pellets when tuna viscera, flounders, dogfish, and pasteurized salmon viscera were fed to young salmon. The dogfish and tuna viscera were rated especially high in these experiments.

A method of rating artificial fish foods involves calculating "food

Table 3

OREGON PELLET FORMULAS

Ingredient	Per cent of total
Dry Mix	
Cottenseed oil meal	23·0
Herring meal	21·0
Shrimp solubles[1]	6·0
Wheat germ meal	3·6
Distillers, dried corn solubles	2·4
Vitamin premix	1·5
Wet Mix	
Corn oil	1·8
Choline chloride (liquid, 70 per cent)	0·65
Antioxidant (Tenox IV)	0·05
Tuna viscera[2]	40·0

[1]Made from equal parts shrimp meat and condensed fish solubles, dried together.
[2]Turbot, salmon viscera, or dogfish can also be used. Salmon viscera should be pasteurized to prevent disease.
Data from Westgate, McKee, and Law, 1964.

quotients" by dividing the weight of food required to produce a known weight of fish flesh. Obviously the closer this quotient is to 1 (quotient of 1 means that 1 pound of food gives 1 pound of fish flesh), the more efficient the food is; and, conversely, the higher the quotient (quotient of 20, for example, means that 20 pounds of food are required to give 1 pound of fish flesh) the less efficient the food. In addition to the selection of foods which give low food quotients, the cost of the food is important.

The ratio of fish which can be obtained from a given amount of food differs greatly with different species, under different conditions, and in different areas. However, a figure of 10 per cent efficiency, or one pound of fish for every ten pounds of food fed, is a generally accepted conversion value. Food conversions of 1·5 and 1·3 have been achieved for fresh water catfish and trout.

Many diseases of man are caused by dietary deficiencies, for example, lack of certain vitamins in the diet cause diseases such as beriberi, rickets, and scurvy. This is also true for fish, and it is important that a well-rounded diet be fed to prevent dietary diseases. A fish with dietary disease will be noticed by its listless behavior, reduced growth, and, under severe conditions, death. Regular feeding can be and is arranged automatically in well-planned plants (*Fig. 39*).

Feeding Practices

Measuring growth of animals is difficult and complex because they grow at different rates at different times of their lives, growing most rapidly when they are young and slowing considerably when they get older. In some species, males and females often grow at different rates. During sexual maturity there is a reduction in the over-all growth because chemicals normally used in growth go into the synthesis of sex products. During the time that tilapia are brooding their young in their mouths they cannot feed and hence do not grow.

Fig. 39. A clock mechanism meters fixed amounts of food at regular intervals at this Danish hatchery.   (*Dansk Orredfoder A/S*)

Most food an animal eats is required for the maintenance of body processes, so that in farming animals, considerably more food is fed to them than is converted to flesh. Maintenance feeding by specialized farmers has made it possible to hold young fish inexpensively throughout the year, for sale to farmers who then raise them to market sizes. This is commonly practiced with milkfish.

Numerous complications arise in attempting to find the best food and rate of feeding for fish. If feeding is either too light or too heavy, it will affect the growth of the animals. In cases where feeding is too light, while the fish may not be starved, they may expend a lot of energy seeking food. If the concentration of food on which shellfish are feeding is too high, some animals, such as oysters, will stop feeding. If the sizes of the fish in the experimental aquaria are considerably different, this, too, will affect growth. There is a size hierarchy effect: the small fish in company with large fish do not eat as much as larger fish perhaps because of the presence of the larger fish. Concentrations of fish will show considerable difference in growth in a fixed amount of water. Because of so many variables, it is impossible to provide accurate figures on amounts of food to feed for for different situations. *Fig. 40* shows one arrangement for satisfactory feeding.

Fig. 40. Compressed air is used in this outdoor feed dispenser set to serve a number of ponds. They can be set for the best rate and the time of feeding.

(*Dansk Orredfoder A/S*)

For the fish farmer to profit, he must experiment to determine if he is able to increase the growth of his stock by using certain foods and feeding rates.

In Honolulu, Java tilapia were fed at the rate of 2 per cent of the total fish weight on eight kinds of food to determine which was best. Feeds of small-sized particles such as powdered rice bran, powdered millrun, and powdered or granular chicken mash were not efficiently consumed, and the uneaten feed tended to foul the tanks. Alfalfa with about 28 per cent fiber, or rabbit food with about 21 per cent fiber, were poorly digested and accumulated on the pond bottoms and caused fouling. Trout pellets were most satisfactory.

Fig. 41. Automatic feeding device used to feed young rainbow trout before transfer to brackish water ponds in background.
(*Australian News and Information Bureau*)

Crowding tilapia in ponds, too, tends to reduce growth despite the food available to them. Concentrations of fifteen tilapia, five per 30 centimeters square (square foot) of pond surface, showed faster growth over twelve weeks than did any other density of fish up through ninety-two per 30 centimeters square (square foot) in the 840-liter (220 gallon) tanks.

Seasonal water temperatures affect the rate at which fish feed. As water warms, fish consume more food, and less as it cools. Fish farmers must adjust the amount of food given as they gain experience in fish feeding behavior and *Fig. 41* illustrates one useful arrangement.

For some species, feeding practices must be modified for an extended period prior to harvesting. The feeds used sometimes may impart a flavor or color to farm-raised fish that is not as desirable to humans as that of wild fish. By feeding special food for limited periods, perhaps for a month prior to harvest, the flavor can be improved. This is often done in trout farms. The color of oyster meats is improved in France by placing them in claires (ponds with certain micro-organisms) (see Chapter 7).

It is difficult to estimate costs of food and fertilizer to raise fish because so many factors cause variations. Costs have been calculated for hatcheries, but these costs involve labor and capital expenditure and the cost of the food alone cannot be easily extracted.

The subject covered in this chapter bears heavily on the future success of sea farming. Advances in our knowledge of nutrition of fishes and new feeds and fertilizers can greatly increase production from sea farms. Examples of required research and development are:

(1) Dried feeds which can be easily stored.
(2) Inexpensive feeds.
(3) Feeds which contain the nutrients required for rapid growth and which do not taint the flavor.
(4) Increasing natural foods in ponds by fertilization.

An exciting possibility of increasing production of fish ponds at low cost lies in new types of pelleted and encapsulated foods. Some research has been devoted to placing nutrients into tiny capsules similar to those used for medical purposes. Under specific conditions, the nutrients inside the capsules will be released to provide a balanced diet.

CHAPTER 5

Improvement Through Artificial Selection

Genetics is the science of heredity which attempts, among other things, to determine the inheritance or the passing on of characters from one generation to the next. In nature, within species, animals mate more or less randomly with regard to those particular characters in which man is interested. When breeding animals for sea farming, man seeks offspring which possess resistance to disease, rapid growth, early-in-life reproduction, and high fecundity. By artificial selection man can breed animals for these characteristics in a species, and the species is thus improved. Artificial selection can be done without a thorough knowledge of genetics, but the results may be far less valuable than if the mechanism of inheritance first were studied, because either the desired characters may not be inherited or other undesirable ones may manifest themselves.

The land farmer can draw upon a huge fund of scientific research pertaining to all phases of his occupation; genetics for stock breeding, entomology for pest control, agronomy for crops, and many other specialities. The sea farmer, on the other hand, must labor in comparative ignorance.

It is well known that by artificial plant and animal breeding man can produce organisms more suitable to his needs by techniques in selection and inbreeding of plants or animals for traits desirable to his plan. Offspring with these special traits are selected and permitted to breed for generations until a new strain is developed which exhibits the desired traits. Offspring of each new generation not possessing the desired traits are then prevented from breeding.

Examples of artificial selection are everywhere. Selective breeding and the perpetuation of mutations (new characters produced by gene changes) have produced many breeds of domestic animals that differ greatly from their wild ancestors. For instance, Plymouth Rock and Rhode Island Reds, chickens which are good meat producers (up to 3·6 kilograms (8 pounds) each), were bred from the wild jungle fowl of India. In their natural state these birds were small and slender. White Leghorn hens, which average anywhere from 120 to 200 eggs per year, were selectively bred from the same Indian fowl which laid only 12 to 24 eggs per year. The selective breeding of beef cattle (Herefords, Shorthorns, Aberdeen Angus) and high milk producers (Holstein-Friesian and Jersey) are classics in the practical application of the principles of genetics. Instances where artificial selection has produced disease-resistant plants and animals are well known. For example, about fifty years ago, in the British Isles,

Fig. 42. Fish spawned and raised in farms can be selected for fast growth and other desirable characteristics. Selected trout are thrown live into boxes as the four men are doing. Rejects are released behind for further growth.

(*Snake River Trout Co.*)

wheat was bred which was superior to existing wheat in many ways, including being resistant to rust, a fungus disease.

But what about selective breeding of fish? Can fish geneticists match or exceed the success achieved by other plant and animal breeders? Fish produce very large numbers of offspring, and many species become sexually mature in a relatively short time, so the fish geneticists have some advantages over, for example, cattle breeders.

Early Experiments

In fresh water, artificial selection has been applied to several fish species such as carp, goldfish, and trout. For instance, in trout hatcheries selective breeding experiments have resulted in marked increases in the rate of growth, egg production, and resistance to disease. After four generations of artificial selection, trout held at a New Jersey hatchery during the 1920s by Dr. G. C. Embody and his co-workers showed an increase in length at the end of their second year from 25 centimeters (10 inches) to almost 35 centimeters (14 inches). In some experimental lots the trout grew two or three times that of other lots during the first summer (see *Fig. 42*).

Since many diseases in fresh water hatcheries are difficult to eradicate, the development of resistant strains of fish provides a promising means of combating disease. Evidence collected at the New Jersey hatchery in 1920

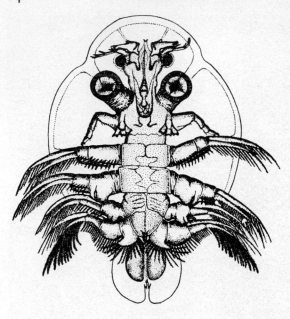

Fig. 43. Artificial selection
can result in strains of fish
which will be resistant to
parasites such as this "fish
louse."
(*United States Bureau of
Commercial Fisheries*)

showed that the offspring from parents selected for resistance to disease
had a much greater survival than other offspring (*Fig. 43*).

When Dr. Embody's results were presented at the American Fisheries
Society meeting in 1925, the experiment was hailed as marking the beginning of a new epoch in fish culture. In the discussion that followed,
fish culturists raised the question of whether failure of the stock might not
result from the crossing of brother and sister, but received no satisfactory
answer. It has been believed for years that inbreeding is dangerous and can
develop undesirable traits, so our society's laws ban humans from marrying
close relatives. Our attitudes in this respect have been projected to animals. It is true that a race, as a whole, subjected to inbreeding tends to
degenerate, but it is just as true that some planned inbreeding with *wise
and careful selection* will improve a race.

Mutations

Sometimes gene changes cause new characters called mutations to
appear. These gene changes are inheritable. Many extreme mutations or
odd individuals occur in nature, but are not seen by man because in the
process of natural selection predators consume those fish that are in any
way handicapped. It is by mutations and this process of natural selection
that fish populations are able to evolve and become better adapted to their
environment. Mutations, however, are not necessarily more desirable to
man. Mutations often appear in goldfish offspring, and have been per-
petuated in the "popeye," "veil tail," and "lionheads," which are familiar
aquaria fish but of no value other than that they are more attractive to
man.

Fig. 44. Spawned earlier from selected parents at this hatchery at the University of Washington, adult salmon return from the sea up this narrow fishway (center, near man). *(K. Waldron)*

Selected Salmon

Scientists are artificially breeding a stock of chinook salmon, *Oncorhynchus tshawytscha*, with desirable characters. Dr. L. Donaldson and his co-workers at the University of Washington College of Fisheries in Seattle have been carrying out selective breeding experiments on these fish for many years. They have successfully bred stocks which are more resistant to high temperatures and disease, which mature earlier, and which have a higher survival rate than the non-selected stocks.

The chinook is a good species for study because, in common with other salmon, part of its life is spent in fresh water and the other part in the sea. The salmon return to their "home streams" to spawn, and, by man's design, it can be so arranged that a hatchery trough becomes the home stream. This is being done at the University of Washington College of Fisheries as shown in *Fig. 44.* Here runs of chinook salmon are released year after year to pass through Puget Sound into the Pacific Ocean. When they reach three or four years of age, after traveling thousands of miles, the survivors make their way back to Puget Sound, up the "fish ladder" (a series of stepped pools), and into the very hatchery trough from which they came years before.

Hybrids

Another type of artificial selection is to cross generic and specific lines to produce hybrids. An example of a hybrid is the mule, a cross between the female horse and the ass.

Fresh water and marine fish are occasionally found in nature that resemble two closely related species, but are midway between them and are considered to be hybrids. For example, crosses are found between trout species. What might be expected from such a cross is greater vitality, resistance to unfavorable environmental conditions, and sturdier offspring than those possessed by either of the parent lines. This phenomenon, common in plants and animals, is called "heterosis" or "hybrid vigor." Crosses between inbred lines bring the dominant genes for vigor forward from one of the parent stocks.

An experiment involving hybrids is underway in Puget Sound, Washington, to produce a salmon more desirable to the consumer from two species of eastern Pacific salmon found in this area. The chum salmon, *Oncorhynchus keta*, which run every year, have a fine flavor but the meat color is light and less appetizing than other salmon, and they will not take a fishing lure. The pink salmon ("humpies"), *O. gorbuscha*, are abundant only during odd-numbered years, have a pink meat, and will take lures. These two species have been crossed with the hope of producing a hybrid with desirable features of both species. First catches of the returning adult hybrids, called "chumpies," are stronger fish than the pinks and have darker meat than the chums. Still to be determined is the possibility of this hybrid reproducing on its own, and the establishment of even-year runs. If this can be done, it will aid the commercial fishery and someday perhaps help in making salmon farming possible.

In Britain a flatfish hybrid of the plaice and the flounder produces a fish that has good eating qualities with a more rapid growth rate than either parent.

Crosses between *Tilapia nilotica* and *T. mossambica* were mated and produced a hybrid which could withstand colder temperatures than *T. mossambica*. *T. nilotica* has a greater tolerance to cold water than *T. mossambica*, and a cross of these two species suggested that the resulting hybrid should have a greater tolerance to cold. The result: the hybrid's tolerance was midway between the two parents; in addition, it showed a better survival rate than the parents, it grew faster and had a more efficient food conversion (fish weight produced for food consumed) than either of the parent species (*Fig. 45*).

In producing hybrids, exact identification of the species of the parent stock is important. Because the characteristics used by biologists to classify species involve minute differences in appearance or numbers, i.e. numbers of fin rays, numbers of scales, etc., and shows further that the characteristics vary, exact identification of individuals used as parents in artificial selection experiments often cannot be determined. Since the identity of parents is often confused, persons wishing to carry out artificial selection on their own may find completely different results from those found in previous work.

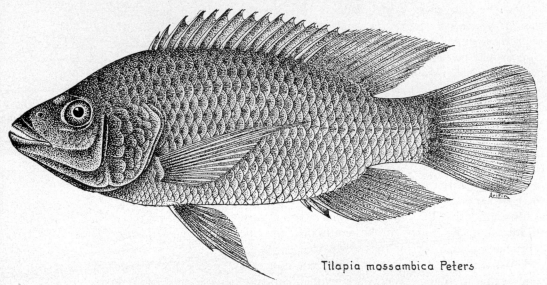

Tilapia mossambica Peters

Fig. 45. Experimental breeding of Java tilapia has produced more desirable fish for farming. (*Indo-Pacific Fisheries Council*)

Advances in Shellfish and Fish Breeding

There is no doubt that the application of artificial selection has proven successful in breeding both fresh-water fish and salmon which live in both fresh and salt water. What about the truly marine fish and shellfish? What progress has been made with them on artificial selection and the management of stocks by artificial selection?

The American oyster, *Crassostrea virginica*, can be cited as an example of a species in need of help from fish genetics. There are estimated to be at least thirty recognized diseases in oyster stocks, and others for which pathologists are at a loss to find causative agents. The combined oyster production of Maryland and Virginia has declined from 22 million bushels in 1890 to less than 6 million in 1961, in part due to disease. Very likely it is possible to breed disease-resistant stocks of oysters, the young of which could be introduced into oyster culture areas. This technique could drastically reduce natural mortality and the result would be greater production.

For many years, man has wanted to cross various species of shellfish to obtain hybrids possessing desirable attributes and thereby increase their value to man. However, to do this one must be able to raise the experimental animals from eggs to adults. In 1950, Dr. Victor Loosanoff and his co-workers at the Milford, Connecticut, laboratory were able, through large-scale research, to find means of rearing from eggs and feeding and holding the delicate larval stages. Former attempts to do this had failed. With this significant contribution they cleared the way for experiments on improvement by selective breeding of shellfish.

One shellfish cross easily made is between the northern hard shell clam, *Mercenaria mercenaria*, and the southern hard shell clam, *M. campechiensis*. An experiment was made to determine whether the resultant cross would be faster growing and larger. The experiment, although appearing simple, was not. These hybrid clams, along with young of the pure-bred parent stock, were sent to different laboratories in the United States to be planted so that biologists could compare the growth of offspring of these lines with the hybrids. Similar environments had to be provided for the young of the hybrid and young of the parent line in order that the comparison could be valid. The results of the experiment were encouraging.

In one of the rearing experiments in Chesapeake Bay, the offspring from these two species of clams were placed in screened boxes and held as long as fifteen months. The hybrids showed superior growth over their northern parents, but the young of the southern clams did not survive the exceptionally cold winter of 1955.

Thus, while the first attempts were not noticeably successful, they do suggest that more experiments are justified. If some parents can be found, the hybrids of which have increased growth as well as equal or lower mortality than native clams, then progress towards greater yields will be made.

In other shellfish experiments, P. E. Chanley, at Milford, Connecticut, reared offspring of a pair of hard clams up to twenty-eight months of age. He selected 120 of the largest clams as brood stock and reared them to forty-four months of age. Out of these he selected a large male and female and crossed them to see if they would beget larger offspring than the average. To obtain measurements of average growth, he bred a female with two males, picked at random from wild stock. At the end of fifteen months, 200 clams were randomly selected from the controls and 200 from the selectively-bred clams. The total volume of the selectively-bred clams was about 60 per cent greater than that of the control clams.

Encouraged by these results, shellfish biologists believe that a rapid-growing strain of hard clams can be developed from stringently selected brood stock in just a few generations.

Russian researchers are greatly concerned over the decreasing supply of caviar. In an effort to obtain more of this valuable fish roe (currently selling at about $40 a pound), studies on cross-breeding of sturgeons with sterlets (both *Acipenser*) are under way. It is hoped that the hybrid offspring will grow faster and produce more caviar by breeding more often, or at a younger age, and that the hybrid will be able to live in fresh water lakes, rivers, and reservoirs in the U.S.S.R. While crosses of these two species have been made by Soviet scientists, it is not yet known how the caviar will taste, or even whether the offspring of the cross is fertile. *Fig. 46* shows one of the hybrids.

Dr. C. F. Hickling, an authority on pond culture, crossed a male of what was thought to be *Tilapia mossambica* from Zanzibar with a female of what was thought to be *T. mossambica* from Malaysia. This mating

Fig. 46. A beluga-sterlet hybrid may produce more caviar for gourmets.
(*N. J. Nikoljuki* in *Fishing News International*)

produced 98 per cent to 100 per cent male offspring, a result which has considerable value since the species has a tendency to over-reproduce. However, when the female from Zanzibar was crossed with the male from Malaysia, the hybrids produced had a ratio of three males to one female. All-male offspring presents some disadvantages. (*Fig. 47* deals with the problem of hand sorting.) In actual farming it is hard to keep some females from getting into the male ponds, and so reproduction goes on and upsets the numbers stocked, although at a much lower rate than if the fishes had been carelessly hand-sorted. Another disadvantage is the male tilapia's nest-making instinct. Simply because no females are present does not prevent the males from building nests. And since hybrid males are large, they make quite large nests, preferring to build near the dikes on the edges of the ponds. After several generations have been raised in a pond there is the possibility of collapse of the dikes. It is suggested that perhaps all-female hybrids should be sought by artificial selection which would thereby avoid the nest-building problem. The growth of the female hybrids in the tilapia crosses to date has been slower, however, than male hybrids.

Still another possible use of artificial selection is the production of fish stocks that are resistant to pesticides. Some fish have been found to survive in areas that are heavily contaminated with pesticides. The young from these fish were also pesticide-resistant, suggesting that it may be possible to produce fish for sea farms that can withstand at least low levels of some pesticides.

Fig. 47. The development of monosex strains of Java tilapia eliminated hand-sorting of young. Fertilization of ponds in many tropical countries is accomplished by housing farm animals at edge of pond as seen in right background.
(*FAO-Jack Ling*)

Controlled Spawning

Controlled spawning may be a boon to successful farm production for some marine fish. Using hormones to induce fish to spawn apparently was started in Brazil about 1932. Experiments with fresh-water channel cat-fish, *Ictalurus lacustris*, in Oklahoma recently were promising. The pituitary hormones from carp, with which the catfish are injected, at first successfully induced spawning. Because carp pituitaries are sometimes hard to obtain, scientists tried the readily available human chorionic gonadotropin. This mammalian hormone also proved effective in inducing spawning.

The catfish experiments provide solutions to obtaining many generations of fish for culturists studying fish genetics, and also permits greater production of young fish in captivity. They were able to increase channel catfish fry production at a hatchery station from 82,000 to about 700,000 or an increase of over 850 per cent. Variations and peculiarities in spawning times, as well as lack of a special spawning season, were overcome by hormone injections.

Hormone-injected fish can simplify a fish farmer's job. If non-injected adult pond fish are permitted to spawn over an extended period, the young will be of different ages, and hence different sizes, so that larger fish (in cannibalistic species) eat the smaller, and in non-cannibalistic species take a disproportionate share of food from smaller fish. For these reasons fish farmers must seine all fish out of their ponds and separate them, by sizes, into different ponds. The use of artificial hormones induces both males and females to mate at a determined time, which permits fish farmers to hand-strip the fish (remove eggs and sperm) and fertilize the eggs by hand. The young in any pond will then be of rather uniform age and size, making extensive seining, separating, and grading unnecessary.

Two disadvantages to keeping brood stocks in ponds with offspring are that diseases are passed from the brood stock to the offspring, and that predation by the adults on the young can occur; both clearly reduce hatchery and farm output. Again, by using hormones and hand-stripping the fish, farmers take over the job of the adults and the brood stock is kept separate from the young, thereby reducing losses.

So we see that with hormones it is possible to produce fantastically large numbers of fish, and, by selective breeding, select strains that grow faster, mature earlier, are more disease-resistant, are less sensitive to their environment, and produce greater yields. The possibilities for improvement in fish farming are great.

Additional Considerations

The fish farmer should not be deluded into thinking that all he has to do is take a few desirable-looking fish, cross them, select desirable-looking young from these crosses, then mate these to produce a new strain which is desirable from a sea-farming standpoint (see *Fig. 48*). In actual fact, work

Fig. 48. Fresh water rainbow trout farms are successful because of the development of strains of desirable fish. Mass rearing of young from known parents and tedious measurements are required to produce new strains.

(Virginia Trout Co.)

on hybrids and artificial selection in general requires considerable space and many ponds because the various broods must be kept separate and measurements made of the individuals. This experimentation is very expensive for the fish farmer because while fish grow rapidly, much time is required to carry the crosses through several generations to observe whether the characters breed true (Table 4). Another practical consideration is that of providing similar facilities for the parent and the offspring of the crosses. The only way it can be decided whether the offspring possess more desirable qualities than the parents is to provide both groups with similar nourishment, environment, and so forth. If there is any difference in the kind or amount of food provided one group or the other, the result of the experiment will have little value because it will be impossible to tell whether there is an increase in the rate of growth as a result of the cross, the care, or the food provided. In general, artificial selection requires considerable care and expense over a long period of time. It is the sort of research which can and should be carried out by government laboratories and biologists. The sea farmer should seek all available literature on the subject of artificial selection of fishes and consult with research laboratories for results of recent studies. There is, however, a dismaying lack of research on fish genetics. This research, if done, would greatly aid sea farming.

It is equally as easy to lose desirable qualities in a fish by artificial

Table 4

DIAGRAM ILLUSTRATING EFFORT REQUIRED TO PRODUCE A
STRAIN OF FISH WITH MORE RAPID GROWTH BY ARTIFICIAL
SELECTION

Parents selected by numerous measurements for rapid growth
male × female
numerous offspring

First generation
1. Raise all offspring to adults for perhaps two years, with uniform care and environment.
2. Measure growth at frequent intervals.
3. Select several pairs with rapid growth and no undesirable characteristics, such as high susceptibility to disease or those which spawn late in life.
4. Cross selected pairs.

male × female   male × female   male × female   male × female
numerous young numerous young numerous young numerous young

Second generation
1. Raise all offspring to adults for perhaps two years, with uniform care and environment.
2. Measure growth at frequent intervals.
3. Select several pairs with rapid growth and no undesirable characteristics, such as high susceptibility to disease or those which spawn late in life.
4. Cross selected pairs.

Repeat until young show consistently more rapid growth and no undesirable characteristics.

selection as it is to breed in desirable qualities. If a fish farmer, for example, by artificial selection, is able to produce more rapid growth in a stock of pond fish, he may lose characteristics such as resistance to disease, and so his work may be for naught. In artificial breeding of rainbow trout, *Salmo gairdnerii,* in Washington State, early maturity was successfully obtained by selective breeding. A high percentage of the stock (about 62 per cent) matured at two years of age rather than as the majority at three; however, it was found that early maturity tended to retard growth to some extent and also lowered the average egg production by the early maturing females. The female rainbows that spawned as two-year-olds produced only between 600 and 900 eggs; the rainbows that spawned at the normal maturity of three years produced 1,500 to 2,000 eggs, with some occasionally producing up to 3,000.

It should not be concluded that very high egg production is a desirable quality per se. In cases where parental care is involved for the eggs or fry, survival, either in the nest or later, may drop off as their numbers increase because there may be a limit to the number the parents can protect or care for.

In the next six chapters we discuss the groups of organisms of greatest importance to sea farming. Each of these groups, except milkfish, involve numerous species which have similar life history patterns. But there is considerable natural variation in biological processes such as growth within even a single species in a single geographic location. This variation increases in different areas and with different, though related, species. Selected important representative species of the various groups and some general farming techniques for them are outlined.

III
PRESENTLY FARMED SPECIES

Chapter 6

Seaweeds

Seaweeds and large marine algae (many of which are called "kelp") are classified by botanists according to several characteristics, including color. Some are blue-green, some green, some brown, and some red, the latter two marine algae being the most valuable commercially (see *Fig. 49*).

Many species of algae occur along the sea coasts, mostly in the intertidal

Fig. 49. These young giant kelp are harvested off the coast of California.

(*California Dept. of Fish and Game, J. W. Schott*)

zones. In Canada, about 300 species grow along the Atlantic coast. Of the numerous species of algae which occur in Hawaii, over seventy are edible.

Commercial algae, with few exceptions, are gathered in public areas. They are used as thickening agents in many processed foods, such as soups and ice cream, and are nutritious foods in their own right. One species of red algae, dulse, consists of about 25 per cent protein, about 44 per cent carbohydrates, and 27 per cent mineral salts. Agar, algin, and carrageenan are important algal products. Agar, a jelling agent, is useful in the home and in the laboratory. Algin, used in ice cream and chocolate milk drinks, has other uses in manufacturing and in laboratories. Carrageenan is used in the food industry as a stabilizer, in drugs such as cough syrups, dental impression material, in cosmetics such as shampoos, and in industry, in such as paper, paint, and rubber. These are but a few examples. Most algae contain important minerals and vitamins valuable to the human body.

Seaweed Cultivation

Increased popularity of underwater diving gear has encouraged visions of, and suggestions about, farming algae. The scuba diver is pictured as planting, cultivating, and gathering algae underwater, much the same as the land farmer works his fields ashore. Algae are farmed in Korea and Japan, but not as yet by such modern means as underwater diving gear. The farms in Japan, the only country in which extensive seaweed culture is done at this time, are in the intertidal zone where no under-water gear is needed.

Cultivation of red algae (they call it "nori" or "amanari") in Japan has been done for many years, probably originated in Tokyo Bay in the late seventeenth century. It was widely practiced there in the early nineteenth century, and as early as around 1900 production was in excess of 22,700 metric tons (25,000 tons), valued at over $400,000. Algae cultivation is still a large industry in Japan, but is mostly a sideline for fishermen and land farmers, with an estimated 70,000 algae farmers engaged in raising this crop. Because it is a winter crop, red algae is uniquely suited as a sideline for land farmers.

Small quantities of nori are eaten fresh, but most is sun-dried before being sold. Sand, mud, and other foreign substances occur together with the seaweed when it is removed from the netting or twigs, so that the seaweed must be washed. The fronds are chopped fine and spread on small bamboo mats, then dried in the open air. After drying, the sheets of nori are stripped from the nets, pressed, and marketed. The customer heats the nori to crispen it, crushes it, and uses it to impart flavor in sauces, soups, or broths. Good quality nori is high in Vitamin A, containing over fifty times the amount found in an equivalent weight of hens' eggs.

The red algae cultured in Japan belong to a group of plants technically called *Porphyra*. About twenty species in this group occur in Japan. *Porphyra* has vivid, purple, gelatinous, widely expanded and lobed fronds about 45 centimeters ($1\frac{1}{2}$ feet) long.

Fig. 50. Old drawing of bundles of brush and conical frame used in Japan in planting brush to catch larval algae.
(*United States Bureau of Commercial Fisheries*)

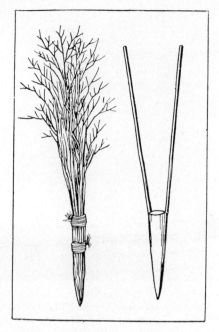

Fig. 51 (below). Working on a soft bottom, these Japanese algae farmers plant bundles of brush on which laver is to grow.
(*United States Bureau of Commercial Fisheries*)

Fig. 52. The floating spores attach to the bundles of brush in the old (vertical) method of laver culture in Japan (From *Marine Botany* by E. Yale Dawson, copyright © 1966 by Holt, Rinehart & Winston, Inc. Used by permission of the publisher.)

In the old method of nori farming (vertical method), still used today, the farmers prepare the grounds by driving numerous bundles of bamboo ("bushes"), about a meter (3 feet) in diameter, into the mud bottom in water that is about 3 to 5 meters (10 to 16 feet) deep at high tide (see *Fig. 50*). Two-man crews make deep holes in regular lines with an elongated wooden frame, which they drive into the mud by their weight alone, and then plant the bushes (*Fig. 51*). The bushes (or indeed any objects in the water) intercept and afford a place of lodgment for the floating spores of *Porphyra* which are barely visible to the naked eye. Once attached, the spores produce the marketable leafy plants (*Fig. 52*).

The modern culture method involves driving rows of bamboo poles into the tide flats between which heavy netting is stretched parallel to the surface of the water (horizontal method) (*Fig. 53*). It is important to place the netting at the proper depths within the range of tides so that it is covered most of the time, yet is occasionally exposed so that the nori can be harvested by farmers who move along the webbing in small boats and remove the algae from the nets by hand. It has been estimated that there are more than 480 kilometers (300 miles) of these nets in use in Japan today. Occasionally, instead of netting, pieces of split bamboo are tied across two pieces of rope, or across long sticks. The drifting nori spores readily attach to the closely-spaced split bamboo (*Fig. 54*).

The quality of this seaweed is best in somewhat brackish water. Too much fresh water is believed to be harmful to it. Rapid growth of nori has been obtained off river mouths in southern Japan. The combination

Fig. 53. Pump loosens bottom mud to ease placement of bamboo supports for holding nets in the modern (horizontal) method of nori culture in Japan. (From *Marine Botany*, by E. Yale Dawson, copyright © 1966 by Holt, Rinehart and Winston, Inc. Used by permission of the pubisher.)

Fig. 54. Nori nets must be placed at the correct depth so they will be submerged most of the time and yet be out of the water for picking. (From *Marine Botany*, by E. Yale Dawson, copyright © 1966 by Holt, Rinehart and Winston, Inc. Used by permission of the publisher.)

of low winter temperatures and the nutrients carried by the rivers to the sea stimulate growth. Tidal flats are dug up by bulldozers, and even plows, to release nutrients trapped in the sediments, and sometimes to channel run-off from the land into the nori farms.

In September and October, when water temperatures drop, "seeding" occurs when floating spores appear naturally in the water and attach on the bushes, nets, or bamboo. No additional cultivation is required, and harvesting of the crop usually begins early in November and continues until about March. After the season is over, the farmer removes his nets and poles and stores them until it is time for the next year's crop.

Research and Increased Production

Despite the early beginning of nori culture, the life cycle of nori was not then completely understood. It was known for many years that the young plants released spores into the water, but where the spores came from in the fall when there were no young plants around was a mystery. Without this knowledge, artificial seeding of the grounds was impossible. Then, in 1949, Dr. K. M. Drew, an English botanist, learned that an English species of *Porphyra* released spores that developed into a form, *Conchocelis*, that bores into oyster shells. Prompted by this discovery, Dr. M. Kurogi, a Japanese scientist, found that the Japanese species of *Porphyra* has a similar life cycle, and that when water temperature drops to about 22° Centigrade (72° Fahrenheit) the *Conchocelis* releases spores free into the sea to find attachment and grow to large plants.

This knowledge enables the Japanese to increase their production. After boiling oyster shells to disinfect them, they place them in the sea and lay ripe nori leaves on top of them so that the nori spores can bore into the shells. When the nets for attachment of the floating spores are placed out in the fall, the oyster shells are placed in bags and hung from the nets or placed on bamboo sticks. The spores, released from the shells by the thousands, easily find a location to settle on with the nets so close at hand.

The nets can be artificially seeded in tanks on shore before being placed in the sea. Oyster shells containing the boring stage are placed in these tanks, and the water temperature is lowered. When the spores are released and attach themselves to the nets, the nets are then ready to be placed in the sea. In some farms, nets seeded artificially have produced over 200 times as many young plants as those seeded naturally.

The Japanese are looking for ways to make use of areas of the sea where it is too deep for conventional nori culture methods. Rafts or other types of floats may be suitable in deep water. They are also considering means to fertilize semi-enclosed waters in areas where the young nori plants are growing, in order to speed up production. Occasionally a disease called red rot becomes a serious problem to nori farmers. If characteristics of the water can be used to foretell the approach of this disease, then the nets holding algae could be moved to a disease-free area. Another suggested means to improve nori farming is to develop a machine to pick the fronds

Fig. 55. Harvesting nori from the nets is a cold, slow job. Mechanical harvesters, if developed, would greatly reduce hand labor. (From *Marine Botany*, by E. Yale Dawson, copyright © 1966 by Holt, Rinehart and Winston, Inc. Used by permission of the publisher.)

from the webbing racks or bushes. A substantial saving of expensive hand labor would be realized thereby, and because nori is a winter crop, hand-picking in low water temperatures is an undesirable job (*Fig. 55*).

Japanese also practice a type of farming of the large kelps that are also used for food. These firm-textured algae have strong holdfasts, capable of withstanding battering by the surf. The *Konbu* kelp requires about two years to reach a favorable size for market. Kelp farmers place clean rocks in the sea so that the kelp will find attachment for their holdfasts. If sufficient rocks are not readily available, large boulders on land are sometimes dynamited to form rocks of suitable size with clean surfaces for spreading over the sea bottom. This is an inexpensive and widely practiced method of increasing production.

A semblance of kelp "farming" is practiced in California. Kelp cutting was begun in 1900, and during the early years rather careless harvesting methods were practiced. Too, the kelp crop became somewhat reduced due to such causes as pollution, sedimentation, water turbidity, diseases, and grazing by sea urchins. In about 1921, the California Department of Fish and Game realized that leases should be established to increase kelp production. A maximum of 40 square kilometers (25 miles) was leased to kelp cutters. These "plots" were awarded to the highest bidders. The plan worked well, and in 1950 leasing laws were changed to permit the awarding of leases on the basis of negotiations rather than on competitive bidding. The negotiations by the State of California were designed to insure harvest of the crop of kelp by reliable firms. The few companies involved in kelp harvesting cooperated fully with the state in this conservation attempt, agreeing to cut the kelp no deeper than four feet below the water surface to perpetuate the crop. Harvesting in this manner removes dense growth of fronds near the surface and allows light to penetrate to the younger plants. The growth is stimulated by increased light, and the new fronds quickly replace the harvested plants. The leasing arrangement does not involve all areas, but leaves some area open for public cutting and to prevent monopolies. The arrangement produces complete utilization of all kelp cut and, at the same time, avoids the danger of depletion.

We discuss leasing arrangements at greater length for other species; however, in general, leasing changes an area from a fishery where each individual grabs everything that can be taken before the next man get it, to one where the individuals who harvest the crop have a proprietary interest in the area. Higher and more profitable harvests for most of the people concerned result from leasing grounds.

Studies on algae farming are under way in Nova Scotia in an attempt to increase production. Wide distribution of algae on any intertidal zone in nature makes harvesting expensive because much labor is required to harvest it. Artificial cultivation permits more concentrated growth and thereby reduces farming costs. If demand for seaweed continues to increase, cultivation of this valuable crop, together with breeding and selection will be necessary to provide an adequate supply.

CHAPTER 7

Oysters

The oyster is a sedentary mollusk with two hard shells, or valves, which are attached by a hinge and are held together snugly by a strong muscle. This calcium carbonate armor shields the fleshy part of the oyster against predators and adverse environmental conditions. Unfortunately for the oyster (and oyster farmers), this armor does not provide complete protection from predators who are able to pry the shell open or to drill through the shell, especially when the oyster is young, nor does it provide lengthy resistance to pollutants since the oyster must open its shell periodically to breathe and feed.

In general, the various oyster species fall into two artificial groups: flat oysters and cup-shaped oysters. The flat oysters, so-called because both shells are flat, constitute two commercially important species of the genus *Ostrea*. The cup-shaped oysters, which are represented by four commercial species belonging to the genus *Crassostrea*, possess a flat upper shell (the one away from the substrate), but the lower shell (closest to the substrate) is cup-shaped or somewhat rounded.

Oysters extend over a wide geographic range, mainly in temperate waters. In addition to native species of oysters occurring in various regions, introduced species are found also, as a result of man's insatiable desire to transplant animals. Oysters are especially suited to his whims because they can be shipped alive over long distances with little or no water, provided they are kept cool (Table 5).

The American oyster, farmed extensively, will be used as a representative species for a discussion of the oyster's life cycle. Dr. Paul S. Galtsoff, U.S. Bureau of Commercial Fisheries, has reviewed much of the vast information on this oyster and the reader who is interested in more detail can consult his works (see References).

The American oyster lives along the Atlantic Coast of North America, southward around Florida, all around the Gulf of Mexico, and has even been introduced to Hawaii and along the Pacific Coast in California and Washington. A single ripe female may release 14 to 114 million buoyant eggs at one spawning. It is probable that under natural conditions females spawn more than once during the breeding season. Egg fertilization is external; in fact, the water becomes milky white by the multitudinous sperm cells released by the males. The fertilized eggs develop in a few hours into free-swimming, delicate larva called "veligers" (*Fig. 56*). These weak swimmers are carried by the current for about two to three weeks, when they attach themselves by a small but well-developed foot to a relatively clean surface. Once attached, the young oyster transforms into a "spat" stage

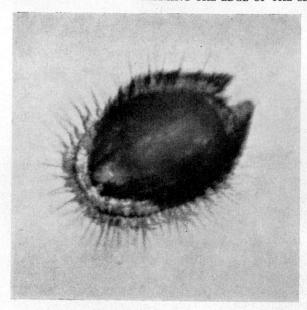

Fig. 56. Photomicrograph of a free-swimming oyster larvae (two weeks old). The fine hairs vibrate rhythmically to keep the larva floating for transport by tidal currents.

(greatly enlarged)
(*Virginia Institute of Marine Science*)

and begins development of its shell. It was thought for years that the spawning female oysters spat out their young which are found attached to surfaces, hence the name. The American oyster, in common with many bivalves, changes its sex during life and changes from male when young to female later in life and will even change back to male between spawning seasons.

Table 5

SOME SPECIES OF COMMERCIALLY IMPORTANT FOOD AND PEARL OYSTERS

Species	Common Name	Geographical Distribution[1]
FLAT OYSTERS		
Ostrea edulis	Flat oyster	Coast of Europe
	Native European oyster	(Maine, U.S.A.)
Ostrea lurida	Olympia oyster	Alaska to Lower California
CUP-LIKE OYSTERS		
Crassostrea angulata	Portuguese oyster	Coast of Europe
Crassostrea virginica	American oyster	Canada, Atlantic coast
	Eastern oyster	Atlantic coast of U.S.A., Gulf of Mexico to Mexico. (California to Washington and Hawaii)
Crassostrea gigas	Japanese oyster	Japan (Alaska to California)
	Pacific oyster	
Crassostrea commercialis	Sydney rock oyster	Australia (Hawaii)
PEARL OYSTERS		
Pinctada martensii	Japanese pearl oyster	Japan
Pinctada emarginata	Margarita pearl oyster	Venezuela

[1]Oysters have been transplanted to locations in parenthesis.

Oysters feed by pumping water between their valves, filtering out the micro-organisms in the water by specially adapted hair-like structures on the gills which also serve to move the food through the mouth. The number

Table 6

SUMMARY OF INFORMATION ON THE AMERICAN OYSTER
Crassostrea virginica

Identification:	The valve closest to the substrate to which the oyster is attached is cup-shaped; the upper shell is generally flat; the shell shapes vary greatly.
Distribution:	Atlantic Coast of North America; Gulf of Mexico from Florida to Mexico; West Indies; San Francisco, California.
Age and growth:	Maritime Provinces of Canada, four to seven years to reach 7·6 centimeters (3 inches); may reach 38 centimeters (15 inches) in 20 years. Long Island Sound of United States, one year to reach 1·9 centimeters (¾ inch), three years to 7·6 centimeters (3 inches), Gulf of Mexico, two years to reach 8·9 centimeters (3½ inches).
Reproduction:	Spawning takes place when the temperature increases within a range of from 20 degrees to 32 degrees Centigrade (68 degrees to 90 degrees Fahrenheit). Individual females release 14 to 114 million eggs free in the water. Fertilization is external.
Food:	Planktonic plants and animals.
Feeding habits:	Food is drawn into gills by the beating of many small hairs (cilia) and is moved along by the hairs to the lips and mouth.

of micro-organisms in the water affects feeding: if they are numerous, the rate of feeding (pumping) will be lower, and if the numbers of organisms are low, the oysters' rate of feeding will be higher. If the temperature of the water drops to a low level, the oysters reduce the rate of feeding or close their valves and cease feeding. Oysters in the intertidal zone close their valves and cease feeding any time they are left high and dry, or if certain pollutants occur in the water. They can extract oxygen from the water trapped within their shells. Numerous and prolonged interruptions in feeding reduce the growth rate. Since good spawning areas are not necessarily good growing areas, oyster farmers might find it is advisable to move the oysters after the spat (attachment) stage to a fertile area which will result in rapid growth and good quality oysters. (*Fig. 57* shows the anatomy of an oyster.)

Since fecundity is, in effect, a means by which animals compensate for mortality, the extremely large numbers of eggs released by female oysters (and other marine animals) foreshadows the extremely high mortality rate caused by unfavorable environmental conditions, competitors, diseases, predators, or a combination of these. By reducing this mortality sea farmers can obtain greater production than occurs naturally (as in *Fig. 58*). However, the extent to which natural mortality can be reduced by careful farming procedures may be small, because in the course of impounding some animals, and in substituting artificial for natural

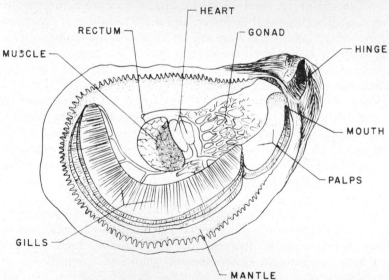

Fig. 57 (below). Anatomy of an oyster.
         (*United States Bureau of Commercial Fisheries*)

Fig. 58 (above). Good growing conditions for oysters are found
in this New South Wales farm.
         (*Australian News and Information Bureau*)

environment, other complications arise. But even a relatively small increase in the survival rate of animals which produce numerous eggs can result in a large number of offspring which survive to market sizes.

If conditions are suitable in Long Island Sound, the American oyster will grow to a length of 9 centimeters ($3\frac{1}{2}$ inches) in four to five years. In the Gulf of Mexico this oyster grows faster, reaching the same length in about two years. Colder water and winter hibernation reduce growth rates at the higher latitudes. It is important to mention at this point that growth figures for shellfish should be read carefully because different measurements of growth are used. For example, if oysters grow in tight clusters, they may be long and thin (see *Fig. 59*). Thus the shell length of these oysters may not be a good measure of their growth, especially if it is compared with measurements of oysters which are allowed to grow individually and are nearly circular in shell outline.

An alternate method of measurement, one of the best ways because of the commercial importance, is the yield of meat. The meat yield of individual oysters from locations along the Atlantic Coast of the United States may be greater than in the Gulf of Mexico despite warmer water in the Gulf. The environment in the Chesapeake Bay region is ideally suited to the requirements of the American oyster; temperature alone does not determine the rate of growth or fatness of the oyster, but the interaction of a number of conditions such as the amount of food and the water temperature, the amount of food and salinity, or combinations of these and many

Fig. 59. Oysters growing on natural reefs on this tidal flat in Florida are subject to the ravages of predators, and because of crowding, produce long, thin shells.   (*E. S. Iversen*)

other environmental factors important in producing rapid growth and high quality oysters for the table.

The oyster native to the Pacific west coast in North America is a small, round oyster, called the Olympia oyster, *Ostrea lurida*. Apparently it is an old-established species, for fossil remains have been found 61 meters (200 feet) or more below the ground. These oysters were fished commercially before the turn of the century, with shiploads being sent to market in San Francisco. Because they were exploited heavily and no attempt was made to conserve them, by 1870 they began to show signs of depletion. In Washington State the Olympia oyster declined rapidly and has not been commercially important there since about 1920. In the last six years there has been increased setting and survival in some locations. Local growers attribute this change to reduced pollution from pulp wood plants.

The American oyster was transplanted to the State of Washington about 1895, and also market-sized oysters were later shipped there. The American oyster became popular there because it was considerably larger than the Olympia oyster. Too, many consumers, who had gone west remembered and liked the American oyster. However, their cultivation was not successful and about 1920 they were wiped out by an unidentified cause. Shipping of market-sized American oysters from the Atlantic Coast was too expensive to be profitable.

Before 1900 when the Olympia oyster catches were declining, consideration was given to transplantation of the Japanese oyster, *Crassostrea gigas*, from Japan to the west coast of North America. Attempts to establish spawning stocks of this species have been unsuccessful. Although the Japanese oyster still does not spawn successfully to any degree in American waters, it does grow very well, reaching about 30 centimeters (12 inches) long. Only 80 to 140 meats are required to fill a gallon container, while the tiny Olympia oyster takes about 1,600 to 2,200 meats to fill the same container. Despite many attempts to get this immigrant oyster to spawn in North American waters it has been accomplished only occasionally in some areas. Except for a few locations as in Canada, spawning is so irregular that a dependable seed stock cannot be obtained for farming. Production of Japanese oysters in the United States Pacific Northwest, which may reach over 3.7 million kilograms (8 million pounds) annually, is solely dependent upon seed oysters brought all the way from Japan (*Fig. 60*).

Farming Oysters

Oyster farming is old. The Japanese and the Romans are the earliest known oyster farmers. Until recently these pioneer farming operations lacked scientific knowledge about the biology of the oyster, and as a result all the early methods were "rule-of-thumb" using trial and error experimentation.

Many biologists have devoted their lives to the study of oyster biology. Havinga and Korringa in Holland, Costé in France, Yonge in England,

Fig. 60. In Washington State, Pacific oysters are raised from Japanese seed stock.
(*E. N. Steele*)

Stafford in Canada, Galtsoff, Loosanoff, A. E. Hopkins, and Nelson on the Atlantic Coast of the United States, and Kincaid on the Pacific Coast are examples. Many oyster farmers also played important roles in further-ing oyster farming—Steele, who pioneered the transplantation of the Japanese oyster in Washington State, and Mikimoto in Japan, who began the cultured pearl industry. To these men, and many more scientists and farmers like them, we owe our knowledge of oyster biology and the success of oyster farming.

Oyster farming has become important in the United States, for 57 per cent of the 1962 production of American oyster in the Gulf of Mexico and the Atlantic Coast of the United States were raised on private grounds. And, furthermore, farming paid off. In 1962 oysters growing wild on public grounds brought about $0.52 per pound for meats, and those raised on private grounds, leased or owned, brought $0.63 per pound. This exemplifies the superior quality of the cultivated oysters.

Suitability for Farming

Oysters are well-suited for farming because they are in demand, they grow rapidly, and since they attach to the bottom, they need not be impounded.

It has long been known that oyster production per unit of area is far greater on private land than on public land. For example, nearly all oyster production in Holland since 1870 has been on private land where the production per hectare has increased. In Holland, leased oyster bottoms have a high rental placed on them to encourage farmers to obtain maximum production and to work their lands on a long-term basis. In some parts of the United States low rentals for oyster leases have encouraged farmers to lease areas for a year or two and then to harvest any wild oysters present in the area. They then violate their lease because they have little investment. In an effort to increase oyster production, biologists and fisheries administrators in the United States have for many years urged that more land be placed under lease with sufficiently large rental to attract seriously interested oyster farmers, but to no avail. In Australia (*Fig. 61*) oyster farming is successfully practiced.

The reasons for greater production on private land are reviewed by Galtsoff (1943). Briefly, the wild oyster populations on public grounds are composed of various age groups, and hence various sizes of oysters, each in competition with the other for food and oxygen. For example, spat will attach to adult oysters and compete with them. Also, on public lands where large and small oysters occur together, when the large oysters are

Fig. 61. These two-year-old oysters, grown on sticks, were transplanted 160 miles north to take advantage of quicker maturing on this Australian farm.
(*Australian News and Information Bureau*)

harvested, the small oysters may be killed in handling or by the teeth of the dredges used to catch the adults. Small oysters attached to adult shells may also perish during culling. On the other hand, bottoms that are planted and managed produce oysters of uniform size and age, thereby eliminating competition for food and oxygen and allowing the oysters to grow faster and reach larger sizes. Furthermore, handling during transplanting tends to break up bunches so that the single oysters usually grow better and obtain a more desirable shape for market. All oysters on private grounds can be harvested about the same time and when only a single-sized group is handled there is little need for culling with the attendant destruction of small oysters. Farmed oysters are so attractive to the consumer that he willingly pays the higher prices that they command. The greater care given oysters on private farms produces a fatter, better-flavored product (as in *Fig. 62*).

Steps in Farming

When water temperatures reach about 20° Centigrade (68° Fahrenheit), the American oyster begins to spawn. After about three weeks, depending on locality, the larvae affix themselves to any firm, clean object, and will settle there for the remainder of their lives if they are not disturbed. At

Fig. 62. Oysters of uniform sizes in quantities to satisfy market demands are raised on trays.
(*Australian News and Information bureau*)

this point in the life history of the oyster it is possible to collect the young. A farmer can provide spat collectors, called cultch, at the proper time and place for the spat to attach to and thereby obtain the most seed possible (*Fig. 63*). Some farmers simply spread clean oyster shells on the bottom, others stir shelly bottoms to make clean surfaces to which the spat can attach. The oysters may remain attached to this surface for the remainder of their lives and be allowed to remain in one area if they have proper growing conditions—food, current, temperature, and salinity for all stages of their lives. However, oysters left in their initial settling area will generally have less market value than those broken into singles because crowded conditions prevent them from growing into well-shaped, large oysters.

Many important steps in oyster farming are similar to procedures used in land farming. One of the most basic is to prepare the bottom on which the oysters are to be planted. For the most part this involves clearing away old shells which may harbor disease organisms or the eggs of oyster predators, and the removal of any predators such as starfish. Bottoms which are too soft for cultch may be made suitable by spreading shells, sand, or gravel over the bottom. These materials form a firm base for the dead oyster shells (cultch). In some experiments plastic sheeting and tar paper have been used successfully to create artificial bottoms. As a rule these materials are too expensive for the average farmer.

Of the diverse ways to collect spat, the best is to provide cultch material that can be broken up so that spat clusters can be separated and grow as single oysters (*Fig. 64*). Some of the best collectors are cardboard egg-crate fillers coated with concrete to hold them together and wrapped in chicken wire to keep predators away from the spat. The disadvantage in using this cultch is that the oysters grow together to form a mat, so that

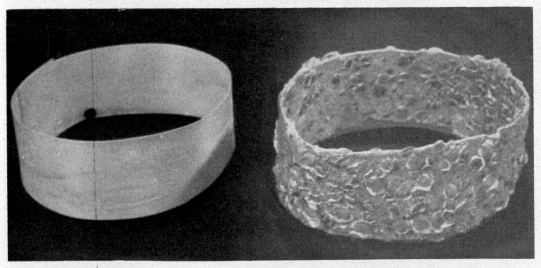

Fig. 63. Cultch made from waste wood veneer and dipped in a cement–lime–sand mixture is a good spat collector.   (*Fisheries Research Board of Canada*)

Fig. 64. An English pasture harrow dragged over oyster beds
removes eel grass and improves spat sets.
(*Washington State Department of Fisheries*)

many are destroyed at the time of separation for distribution on the
growing beds. In France, farmers use limed tile to collect spat. The lime
tile allows the spat to be easily scraped off the tiles for planting. In Japan,
bamboo and twigs are used as spat collectors.

It is highly advantageous to place cultch in oyster-spawning areas as
close as possible to the time that large numbers of young oysters will settle
to prevent the cultch from becoming fouled with worms or other organisms. This practice allows the maximum number of spat to settle on
the cultch and not be crowded by the fouling organisms which have
settled first. The proper time to put out collectors can be determined by

recording the temperature trends to find when the oysters are most likely to spawn in the area, by sampling bays with fine-mesh net to locate the drifting spat, and by periodically examining sample spat collectors (cultch).

The amount of spat available in different areas varies greatly. Some areas may be almost barren of spawn, either because of an inadequate number of spawners or unsuitable spawning conditions, while other areas may have so much spat that it can be collected or cultched and sold for seeding other grounds. For example, from the very successful spawnings they have in their home islands, the Japanese sell seed to oyster growers as far away as the Pacific Coast of North America. In the United States, from 1950 to 1963, slightly more than 75 per cent of all the seed that was sold came from private grounds. The seed raised on private grounds brought $1.21 per bushel, whereas those from public grounds brought only $0.81. In New England where local seed is very scarce, the price in 1965 rose to $10.00 per bushel.

Devices have been constructed to grind the spat collectors into small pieces, leaving the individual oysters attached. Unfortunately, as with any of these techniques, some young oysters are killed in the process.

During the spat stage and until oysters grow to bedding size, 3·8 to 5 centimeters ($1\frac{1}{2}$ to 2 inches), very high mortality may occur. Spat can be reared up to bedding size on trays, but in most countries today the expense rules out this technique for commercial operations. Trays, while increasing survival by keeping predators away from the young oysters from being smothered by sediments, or from being washed upon shore by waves, occasionally have the disadvantage of producing oysters with shells which are softer, flatter, and less symmetrical than the shells of bottom-reared oysters (*Fig. 65*).

It is important to plant the spat evenly on the bedding ground so that food and dissolved oxygen will be available to each oyster, even though the density of young oysters can be as high as 3·7 million per hectare (1·5 million per acre). Planting intertidal zones when the tide is in over the flats allows the oysters to sink to the bottom, right side up, and to be evenly distributed over the bottom. If the farmer plants oysters on flats at low tides, large numbers of the oysters may land wrong side up and eventually smother. It is good practice to cultivate the oysters from time to time, which simply means collecting the oysters and breaking up any clusters that may have formed, removing fouling organisms, including spat which may have attached to their shells, and returning the cleaned individual oysters to the bottom.

If healthy, wild bedding oysters are available for farming, the farming operation can be started by collecting and transplanting them into areas where they can mature to market size.

The last stage in raising oysters involves the maturation. Particular care should be given to placing the individual oysters in an area with the proper depth, proper salinity, an abundance of food, and where disease, pollution and predation are not serious problems. Just as with bedding

Fig. 65. Tray-reared oysters are expensive, but generally survive better than oysters reared on the bottom. (*Australian News and Information Bureau*)

oysters, maturing oysters should not be planted so thickly as to cause serious competition with each other for space. Cultivation should continue through the time the oysters are maturing until they are marketed. This takes two to five years, depending upon the location.

As in many other areas where oysters are cultured, few Japanese are engaged exclusively in oyster culture. Most of them devote the majority of their time to fishing or land farming. Oyster culture, like land farming, requires much labor at certain times. Most labor is needed for the separation of clutch into individual oysters, transplanting oysters, and harvesting. When the crop is growing, labor requirements are minimal.

Productive Areas

Since about 1942, commercial oyster culture has been carried out in the long inlets, or *rias* of the river mouths in Spain where conditions are exceedingly favorable for oysters. Spat is collected on limed tiles, and the larger oysters are placed in cages which are held above the bottom by racks. The rate of growth in these cages is much faster than on the bottom, for at nine months they reach a size of 6 centimeters ($2\frac{1}{2}$ inches).

In the Netherlands oyster farming is on sound footing because all natural beds and potential fattening grounds are leased. The high rent charged oyster farmers encourages only the ambitious to attempt the operation and discourages the practice of harvesting only the wild stock without replanting or farming the grounds. This changeover from a free fishery into which anyone could enter, to the private oyster farm with high leases, was not easily won because many fishermen claimed a loss of their rights. However, since about 1870 the grounds have been leased, and many areas where oysters did not occur naturally owing to a lack of suitable collectors for the spat to settle on have since become good farming areas because of bottom preparation and planting. The Netherlands government has an active program to provide scientific advice to oyster farmers, especially in helping them to combat oyster diseases and predators. This program has been in effect for decades. Oysters grown in polluted beds must be removed to clean beds for purification before they can be marketed. Bacteriologists in charge of shellfish control regularly sample oysters to determine if there is any danger to public health, and the government issues certificates of cleanliness for oysters which are safe to eat. Consequently, the Netherlands has an excellent record of oyster sanitation.

In the Philippines oysters are farmed extensively, but only as a local subsistence item. Few of them appear on the market, possibly because of lack of ice or adequate transportation to get them to markets. In the Manila Bay area where there are no firm bottoms as required by oysters, hanging methods and tray culture are used. The most common method is to drive bamboo poles into the bay bottom with tin cans or oyster shells impaled on the stakes to collect the spat. So many farms of this type have been established on the southeast shore of Manila Bay that it has become a forest of bamboo poles. They have caused increased accumulation of sediments normally carried through by the currents, and have decreased the current velocity. Despite such local problems, apparently considerable expansion of oyster culture is possible in the Philippines because of the extensive tidal flats.

Some oysters are cultured along the English coast, but there are no large natural beds where they are fished or where oyster farmers can obtain seed for their farms. Over the past forty years or so oyster culture in Britain has declined, due in part to industrial and sewage pollution, adverse winters, disease, and predation. Oysters here are planted below the low-tide mark, because in the intertidal zone they would be exposed to low temperatures that would result in high mortality. Planting below low-tide marks requires harvesting and predator removal by dredges from boats. (*Fig. 66* shows an English technique.)

The most successful species of oysters farmed on the Pacific coast of Canada is the immigrant from Japan, the Pacific oyster. Production is about $650,000 annually. In British Columbia, the grounds are leased for periods of ten to twenty years. Farmers lease about 16 hectares (40 acres) as a rule, but there are some areas of several hundred acres under lease. The Pacific oyster breeds successfully in British Columbia (see *Fig. 67*) in contrast to other areas along the Pacific coast where seed must be

Fig. 66. Oyster storage pits operated by the Ministry of Agriculture, Fisheries and Food in England. The backwater at left of the picture is an added source of water for the pits. *(P. J. Warren)*

Fig. 67. Styrofoam seed racks used for rearing Pacific oysters in Washington State. *(E. N. Steele)*

Fig. 68. A boat-load of coated tile spat collectors being moved to oyster flats in France.   (*Outboard Marine International*)

imported from Japan. Recently sufficient local oyster seed has been available here. Young are collected on cultch which is suspended from log rafts. The young oysters are separated from the mother shell and placed directly on the bottom. They are planted in the intertidal zone and harvested by hand or by using rakes or forks.

In eastern Canada, modern oyster farming began about 1930. Conditions are suitable for the American oyster in the Maritimes, and extensive oyster farming of this species takes place there. The growing season is short, and it requires five to seven years for the oysters to reach the minimum legal size of 7·6 centimeters (3 inches). Farmers collect the spat on cardboard collectors, then raise the oysters to market size on the bay bottoms. Despite some poor years due to heavy mortalities from disease, hope is held for increasing production in the future. Oyster farming here is a part-time occupation. It is generally done in conjunction with land farming, or fishing.

In France the method was conceived in 1865 of collecting spat of the European oyster on coated roofing tiles (as in *Fig. 68*). The tiles, coated with a mixture of lime and sand to make it easy to scrape the spat from them, can be used again and again. Before this coating method was devised. tiles were used, but they had to be broken up to separate the attached spat. This was expensive, and coating the tiles was a big step forward in oyster farming in France. Tile coating began in the Bay of Arcachon, one of the great oyster-rearing areas in the world today. More than 400 to 500 million oysters are exported from there every year. The young oysters, after they are removed from the tiles and distributed over the bottom in the intertidal zone, are protected from predators by sticks and twigs driven into the bottom to form palisades around the growing areas. Because oysters can be raised between the tide marks, farmers can reduce the enemies of the oysters which might slip into the growing areas.

In some regions of France special ponds are set aside to fatten oysters. These shallow ponds, called *claires*, are flooded in the spring, and during the summer the microscopic organisms which serve as food for oysters appear and multiply rapidly. Oysters placed in these ponds from less fertile areas grow at amazing speed toward suitable market size. It is in these claires that the esteemed green oysters are produced. One of the food organisms, a tiny plant called a diatom, imparts the green color to the flesh but does not alter the taste.

Oyster farming is an important industry in Japan. Two general types of oyster farming (for food) are practiced there. In one, only seed oysters are raised for sale, and in the other the farmer purchases the seed and raises the young oysters to marketable sizes. Three different culture methods are in common use: hanging, stick, and bottom planting. This latter method is not popular because the production is low and the grounds must be fenced off to protect the young oysters from predators living on or near the bottom. The stick method involves collecting the young oysters on bamboo sticks or stones. The young oysters are not removed from these objects, as is the practice in many areas, but the collectors are placed in piles so that they can be handled more easily. The hanging method involves the racks or rafts being anchored in areas generally deeper than

Fig. 69. The spat of rock oysters, *Crassostrea commercialis*, attaches to sticks in this farm in New South Wales. (*Australian News and Information Bureau*)

about 3·6 meters (12 feet). In some areas long ropes are stretched between floats made from oil drums and the cultures of oysters are hung from the ropes. A recent improvement has been to use cast concrete floats to replace the wooden barrels or oil drums. The concrete drums have walls about 1·9 centimeters ($\frac{3}{4}$ inch) thick which are non-porous.

One oyster lease in George River near Sydney, New South Wales, has been used by three generations of one family. At this farm, in operation for over sixty-five years, spat of the rock oyster, *Crassostrea commercialis*, attaches to tarred sticks placed on rocks near the lower reaches of estuaries. After spat-fall the 2·5 centimeters (1 inch) square, 1·8 meters (6 feet) long sticks are moved into the waters of lower salinity where more rapid growth takes place (*Fig. 69*). After about two years of stick culture, the oysters are scraped loose and laid out in chicken-wire trays for another year before they are ready for market. The annual production of rock oysters in the many areas of New South Wales is about A$2.5 million.

The rock oyster was transplanted to Hawaii during about 1925–28 where small numbers still exist.

On the east coast of the United States and along the Gulf of Mexico, the spat of the American oyster, the only commercially important oyster, are caught on oyster shells. Although the hanging culture technique is being studied, it is not being done commercially. Oysters are freely transplanted to fatten them and improve their flavor. *Figs. 70* and *71* show two methods of culture.

On the northwest coast of the United States, the Pacific oyster seed is imported from Japan and raised on tidal flats. In the Puget Sound district production has increased about threefold between 1935 and 1963. In areas which lack suitable tide flats, oysters are planted below the low tide mark and various types of boats are required to dredge or tong the oysters from the bottoms just as is done on public fishing grounds.

Oyster cultivation is carried out in closed or semi-closed ponds at the heads of fiords in Norway. There fresh water run-off from the mountains flows onto the surface and forms a layer over the saline water. Circulation is poor in these fiords and the bottom water, very low in oxygen, supports sulphur bacteria. Only in the mid-depths where the oysters are suspended in cages, is found oxygen, food, temperature, and salinity which produce good growth and spawning. Norwegian oysters are marketed when they are about three years old. Two factors make this operation an expensive one: first the oyster exists in a delicately balanced environment; marked changes in the system, such as the bottom water being mixed with the water from the mid-depths, can cause high mortality, as can low temperatures and low salinities which sometimes occur during a cold winter. The second expense factor is the considerable labor necessary during the three years required to grow marketable oysters.

The excellent natural conditions for oyster breeding in Norway yield high-grade oyster spat that survive well even with large temperature fluctuations. In recent years Norway sold large quantities of young oysters for bedding to Denmark and France. Early in 1966, a special project used

Fig. 70. Oysters grown on strings have round shells and are safe from bottom-dwelling predators.
(*United States Bureau of Commercial Fisheries, W. Shaw*)

Fig. 71. This experimental fiberglass raft for holding strings of oysters has two rows of string extending its length.
(*United States Bureau of Commercial Fisheries, W. Shaw*)

three airplanes to carry 20 tons of one- and two-year-old oysters from Norway to France for planting.

Shell and Pearl Farming

The pearl and pearl shell markets are of considerably less importance than the food oyster market. Also, they are restricted geographically and show less potential for farming than food oysters.

The 1922 world slump in commodity prices lowered the value of pearl shell, from which decorative buttons are manufactured, to an uneconomical level. As a result, the industry in the Red Sea was abandoned. After a survey by the Food and Agriculture Organization of the United Nations, a government-sponsored pearl shell farm was begun in 1959. The success of this farm encouraged 120 local fishermen to start similar farms. Farming oysters for pearl shells is similar to farming oysters for food. In Sudan, the pearl shell farmer collects spat on bamboo rakes or frames. The nurseries where the young oysters grow are built up off the sea bed and are made of wire netting to discourage predatory fishes. After a year in the nurseries, the shells are sufficiently strong to withstand attacks by most predators. At this stage they are transferred to growing trays. About two years more are required for oysters to be ready for the shell market.

Mikimoto, who raised his first cultured pearls in Japan in 1883, vowed he would adorn the necks of women the world over with his pearls. He was not the first to consider the possibilities of pearl culture. The Chinese are credited with discovering the techniques during the fourteenth century. They used mud pellets, nacre beads, and even small leaden images of Buddha to form the nuclei of pearls in the oysters. In 1897 the French unsuccessfully attempted to produce pearls using abalones. To Mikimoto goes the title, "King of Pearls," for it was he who produced the first good, cultured blister (or half-pearls) which eventually led to the culture of fine, spherical pearls. At least three other Japanese have since become prominent in pearl production.

Pearls can be produced in other mollusks such as oysters, abalone, *Pinna* (sea-pen), and some fresh-water mussels. The oysters that are desirable as human food do not produce pearls, nor do clams, scallops, or mussels, since their shells have no nacre layer. While some pearls are fished in Venezuela and Tahiti, Japan is the greatest producer of cultured pearls. Mikimoto's process, patented many years ago, requires great skill and patience to be successful. A small piece of the mantle is cut from a living Japanese pearl oyster, *Pinctada martensii*, and a small, spherical, shell fragment, which will be the nucleus of the future pearl, is placed on top of the mantle. The mantle is formed into a small bag around the nucleus and tied with a thin thread. The tiny bag is placed in the subcutaneous tissue of a living pearl oyster about two or three years old. Then the thread is removed from the sac and the wound disinfected. After the operation, the oysters are placed in culture cages on rafts and the grafted pieces of mantle grow into a "pearl sac" which forms a nacreous layer over the nucleus. Pearls may be harvested as early as five months or as late as seven years. About 60 per cent of the operations performed are successful. In the unsuccessful cases the oysters either die or do not produce pearls. Only about 5 per cent of the surviving oysters produce pearls of sufficient beauty to be marketed.

Just like gold nuggets, the larger and heavier pearls sell for higher prices than do small ones. Luster, color, and smoothness of the pearls also affect price. The first good quality spherical pearls, reared in 1919, competed with natural pearls from wild oysters. But growth of the culture industry in 1920, and by 1926 about 700,000 pearls had been produced on thirty-three farms. In the late 1930s this pearl culture reached its peak, but World War II intervened. Soon after the war, pearl culture was resumed. In 1962, the total export was valued at over $35 million. Half of the pearls were imported by the United States. The size of pearls has increased over the years: in 1919 no cultured pearls were larger than 7 millimeters ($\frac{3}{8}$ inch), but during the 1930s pearls of 1·2 centimeters ($\frac{1}{2}$ inch) were produced. The number of rafts in use during 1960 was over 3,400. The individual farms, which are household units owned and operated by families, consist mostly of a dozen or less rafts.

In 1956, pearl farming was introduced in northern Australia. Although the growth rate of Australian pearls is slow, they make up for this deficiency by their large size, for in Australia the largest pearls are produced, some of which reach about 1·7 centimeters ($\frac{3}{4}$ inch). Today there are about fifteen pearl culture farms there which produced in 1965 over A $2.7 million worth of pearls. A dozen of these farms are joint Australian-Japanese companies, while the remaining three are Australian ventures. The recent trend in this operation has been to process the blister and round pearls in Sydney, rather than sending them to Japan as was done previously.

The Future of Oyster Farming

Despite the size of the oyster industry (for food) today, there is considerable room for increased production through more effective use of leased bottoms and off-the-bottom culture techniques. Although a great knowledge exists about the biology of oysters, there are numerous gaps which, if filled, could add substantially to production. Disease research (discussed later) and stock improvements through artificial selection are examples of such gaps.

CHAPTER 8

Clams and Mussels

Clams and mussels are important species to the sea farmer in many coastal areas of the Northern Hemisphere. They are not farmed as extensively as oysters, but they have considerable farming potential. Because they are sessile, feed low on the food web, and are in demand by consumers, they are admirably suited for sea farming. The hard clams possess additional advantages in that they can be spawned artificially, and when only half-grown, are marketed in the United States at a good price as "cherrystone" clams.

Hard Clams

The hard clam, *Mercenaria* (= *Venus*) *mercenaria*, lives all along the Atlantic coast of the United States, from Maine to Florida (*Fig. 72*). In

Fig. 72. Hard clams, *Mercenaria mercenaria*, have thick, heavy shells.   (*E. S. Iversen*)

New England it is called "quahog," or "quahaug," in the Middle Atlantic states it is called "hard clam," or "hard-shelled clam," or "little-neck clam." Its abundance differs greatly, with the Massachusetts to Virginia area having the largest concentration because of the excellent living conditions for them there. This clam occurs in waters as deep as 15 meters (50 feet), with the greatest numbers just below the low tide mark. The hard clam lives equally as well in sand or mud bottoms. The hard clam like its close relatives, the soft clams and the mussels (also mollusks), releases eggs free in the water where they are fertilized. The young hatch as veligers, capable of swimming with a spinning motion, but are largely carried by the current away from the area where they were born. There is survival value in this free-swimming stage of the life history of mollusks. The adults are largely unable to move about, so they are dependent upon currents to carry food and dissolved oxygen to them and remove their wastes. Since crowded animals must share the benefits of the currents, crowding reduces their survival chances. Hence, through the free-floating (veliger) stage of its early life, a sessile species avoids high competition for food and dissolved oxygen so necessary for its growth and survival.

Table 7

SUMMARY OF INFORMATION ON THE HARD CLAM

Mercenaria (= Venus) mercenaria

Identification	Thick, hard, equal-sized shells (valves) with ridges. Two equal-sized adductor muscles. Siphons short.
Distribution	Gulf of St. Lawrence to Gulf of Mexico. From intertidal zone down to 15 meters (50 feet).
Age and growth	After about five years, may reach 9 centimeters (3.5 inches). May live 20–25 years and reach 14 centimeters (5.5 inches).
Reproduction	Most spawn when one year old. Eggs pumped out of siphon, fertilization external, young stages settle on bottoms after about twelve days.
Food	Plankton; mostly phytoplankton.
Feeding habits	Draw food into mouth through short siphons.

After the veliger has drifted for about a week or two, its swimming hairs gradually disappear, and it settles to the bottom to begin its sessile existence. A strong muscular foot develops, and at the same time siphons and gills form. At this stage, the young hard clam—only slightly larger than a pinhead—secures itself by byssus (a tuft of strong threads) to sand grains, plants, or other materials which prevent it from being swept away by the current. The young clam has the ability to cast off the byssus and move short distances on its muscular foot. It can secrete more threads as needed. When the clam is about 5 millimeters ($\frac{1}{4}$ inch) long it uses its foot to dig a burrow in the bottom, sometimes making several trial digs before it settles down. Once it has buried itself, the byssus holds it secure for a while; however, as the young clam grows, the byssus-forming glands disappear. The clam usually remains buried for the rest of its life. It may live as long as twenty-five years and attain a length of about 14 centi-

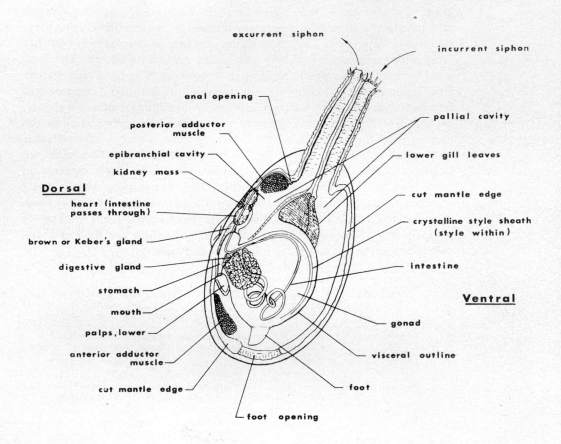

Fig. 73. Internal anatomy of soft clam.
(*United States Bureau of Commercial Fisheries*)

meters (5·5 inches). In New England, where conditions are best for its growth, it takes a little over five years for a hard clam to reach about 7·5 centimeters (3 inches).

Soft Clams

The soft-clam, *Mya arenaria* (also called soft-shelled clam or long-necked clam) (*Fig. 73*), is similar in appearance and life history to the hard clam. It is found in greatest abundance from Labrador to North Carolina. The soft clam was accidentally, yet successfully, transplanted to Washington State, about 1880, when the American oyster was transplanted from the east coast of the United States. Today it occurs from

Fig. 74. The traditional short-handled hoe used by New England clam diggers.
(*United States Bureau of Commercial Fisheries*)

Monterey, California, north to Alaska on the west coast of North America, and from Norway to France, and in Japan. The soft clam, like the hard clam, is rarely found on tidal flats, inlets and bays, but rather it occurs in more exposed areas of the coast line. This species survives best in gravel to mud bottoms where it buries itself, leaving only its long siphons protruding; harvesting them therefore, requires digging to remove them from their burrows (*Fig. 74*). The hydraulic dredge developed in Maryland, has made harvesting of clams in deep water possible and has revolutionized the industry. Since the soft clam depends on plankton (minute free-floating plants and animals) for food, its growth and survival requires an adequate current passing the siphons close to the bottom. Currents carrying large amounts of silt are undesirable, for silt will interfere with their breathing and feeding.

Suitability of Clams for Farming

Both the hard clam and the soft clam are suitable for farming. On the east coast of the United States, about 22 per cent of the hard clams sold in 1962 were raised on private grounds. These clams, farmed only to a limited extent, have considerably greater potential especially if they can be mass-reared cheaply. Clams are not as desirable for farming as are oysters. They have a slower growth rate, it is difficult to collect sufficient seed stock, and their market price per pound is less.

Answers to questions concerning the growth, production, and practicality of farming hard clams are vitally needed. Recognizing this, Dr. R. W. Menzel and his colleagues at Florida State University planted the young of this species on mud-sand bottoms below the intertidal zone and measured their growth and mortality rates. Some were planted in pens and others outside to determine the importance of predation. Predatory blue crabs killed nearly all clams outside the fences, the rest fell to other predators. Despite the 6-foot high fences placed around the pens, a few crabs found their way inside, avoided the baited traps set for them, and destroyed some of the young clams. Losses of approximately 18 per cent occurred in some of these pens. Growth was rapid in these warm waters; the hard clams reached market size of about 6 centimeters ($2\frac{1}{2}$ inches) in two years, whereas about five years is required to reach this size in New England.

These and other experiments point up the many difficulties facing successful clam farmers. Good grounds for planting, of primary importance, must not have excessive sediments. Too firm a bottom will prevent the clams from burrowing and make harvesting more awkward. Maintaining a consistent supply of seed stock at a reasonable price is another problem that must be solved. Since it has been demonstrated that clam hatcheries are feasible, mass-rearing of clams in private hatcheries may become a reality and will lessen the need for relaying wild seed as is presently done. The high mortality of the unprotected clams in certain areas emphasizes the need for providing fencing to protect them from predation. But this is not all. The fencing must be inspected frequently to make sure that there have been no breaks and to locate and destroy any predators which may have slipped inside. An unfortunate result of placing fencing in the water is that in some areas it tends to restrict the current. If the water is carrying a considerable sediment load, and fencing slows the current, much of the sediment will be dropped and will suffocate large numbers of clams.

Experiments with monofilament plastic screen have been conducted in an attempt to prevent the high predation of the very small (a few millimeters) soft clams. In Massachusetts a screen was placed over the bottom of the tide flats to prevent predatory green crabs, horseshoe crabs, and snails from devouring the young clams. While some predators managed to get through this screening or burrow in under the screening on the sides, survival was considerably higher in the screened area. However, the screen is fairly costly.

The growth of soft clams in the Bay of Fundy, Gulf of Marine, Gulf of St. Lawrence, and Chesapeake Bay shows striking differences in the shell, weight, and dry body weight. Considering clams of the same size, the shell weight of the Bay of Fundy specimens was approximately twice that of those from the Chesapeake Bay. Clams from the Gulf of Maine and the Gulf of St. Lawrence have less shell weights than those from the Bay of Fundy. Shell weights seem to correspond very closely with temperature: the colder the temperature, the heavier the shell. Thus, weights of meat give a more accurate measure of production than weights of the total animal.

Steps in Clam Farming

Most of the procedures used in oyster farming are also applicable in clam farming. A suitable area with a firm bottom and a flow of water to provide plankton are required. Unlike the oyster, the clam does not require cultch on which to settle, but will settle directly on the bottom. If the farm location is properly selected, larval clams will drift naturally with

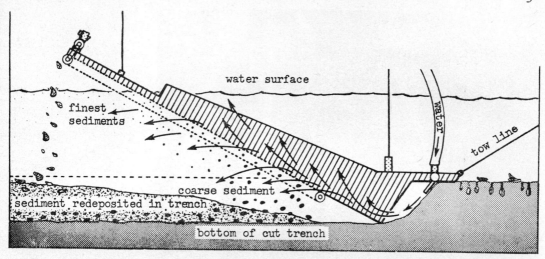

water surface

finest sediments

water

tow line

coarse sediment

sediment redeposited in trench

bottom of cut trench

Fig. 75. Diagram of a hydraulic dredge used for harvesting clams. Attached to the side of a vessel, this device washes a high proportion of clams from the bottom.
(*United States Bureau of Commercial Fisheries*)

the current into the fenced-in areas and settle down. If such a location cannot be found, the farmer may have to purchase the seed, or raise the young clams himself. After the young clams are planted, he must continually inspect the enclosures to remove predators such as starfish and crabs that eat young clams. Harvesting requires either a dredger (*Fig. 75*) which uses water under pressure, to loosen the bottom and suck up the clams, or the old traditional hoe that requires back-breaking labor. Escalators can be used to minimize labor (*Fig. 76*).

Few countries practice clam culture today. Japan, the United States, and Britain to a very small extent, are probably the only areas where clam culture of a commercial nature is worth consideration.

Clam culture is practiced all over Japan, in the inland seas and bays. The care Japanese farmers provide to the clams varies considerably; in some cases the only effort they make is to transplant clams to less crowded areas. In others, they prepare the bottoms, sow the young clams uniformly, remove predators, and fence off a portion of the bottom. Japan's clam farming depends on several species. The most important of these is the asari, *Tapes semidecussata*, or what is sometimes called the "baby clam." This species prefers a bottom which is composed of between 60 per cent and 80 per cent sand, with gravel and dead shell mixed in for the young clams to attach to before digging into the bottom. The asari, which lives at a depth of about 3·6 meters (12 feet) below the low tide, grows rapidly from April to December, with virtually no growth in winter. If the clams which have been distributed over the grounds are crowded together by wind and wave action, they must be recollected and redistributed over the grounds. Harvests of asari as high as about 227 liters (60 gallons) have been obtained from 11 square meters (36 square feet) in Japanese

Fig. 76. Escalators bring shellfish from the bottom to the
rail of the vessel for sorting.
          (*United States Bureau of Commercial Fisheries*)

farms. By spreading a layer of sand and gravel over the young, recently-
settled clams to keep them from being carried away and to protect them
from predators, a higher yield can sometimes be obtained. Between one
and two years is required to grow clams suitable for market. In some areas,
bamboo fences are used to obstruct or sufficiently slow the current movement so that the young drifting clams being carried in the current will
settle within the fenced-in area. Predators such as ducks, snails, and starfish are a constant threat. The mature clams are harvested by rakes and hoes.

There is considerable interest in clam farming in Britain, although little
of it is done. The most important works being carried out there are experiments to determine if there is a future in clam farming using effluents
from power plants (Chapter 3). The hard clam has been introduced often
in Britain since 1864 and as recently as 1962, but only in one area, at
Southampton Water, has it apparently become well-established and able
to breed naturally. Across the Channel, in France, the hard clam was
planted in Arcachon Basin in 1861, and again in 1863. But it was not until
about 1910 that successful introductions into France were made. The hard
clam flourishes there now as a result of transplantations from the United
States.

Mussels

The common mussel, *Mytilus edulis*, has a dark purple- to black-colored thin shell, and differs from the clams we have referred to so far in that its byssus, which it uses to hold fast, remains with it throughout its life. It is distributed in all north temperate regions. It is cultivated in Spain, Holland, France, and Italy, but not in the United States. The larval stage of the mussel, called the veliger as with the oyster and clam, floats briefly before it attaches by its byssus to a resting place. In many places where environmental conditions are favorable, large accumulations of mussels are found. In the areas where mussels have concentrated for many years, a bluish mud often is seen.

On the American oyster grounds in the United States the mussels crowd and compete with the oysters. Land farmers in New England with farms near shore used the species as fertilizer because it was abundant, cheap, and readily available. A number of attempts to encourage the consumption of mussels in the United States have been unsucessful. In 1963, just over 2·3 million kilograms (5 million pounds) of mussels (live weight) valued at $66,000 were collected from public grounds. Although mussels are highly nutritious, being a good source of proteins, vitamins, and iron, to name a few, they are little utilized in the United States. The value of mussels as food was publicized early in 1900 and again just before World War II, but this publicity apparently had little effect on the demand or production. Soon after the turn of the century, attempts to sell canned mussels, pickled mussels, deviled mussels, and mussel cocktail failed. The color and general appearance of mussels is unappetizing to most Americans. Such a prejudice is hard to overcome. The mussels sold in the United States today go to Spanish or French restaurants. The State of Maine has giant mussel beds, yet they are little harvested and it is almost impossible to find them in stores and restaurants there.

There is a great demand for mussels in Europe; however, even in Europe mussels are not a luxury item.

Information on the biology of the common mussel found in Europe and on the east coast of the United States is brief. Classic work on the biology of this species was done in 1922 by Dr. Irving Field (Table 8). In addition to describing the anatomy and biology of the mussel, he told of the Irishman, Patrick Walton, who, stranded without funds in France, accidentally discovered a way to cultivate mussels. Walton was using a long net placed at the surface of the water to catch skimming birds to eat. He observed that the mussels which attached to the posts he had driven into the tide flats to support his nets had a superior flavor to those he got from the mud flat. From this start, the *bouchot* system developed which involves placing rows of stakes at various depths for the young to attach to by their byssus. The mussel farmer moves the stakes holding the growing mussels, as they mature, from deep water closer to shore. Finally the stakes are placed in the upper part of the intertidal zone, out of the water for a substantial portion of each day. By conditioning the mussels to withstand

Table 8

SUMMARY OF INFORMATION ON THE SEA MUSSEL

Mytilus edulis

Identification	Bivalve mollusk characterized by a byssus secreted from a gland at base of foot. Shell thin, black to bluish-black.
Distribution	Widely distributed in north temperate regions.
Age and growth	About 25 millimeters (1 inch) per year for the first three years; in England and Wales, four years to reach 5 centimeters (2 inches).
Reproduction	Single females spawn 5 to 12 million eggs annually, a ciliated larva formed about four hours after fertilization. After ten weeks all organs are present.
Food	Plankton, small diatoms (29 species), protozoans (9 species), and detritus.
Feeding habits	Currents, set up by gills, draw floating food into mouth.

longer periods out of the water, they arrive in the market fresher than if they were continually submerged. An interesting description given by Dr. Field is the use by the mussel farmers of a small "foot canoe" with a turned-up bow, called an *acon*. A pole and a paddle are standard equipment. With this little boat the operator can move over the mud or tide flat by pushing with one leg much as a child propels itself in a wagon, or in deeper water he pushes with the pole. If the water is too deep, he paddles. Field remarked that this versatile little boat can be propelled around the mussel farm at the speed of a trotting horse. The mussels are transplanted from natural beds in areas open to the sea into beds in shallow, sheltered areas when they purify themselves (rid their digestive tracts of sand). They are marketed in France, Belgium, and England.

Mussel Farming

In Holland, Spain, Italy, and France, both hanging and bottom-culture techniques for mussels are similar to those used to raise oysters. Farming mussels off the bottom increases survival just as for oysters since the same bottom-dwelling predators kill mussels. Mussels are prolific, and getting seed is easy. In fact, wherever conditions are suitable and there are places to attach, the young settle and form thick banks or shoals. Dredging on these shoal areas provides seed mussels which can be used for planting other areas. The young or seed mussels, about 13 to 25 millimeters ($\frac{1}{2}$ to 1 inch) long, must be sown in thin layers and distributed evenly over a carefully selected area on the bottom where it is firm enough to permit the mussels to attach and not be suffocated by shifting sand or detritus. Too, heavy waves may destroy large numbers of the thin-shelled mussels. If growing conditions on the bottom are suitable, the young can grow 25 to 50 millimeters (1 to 2 inches) long in a year.

Some farmers deliberately plant mussels in thick layers to insure a reserve supply of young (*Fig. 77*). Heavy planting increases competition for food which causes stunting and thus provides brood stock. Mussels, given adequate food, will rapidly grow to marketable sizes. Mussels grown

Fig. 77. In tight clusters, these young mussels find competition keen for the necessities of life.   (*B. Havinga*)

from seed in Holland require about three years to reach the marketable size of 6·3 centimeters (2½ inches). In Sardinia, mussels reach marketable sizes in one year. About a year and a half is required for marketable mussels grown on ropes supported by stakes in the Gulf of Spezia in northern Italy.

In Holland, mussel culture is done on the bottom of the Waddensea. Here the farmers are assigned portions of the sea bottom, divided into "parks," each of which comprises an area of 5 to 18 hectares (12 to 45 acres) (*Fig. 78*). Farmers are permitted more than one park in their care at one time. The mussel farmer collects, from public grounds, young mussels or seed when they are less than 25 millimeters (1 inch) long using large dredges to collect them, then distributes young mussels over his park or mussel farm. Before planting, he prepares his leased land by removing as many predators as possible. The small streams emptying into the Waddensea are exceptionally rich and suitable for the growth and fattening of mussels. To obtain maximum growth, the farmers must break up clusters and replant them. Farmers must be especially alert for starfish because their crop is growing on the bottom where this predator can destroy it.

Over 200 boats are used in mussel farming in Holland (*Fig. 79*) and during recent years the production has varied from 67,000 to 82,000

Fig. 78. Boundaries between mussel parks or farms in the Netherlands are in-
dicated by poles.   (*B. Havinga*)

Fig. 79. Vessels of this type are used to dredge oysters and
mussels on farms in the Netherlands.   (*B. Havinga*)

Fig. 80. Mussels being removed from poles. Baise de
l'Aiguillon.   (*H. Cole*)

metric tons (74,000 to 90,000 tons) live weight. Part of this mussel production is sold to canneries, but the majority is sold fresh in the markets
of western Europe.

On the west coast of France, mussel farms are numerous. Unlike the
system used in Holland, mussels here are grown above the bottom. The
young mussels are collected on poles imbedded in the sea bottom (*Fig.
80*). When they are about to spawn, the farmers remove them from the
poles and place them in netting fastened between twigs which are entwined among the rows of poles.

Annual production along the west coast of France is about 10 thousand
metric tons with the greatest production coming from the large, shallow,
muddy bay named Anse de l'Aiguillon. On the Mediterranean coast of
France, mussels are grown on ropes which hang from wooden frames over
water. While this hanging procedure and the twig method require more
labor and material than the bottom method, there is less predation, and
since the mussels are off the bottom they do not contain as much sand as
those grown on the bottom, hence eliminating the purification step. Spain
occupies the third place (after Holland and France) in mussel production
in Europe. In the Bay of Vigo on the Atlantic coast of Spain, hanging
mussel culture is practiced using large rafts. In about one year in this
extremely rich area the mussels reach about 8 centimeters ($3\frac{1}{4}$ inches).

Mussel farming has been attempted in the Gulf of Cariaco in Venezuela.
Scientists from Spain came to Venezuela to assist the Venezuelans in
building rafts to start culturing the local mussel *Perna perna*. They built
large rafts, 7 meters square (24 feet square), which floated on styrofoam

Fig. 81. Mussel rafts off the coast of Venezuela.   (*E. S. Iversen*)

from which were suspended vertically about 100 bamboo poles on which the mussel seed was attached. The few experimental rafts that were set out by the government looked promising because they grew rapidly and a very favorable meat to total weight ratio was obtained (*Fig. 81*). However, the first large-scale farming venture, 122 rafts, was unsuccessful because the bamboo poles became riddled by marine borers and fell into the sea. The mussels remaining on the parts still attached to the raft were almost valueless because their meats were small, only about 10 per cent of the total weight, which is less than the minimum required by the market (*Fig. 82*). New studies are being launched to determine the abundance of minute planktonic organisms eaten as food by the mussels to determine their seasonal and geographic abundance. Smaller rafts allowing fishermen to enter business with less capital are being constructed in the hope that local mussel farming will be profitable in Venezuela. The borer menace is revealed in *Fig. 83*.

Very limited mussel culture is being practiced in Great Britain. Usually the live mussels are dredged from one area and replanted in another where they will grow larger and get fatter, but nowhere in Great Britain is the culture of mussels practiced at the level that it is in Holland and France.

Mussel culture is virtually unknown in Canada, the United States, or Japan. On the island of Sardinia, mussels are cultured in strands of rope or in baskets suspended from racks. They are generally marketed when less than one year old.

Future of Clam and Mussel Farming

In the United States and Great Britain, clam and mussel farming could be developed. Both of these groups have potential for extensive future farming. They are flavorful, therefore desirable to consumers, and are hearty animals which are widely distributed in temperate waters.

In many areas in the United States clam farming and clam fishing has been suppressed because of laws and tradition which required hand digging with a short-handled hoe. In addition to this drudgery, harvesting

Fig. 82. The mussel, *Perna perna*, raised on poles suspended from rafts in Venezuela. (*E. S. Iversen*)

Fig. 83. Boring organisms can make short work of shellfish rafts. (*E. S. Iversen*)

by this method is inefficient because numerous clams are missed. In 1951 the escalator dredge was first tried on clam beds in Chesapeake Bay. It has revolutionized clam fishing on public grounds. As high as 95 per cent of the large clams can be collected. Water under high pressure washes the bottom sediments away from clams as the dredge moves along the sea bottom. The clams fall onto a chain-web endless belt and are carried up the belt to the side of the vessel, where they are sorted. Small clams can be easily separated and returned to the water. Large clam farming operations could be profitable by using this device, if law and tradition will accept it. The recent development of artificial hatching and rearing techniques also promises to expand clam farming because obtaining seed stock from natural spawning grounds has long been a deterrent to increased clam farming.

Mussel consumption, although nearly nonexistent in North America because of lack of demand, might be increased markedly by consumer education which would pave the way for farming them. This tasty bivalve can be produced in great abundance, in relatively small areas, by rafting. Such hanging culture techniques require careful planning because of the high labor and material costs involved. However, energy coupled with knowledge can produce enormous quantities of this fine seafood by cultivation. The annual production of Holland (48,000 metric tons), France (10,000 metric tons), and Spain (3,500 metric tons) demonstrates this.

CHAPTER 9

Shrimps

Shrimps are more advanced on the evolutionary scale than any of the species that we have considered so far. They are crustaceans with jointed legs and a hard exoskeleton (external covering) of chiton-like material. Unlike the mollusks which grow by adding material to the edge of their shells, the shrimps must shed, or molt, their exoskeleton and replace it with a larger one to grow. Periodic molts cause step-wise, abrupt growth. Shrimps pass through many more larval stages than mollusks. Warm water shrimps of commercial importance are migratory and generally move from salt water into brackish water, then return to salt water. During nearly all their lives shrimps live near the bottom and eat organic detritus, algae, small crustaceans, and small clams.

Pink Shrimp

Considerable study has been devoted recently to the biology of the pink shrimp, *Penaeus duorarum*. The life history of this penaeid shrimp is similar to that of other commercial shrimps being farmed throughout the world. While details of biology of different shrimp species may differ, the life cycle pattern and the requirements of the pink shrimp in nature are reviewed here to determine the problems of shrimp farming.

Pink shrimp is an Atlantic Ocean species, most abundant in tropical and sub-tropical waters. It extends from as far north in the United States as Delaware Bay and continues southward along the Atlantic Coast into the Gulf of Mexico to Mexico. Even Bermuda has a small population. Pink shrimp occurs near islands in the Caribbean and on the east coast of South America as far south as Brazil. Biologists recognize slight differences in the anatomy of pink shrimp in Cuba, Jamaica, and those populations southward, but they are probably all the same species. It has also been reported off the west coast of Africa from Senegal to Angola.

Areas of high abundance for commercially desirable shrimps are revealed by the occurrence of large trawling fleets such as those which operate from South Carolina southward. Pink shrimp are very abundant in the area near Key West, Florida, on the Dry Tortugas grounds as *Fig. 84* demonstrates. To the south and west of there, across the Gulf of Mexico, lies the Campeche fishing grounds where Mexicans, Cubans, and Americans harvest this abundant crustacean. One of the common features of all these productive shrimp areas is the very wide, gradually sloping continental shelf that is covered with a layer of soft mud and sand. Adjacent to this shelf are large estuarine areas that biologists call "nursery grounds," where many of the young shrimp spend a portion of their lives

Fig. 84. Shrimp are harvested from the continental shelf in large numbers by trawlers. Demand for shrimp has overtaken supply. (*Florida State News Bureau*)

Some portion of the population may never enter the estuaries, but spend their early life in shallow near-shore water. An important feature of these productive nursery areas is both offshore and onshore currents. Such a current system is apparently needed for the shrimp to complete its life cycle. During the larval stage it is impossible for the weak-swimming larvae to move into the nursery grounds without the aid of currents; the juveniles returning to the nursery grounds, although able to swim, also require favorable currents to assist them on their long trip back to deep water where they spawn.

Table 9

SUMMARY OF BIOLOGICAL INFORMATION ON THE PINK SHRIMP

Penaeus duorarum

Identification	Red, grading to a pale white, in some areas brownish. A red spot usually on the third or fourth segment. The shape of the sex organs used for identification usually requires microscopic examination. Nocturnal habits.
Distribution	Lower Delaware Bay into Gulf of Mexico, to Vera Cruz, Mexico; Bermuda. Many of the Caribbean Islands, south to Brazil.
Age and growth	Estimated to live about one year (perhaps as long as twenty months), females may reach 28 centimeters (11 inches), males 19·5 centimeters (7·5 inches). Larval development lasts less than three weeks.
Reproduction	Male attaches a packet of sperm cells to the female's thelicum (sex organ) soon after she molts. Non-buoyant fertilized eggs (500,000 to 1,000,000) released free in the water at a later time. First spawning occurs when female is about 10 centimeters (4 inches). More than one spawning during the life of a shrimp is possible. In southwest Florida, spawning takes place throughout the year.
Food	Variety of small plants and animals plus organic and inorganic detritus eaten; dinoflagellates, nematodes, foraminifera, algae, fish, snails, squids, clams, annelids, insects, shrimps (cannibalistic).

The difficulty of identifying various closely related shrimp are manyfold. One reason is that many species of shrimp are very similar in appearance. However, within a species variation occurs. The color of the pink shrimp, for example, is quite variable in different geographical areas and at different stages of its life. The shape of the sex organs varies in different species, but differences—although consistent—are so minor that identification is difficult (see *Fig. 85*).

Reproduction

As a rule it is easy to detect a shrimp that is ready to spawn. The ovaries, usually visible through the shell, are noticeably larger and of a different color just before the hundreds of thousands of eggs are released. Mating occurs just after the female has shed her skin (the male need not be in molt condition). The male attaches a packet of sperm cells to the thelicum on the female's underside, where it remains until she lays her eggs. As the

Fig. 85. The anatomy of different shrimp species differs slightly. Although similar in appearance, there may be several species present in this catch.
(Florida State News Bureau)

eggs pass through the exits at the base of her third pair of walking legs, they are fertilized by sperm cells as they are released from this packet. Spawning takes place in deep water well offshore. On the Tortugas grounds it occurs at about 8 to 26 fathoms.

Life Cycle

The eggs may be released at any time of the year but most on the Tortugas grounds are released when the temperature is rising. The embryonic shrimp puncture the egg shell with a special spine after about twelve hours in sea water. A larvae called a nauplius emerges from the shell and swims convulsively for short periods. Five naupliar stages follow, most of which do not resemble adult shrimp in the least. Rather they look more like hairy-legged insects. During these stages, which last about two days each, the larval shrimp uses food stored in its yolk. Molting continues periodically. The young shrimp enters a difficult and critical stage

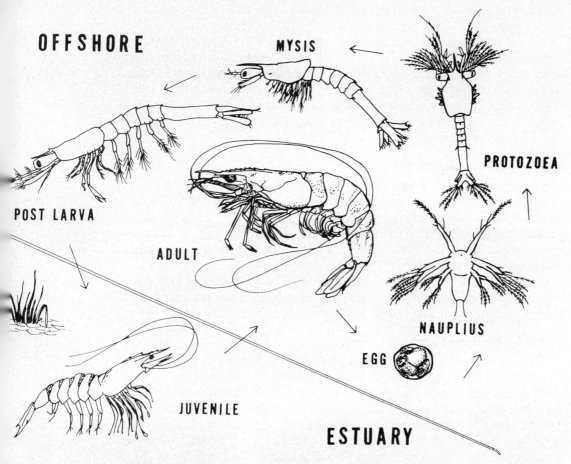

OFFSHORE

MYSIS

PROTOZOEA

POST LARVA

ADULT

NAUPLIUS

EGG

JUVENILE

ESTUARY

Fig. 86. Diagrammatic drawing of the stages of a species of penaeid shrimp. The many drifting stages develop from the eggs which are released in deep water. The young move to the estuaries and inshore waters, later go offshore to deep water to spawn.   (*J. Z. Iversen*)

of its life during the first protozoeal stage after it has consumed its stored yolk and must find food on its own. Its food, which consists of tiny microscopic drifting plants, must be within easy reach or the shrimp will die in a short time. If it survives this protozoeal stage, it develops into another series of stages called mysis and at last becomes recognizable as a shrimp. At about three weeks of age it next passes into post-larval stages and is about 100 miles from where it hatched. These weak swimmers, capable of only limited vertical movement, make a significant journey, apparently without much effort on their part, into a nursery area (estuarine or shallow-inshore bays). At the entrance to the nursery area, the post-larval shrimp allow only the flooding tides to carry them into the estuaries areas and shun the ebbing currents which would return them to sea, apparently by attaching themselves to the bottom or sides of the inlets leading to the nursery grounds. Once inside the nursery grounds they bury themselves during the day in the soft bottoms where they find protection from predatory fishes as well as abundant food for rapid growth. *Fig. 86* shows the life cycle of the shrimp.

After an unknown time, perhaps three to six months in the nursery area, the young juveniles, now about 7·5 centimeters (3 inches) long, retrace their earlier route which led them to the nursery areas. They ride the ebbing tidal current back to the sea, growing and maturing as they move toward the deeper water on the continental shelf. Here they reach maturity, spawn, and the circle is completed.

Suitability for Farming

Rapid growth, which yields shrimp of marketable size in less than a year, is one factor which makes them suitable for farming. Another factor is the short larval life (about two weeks), characteristic of some species, which means that extensive care to rear from the eggs is required for only a short time. A third favorable factor is the high market value of shrimp, which seems to have no upper bounds.

On the debit side of the ledger, the juvenile and adult shrimp in ponds require feed and considerable care and protection from predators for several months which raise their selling price to a prohibitive level.

Japanese Shrimp Farming

There are several ways of obtaining brood stock for shrimp farming. In some areas the post-larval stages may drift with the current into judiciously-placed impoundments. Another possibility is that post-larval or juvenile shrimp may be caught in the sea and placed in ponds to grow to market sizes. A third method is to raise brood stock from eggs as Dr. Motosaku Fujinaga is doing in Japan. He studied the Japanese shrimp, *Penaeus japonicus*, for ten years and obtained about twenty years of experience rearing shrimp before he began farming them. When he started his study on the biology of Japanese shrimp in 1933, nothing was known about their life cycle. Since shrimp eggs are naturally released in the sea where they sink to the bottom, he had tried to collect some there with fine mesh nets. Finding this technique unsuccessful, he placed fertilized female shrimp in tanks where they released their eggs. When they hatched and the nauplii emerged, he was sure that he could begin shrimp farming in the near future. However, it took him years to learn to successfully raise the shrimp from eggs, through all larval stages, to market sizes (see *Fig. 87*).

Fujinaga worked on raising shrimp and learning about shrimp biology until 1941 when the war interrupted his research. After the war, in 1949, he became chief of the research fisheries agency of the Japanese government. Here he was concerned with many problems quite unrelated to shrimp. Many, in fact, were of international nature, having to do with the regulation of high-seas salmon, king crab, and seals. In this capacity he came to the United States in 1955 and visited the Marine Biological Laboratory, University of North Carolina, where they were experimenting

Fig. 87. Farm-raised Japanese shrimp, Kuruma-ebi, *Penaeus japonicus.* *(C. P. Idyll)*

with shrimp raising. They fed brine shrimp eggs and nauplii to young shrimp. This was an important piece of information for Fujinaga because one of the stumbling blocks in attempting to rear the Japanese shrimp had been to find suitable-sized food for the immature shrimp.

Dr. Fujinaga purchased some salt fields around Seto Island in Japan which had been held by the government, and with the information he had learned on feeding, he felt he was ready to begin shrimp farming. He believed that shrimp farming would be successful because shrimp commanded

Fig. 88. Small holding baskets or cages used in Dr. Fujinaga's shrimp farm.   (*C. P. Idyll*)

high prices for use in *tempura* and *suki*, popular Japanese dishes.
Also, catches of shrimp in the fisheries around the coast of Japan were decreasing as a result of pollution. Fujinaga purchased ripe female shrimp
from fishermen, and, using tanks supplied with compressed air, began his
venture into commercial shrimp farming. The number of eggs released by
P. japonicus varies greatly depending on the size of the female. One female
may release between about 400,000 and 1,200,000 eggs. After the eggs
hatch they are held in small indoor tanks until they become post-larvae,
at which time they are placed in outdoor ponds. At first they are held in

Fig. 89. Shrimp rearing ponds in Japan are fed by water
from the Inland Sea. *(C. P. Idyll)*

small baskets in the ponds and are fed clams, worms, and squid, until they
are of sufficient size to be transported to the large rearing ponds he
established in the old salt fields (*Fig. 88.*) The shrimp in these large
rearing ponds are fed only on crushed clams (both meat and shell). This
food is distributed over the ponds by boat. He found that the young
shrimp eat several times during the day. When they exceed 2 grams (a
fraction of an ounce) they are fed only once a night. The ponds, 1 to 1½
meters (3 to 4·5 feet) deep, are flushed by the tides (*Fig. 89*). He obtains
about 10,000 shrimp from each female that he has caused to spawn. These
shrimp weigh 20 to 30 grams (1 ounce) each at the end of about five to

six months. He can raise shrimp from his own brood stock. Brood females release fewer eggs than the wild individuals caught by the fishermen; still, approximately 300,000 to 400,000 eggs per domestic shrimp are laid.

Fujinaga sells his shrimp alive. They are packed for shipping in a special dry sawdust, in corrugated cardboard boxes. In summer, the live shrimp are cooled down to about 12 degrees centigrade (54 degrees Fahrenheit) which makes the shipping operation easier by reducing the activity of the shrimp. To maintain the low temperature, plastic bags containing ice are placed in the sawdust with the shrimp. In winter, trains transport the shrimp rapidly enough to prevent high mortality, but in summer air transport is necessary. Summer trips lasting as long as seven hours might kill about 5 per cent of the shrimp. On the other hand, mortality in winter is close to zero for trips lasting as long as three days. Dr. Fujinaga has a unique market for his product in that the shrimp he sells must be alive, need not be full-grown, and because of the high demand, he receives a good price. He hopes eventually to export shrimp from his farming operations to other countries (*Fig. 89a*).

Shrimp Farming in the Philippines and Southeast Asia

In the Philippines, the sugpo shrimp, *Penaeus monodon*, is usually not raised as a primary crop, but often as supplement to the production of milkfish farms. Since brackish water ponds are screened at the inlets from the sea, some milkfish farmers who find juvenile sugpo in their harvests believe in spontaneous generation (that the shrimp arise from non-living materials). They know that they have not planted the shrimp in the ponds, yet shrimp appear during harvest. Actually many tiny sugpo larvae drift in with the tides and pass easily through the coarse screen used to keep predatory fish from entering the ponds and eating the milkfish.

In those farms where sugpo are reared alone, or are intentionally stocked with milkfish, the juvenile sugpo which drift into the ponds are supplemented with others that are collected from the sea. *Fig. 90* gives the layout of a Philippine pond. The juvenile sugpo are collected with dipnets manned by fishermen from wooden dugouts. The young post-larval shrimp or juveniles, may also be collected on lure lines, or *bon bons*, which consist of bunches of small aquatic plants or grasses arranged in a circle and tied to long lines at intervals of 25 to 50 centimeters (10 to 20 inches). The young shrimp attach to the plants and can be netted.

Most fish farmers in the Philippines regard the rapid-growing sugpo (it reaches 25 centimeters (10 inches) in one year) as a supplementary source of income and usually provide no care for them. They simply harvest any that drift into their milkfish ponds. This type of sugpo farming constitutes one of the most primitive forms of brackish water culture, and therefore production fluctuates widely because of the difficulties and uncertainties of obtaining the young and harvesting the adults. The time of peak abundance of juveniles varies seasonally as well as yearly.

The price that fishermen who catch shrimp in the sea charge farmers for young sugpo is usually several times that a young milkfish. This high cost,

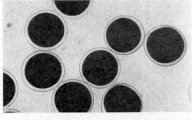
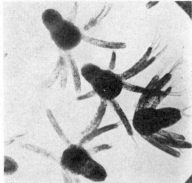

Fig. 89a. Prawn culture in Japan to illustrate the methods developed by Dr. Fujinaga. Top left shows prawn eggs (much enlarged)—females may lay from 400,000 to 1,200,000 eggs at a time. Next stage shows development into nauplius in 14 hours. After moulting six times in 36 hours the nauplius turns into a zoea and at this stage begins to take feed. In suitable ponds these are then carried on to full maturity ready for marketing (as above). That process occupies some six months. Below is pictured a large prawn farm in Aoi, Yamagushi Prefecture. This farm covers some 123 acres. (*Japan Times Weekly*)

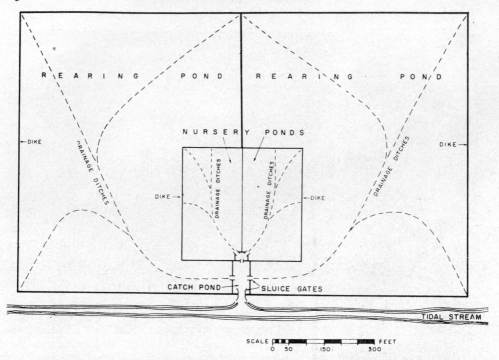

Fig. 90. Philippine shrimp pond showing general layout and drainage ditches for expediting the harvest of stock and removal of undesirable species.

(From D. Allen, 1963)

a major factor in the lack of interest in extensive culture of shrimp by fish farmers in the Philippines, apparently results because sugpo are hard to find. Also, the farmer is somewhat uninterested in farming the shrimp because, after paying a high price for the juveniles, he may recover only between 10 and 50 per cent of those in his ponds when they reach market sizes. Part of this loss is due to predation by fishes, with the remainder due to the inability of the farmer to catch the burrowed sugpo which are scattered over the entire bottom of the pond. Those farmers who raise only sugpo generally drain and sun dry their ponds between crops to kill any predators in the ponds and to later encourage the growth of minute plants which serve as food for young sugpo. The ponds are filled with a few inches of tidal water which enters through fine screens. Later, after the water level is raised to about 2 meters (6 feet), the young shrimp either enter with the tide when sluice gates are opened, or are stocked from catches made in the sea and nearby estuaries. Sugpo farmers harvest their crops in several different ways. They may drain the pond and collect the shrimp by hand, or in a net attached to the down-stream side of the sluice gate (see *Fig. 91*). By draining the pond on a low tide the shrimp are carried into the net. Another harvesting method involves an elaborate bamboo trap which leads the shrimp into a heart-shaped chamber from which they can be dipped.

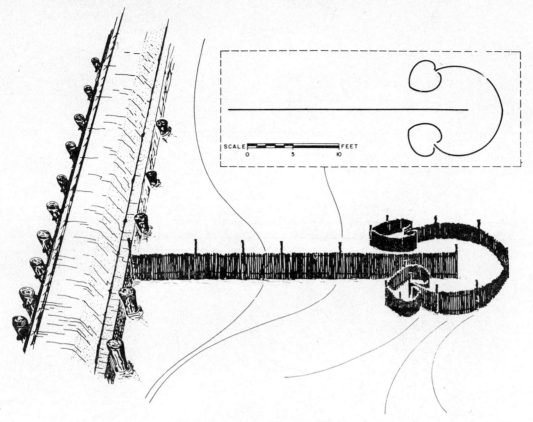

Fig. 91. A bamboo trap used in the Philippines to catch shrimp in ponds.
(From D. Allen, 1963)

The most important species of shrimp farmed in brackish water and sea water in the Philippines and southeast Asia are summarized in Table 10.

Shrimp Farming Research

In 1963, J. Jay Ewald, Institute of Marine Sciences, University of Miami, obtained ripe females from a catch of shrimp made by trawler fishing off Key West. He transported the ripe female shrimp to the laboratory at Miami and put them into aquaria. Several of the shrimp spawned within a few days, and the eggs hatched in a matter of hours. By very careful attention to the needs of these young shrimp, he reared them through all stages to the adult. This advance provides the shrimp farmer with knowledge on how to mass-culture seed stock, so he need not depend on natural breeding to stock his pond (*Fig. 92*).

To raise stock from eggs, the shrimp farmer must obtain a female shrimp ready to spawn, provide the proper food for the larval stages, and a tank or aquaria in which the larval states find conditions suitable for feeding. Much time and money are required to perfect these techniques.

Table 10

SOME IMPORTANT SPECIES OF CULTIVATED SHRIMP[1]

Species and country	Salinity range	Preferred habitat	Spawning and fecundity	Food	Longevity and growth records
Metapenaeus dobsoni India	Ranges between sea water and brackish-water of varying salinities.	Larvae appear in shallow inshore waters of the sea. When about 15 millimeters ($\frac{5}{8}$ inch) long, the young migrate with tidal assistance to coastal estuaries and backwaters. When about to spawn they return to the sea. Males, however, mature in brackish-water.	Breeds in the sea all the year round with peak from August to January. Impregnation occurs when females are 65 millimeters ($2\frac{1}{2}$ inches) long. When inshore waters are turbid on account of rain or inland discharge, the majority of eggs seem to perish without hatching or the nauplii die soon after hatching.	Foraminiferans, nematodes, copepods, amphipods, cladophorans and diatoms.	Life span about three years; grows to 114 millimeters (4·5 inches).
Metapenaeus (or *Penaeopsis*) *monoceros* India Formosa Indonesia	Thrives in sea, brackish and fresh waters	Sea for breeding and brackish waters for growth.	Observed to spawn from late July to early September.	—	Life span about one year; grows to 127 millimeters (5 inches).
Penaeus indicus longirostris India Philippines Pakistan	Sea and brackish waters.	Larvae appear in sea. When 5 millimeters ($\frac{1}{4}$ inch) long the fry move into brackish water. Adults return to sea before attaining sexual maturity.	Spawn in sea.	—	Grows to 203 millimeters (8 inches) in ponds.
Penaeus monodon Philippines	Ranges from sea through brackish to fresh water.	Larvae appear in sea. Fry move up to brackish waters where they thrive better than in fresh water. Half-year-old adolescents get back to shallow sea for spawning.	Spawn in sea.	Organic detritus, filamentous blue-green algae, diatoms epiphyton, small crustaceans and fish and dead and decaying fragments of larger organisms. In farm pond is given rice bran and meat of oyster and sardine.	Grows to 250 millimeters (9·8 inches) in about one year.

[1] Adapted from Kesteven and Job (1958).

Fig. 92. The pink shrimp, first raised in the laboratory in compartmented plastic trays, required careful attention.

(*W. M. Stephens*)

Ewald provided far more attention to the individual shrimp than could be given by a farmer (mass raising shrimp for profit), because he changed the water in his containers holding individual shrimp each day to prevent fouling and fed the shrimp individually. Of the 1,200 late larval stages which he reared fifty survived to become adults. Hence, survival was about 4 per cent. If the young can pass through the first protozoeal stage when they begin to feed, they have a fairly good chance of surviving. After the protozoeal stage, they transform to the mysis stages, and the mortality drops. Ewald found little difficulty in maintaining the late mysis and post-larval stages. They are relatively sturdy.

The refinement of pink shrimp rearing techniques *eventually* may result in large-scale commercial shrimp culture.

In 1939, in France, Jeanne H Heldt, reared *Penaeus trisulcatus*, *Parapenaeus longirostris* and *Sicyonia carinata* from eggs to post-larval stages. In 1956, near St. Augustine, Florida, the white shrimp, *Penaeus setiferus*, was reported to have been raised in captivity from egg to pre-adult which measured about 50 millimeters (2 inches) long. Another species, the brown shrimp, *Penaeus aztecus*, was reared by biologists at the United States Bureau of Commercial Fisheries Laboratory in Galveston, Texas. About five years of concentrated effort was required before individual brown shrimp were successfully raised in the laboratory.

In the United States, the brown shrimp, the pink shrimp, and the white shrimp, all of which are of considerable commercial importance, have now been raised from eggs to adults.

Recently attempts have been made to mass-rear the brown and the white shrimp at Galveston, Texas. Several thousand brown shrimp hatched under laboratory conditions were placed in stagnant ponds, but the nauplii failed to survive. Large numbers of post-larval shrimp also were placed in stagnant ponds, but apparently inadequate water supply and high water temperature caused mass mortality. Brown shrimp held in circulating sea water and fed daily produced about 250 kilograms of shrimp per hectare (225 pounds of shrimp per acre) in three months. In these experiments brown shrimp grew from 12 millimeters ($\frac{1}{2}$ inch) to 76 millimeters (3 inches) during this time. Use of fertilizers in the stagnant water ponds to cause growth of plankton also caused high mortality of the young shrimp, which led the investigators to believe that the fertilizers may have been toxic. The important findings from their work suggest that white shrimp are more suitable for rearing than brown shrimp, yet a great deal of investigation must be done on diet and, generally, on the over-all technique of raising shrimp.

Collecting Post-larvae

Dr. G. Robert Lunz, at his laboratory in South Carolina, has for years allowed post-larval shrimp to drift into the ponds in the nursery area following the Asian technique. He has never had adequate financial assistance to remove predators or give extensive care to these ponds; however, he has obtained yields up to about 350 kilograms per hectare (310 pounds per acre) per year when the shrimp were fed. In his attempts to breed white shrimp he experienced some of the same difficulties that were experienced in the white shrimp experiments at St. Augustine, in that the spermatophores which had attached to the female fell off as the shrimp were being transported to the laboratory. Therefore, the eggs, when released, were infertile. *Fig. 93* shows Dr. Lunz's farm pond.

Other Shrimp Species

A number of cold-water species (i.e. *Pandalus*) in Europe and North America support substantial fisheries. However, due to the small size and to the relatively long lives of these shrimp—two to four or five years in some species—and the costly care required, they would probably not be

Fig. 93. Farm pond in South Carolina used by Dr. Lunz in his shrimp experiments.   (E. S. Iversen)

suitable for culture. No attempts have been made to rear these cold-water shrimp on a commercial basis.

Research on the English prawn, *Palaemon serratus*, carried out at the Ministry of Agriculture, Fisheries and Food, Fishery Experiment Station at North Wales, has demonstrated methods of obtaining larvae from mature adults in the laboratory. The environmental conditions required by this species have been studied. From a biological standpoint, rearing the English prawn is feasible, but at this time considerably more information is needed on the economic feasibility of farming the species before any recommendation can be made.

The giant prawn, *Macrobranchium rosenbergii*, distributed widely in most tropical and subtropical areas of the Indo-Pacific region, has farming potential. It lives in fresh or brackish water, is omnivorous, and has been cultured from larval to adult stages. This species and other *Macrobranchium* and *Cryphiops* with abbreviated larval lives, or direct development, are being studied for increased use in brackish and fresh water farms.

Bait Shrimp Market

Up to this point we have considered rearing shrimp from the standpoint of providing food for human consumption. But since shrimp are caught

Fig. 94. A cast net is used in many areas in the Gulf of Mexico to catch bait shrimp.
(Outboard Marine International)

by a large number of predators (as is discussed in more detail in Chapter 14), they are a desirable bait for sport fish. In the southern Atlantic states, and in the Gulf of Mexico, bait demands of sportsfishermen are being met as fully as possible by commercial fishing (as in *Fig. 94*). In the State of Florida the wholesale value of bait shrimp alone was over $240,000 in 1965. Since anglers generally require only small shrimp and will pay rather high prices for them, the possibility of rearing these species to bait size has potential.

Status of Shrimp Farming

There are a number of reasons why shrimp are suitable for farming. Shrimp grow rapidly and are in great demand. They are reared extensively in several countries either by catching the young and placing them in ponds, or by situating ponds where tidal currents will carry the young into them. Production by this technique is limited by the presence of larval forms of predators which eat the young shrimp, but eliminating these unwanted species is a big problem. Natural spawning and the currents cannot be relied on for the supply of young. In Japan controlled spawning and very high prices for young shrimp have permitted successful shrimp farming. Recently there has been much interest in the United States to farm shrimp, and the laboratory-rearing of the several important species found in the Gulf of Mexico has stimulated additional interest. Additionally there are many suitable areas for shrimp farming in southeastern United States, however, many problems remain to be solved before commercial ventures are successful.

CHAPTER 10

Milkfish

A fish popular to millions of people in the islands and many tropical countries bordering the Pacific and Indian Oceans is the white-fleshed milkfish, known as "chanos" or "bangos," and other local names. In these countries the milkfish in the market come from both wild stock caught offshore and from those raised on farms. The difference between fish caught and fish farmed is in the dependability of supply achieved by controlled feeding so that when catches by fishermen fluctuate greatly or fail completely, milkfish are available from farms.

This fish is practical for farming—it grows fast, it needs no supplemental feeding, and it is not cannibalistic. The milkfish is valuable in pond culture almost everywhere it occurs. Milkfish farming is an important and profitable industry in the Philippines, and many people gain income from the numerous stages of the operation. In addition, thousands of acres of wetlands of otherwise limited use are utilized for food production. Following World War II considerable salt marsh area in the Philippines was unused but suitable for fish farming. The government estimated that they could put in excess of 100,000 hectares (250,000 acres) into fish farming. Using the latest figures available to him, Schuster (1960) estimated that over 88,000 hectares (220,000 acres) of ponds were under milkfish cultivation in the Philippines, 128,000 hectares (320,000 acres) in Indonesia, and 13,000 hectares (32,500 acres) in Taiwan.

Description and Range of Milkfish

The milkfish is a herring-like fish with a sturdy body and a large, deeply-forked tail. It has large eyes and a small toothless mouth adapted for eating plants. It also possesses long intestines, characteristic of herbivores, which may be over thirteen times the body length. A large, powerful fish, the milkfish weighs up to 20 kilograms (50 pounds).

The species is distributed in the Pacific and Indian oceans, in tropical and subtropical waters, and is apparently most abundant near coastlines (*Fig. 95*). It does not occur in the Atlantic Ocean nor in the Pacific where environmental conditions are unsuitable.

Adult milkfish spawn close to coasts. The fry and fingerlings of the milkfish spend their first days very near shore in coastal waters. Some young enter fresh-water rivers, but they do not reach large sizes or even attain sexual maturity there. Apparently even those in fresh water return to sea to spawn.

In some areas within their range, milkfish spawn throughout the year, however, milkfish in the Philippines spawn from March until July.

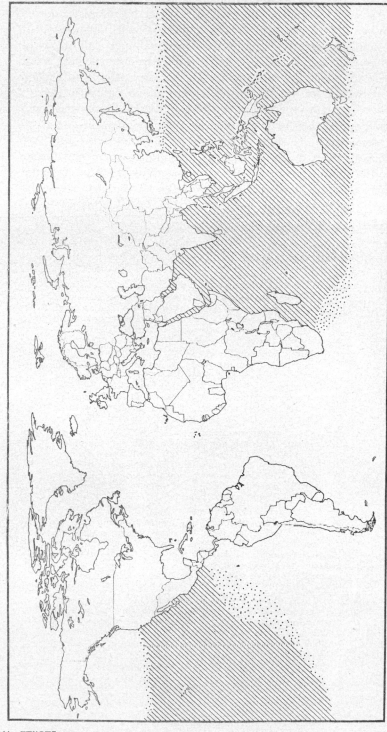

Fig. 95. The world distribution of milkfish is shown by the shaded area.
(*From W. H. Schuster, 1960*)

Females release between 1·5 and 7 million bouyant eggs during a single spawning (*Fig. 96*). External fertilization of the eggs by the males occurs in the sea. When the fry are about 1·3 centimeters ($\frac{1}{2}$ inch) long, they drift toward the shore, apparently living on the considerable growth of phytoplankton found there which results from the runoff from fertile land areas. Fry are most abundant three days or so before and after a full moon during the spawning season. When the fry are about 1·3 centimeters ($\frac{1}{2}$ inch long) they have consumed the stored food in their yolk sacs and begin to search for food. At this fry stage, they eat an assortment of blue-green algae and associated organisms (bacteria, protozoans) until they are fingerling size, about 15·6 centimeters (6 inches) long, when they change their diet to filamentous green algae. They grow rapidly, reaching about 0·8 kilograms (2 pounds) in their first year and 2·7 kilograms (6 pounds) by their fourth year of life. Little is known of their later life history in the sea (Table 11).

Table 11

SUMMARY OF INFORMATION ON MILKFISH,

Chanos chanos[1]

Identification	The body is elongate and slightly compressed, with a pointed head and has a deeply-forked tail. Eyes are large and mouth is weak. The fish is bright silvery or bluish above, and a golden luster along the sides of some specimens is reported. There is a yellowish cast to the rather strong dorsal and pectoral fins.
Distribution	From longitude 40 degrees E. to about 100 degrees W. and from latitude 30 degrees to 40 degrees N. to latitude 30 degrees to 40 degrees S. Milkfish occur in the tropical and subtropical areas of the Indian and Pacific Oceans. The species has not been reported from the Atlantic nor from the Pacific coast of Central or South America.
Annual yield per acre	"The average production per hectare [2·47 acres] per annum is 300 kilograms [660 pounds] in the Philippines, and about 2,000 kilograms [4,400 pounds] in Taiwan, where heavy fertilization and artificial feeding is applied." In Indonesia where sewage is allowed to flow into the ponds production per hectare per annum is 5,000 kilograms (11,000 pounds).
Age and growth	The growth of chanos is easily adjusted by the amount of food provided to them, and by the stocking rates in ponds. They may reach as high as 800 grams (1·8 pounds) after one year and between 1,500 grams (3·3 pounds) and 2,000 grams (4·4 pounds) at the end of two years. At about four years of age, chanos may reach a weight of about 2,500 to 3,500 grams (5·5 to 7·7 pounds) in ponds.
Reproduction	Fertilization is external and the eggs are released in the open sea near shore and float to the surface. As many as 7 million eggs have been estimated to be produced by a single large female. All attempts to obtain eggs from females either by natural spawning or stripping them in ponds has failed.
Food	Milkfish are herbivores and eat diatoms, blue-green algae, filamentous algae, and occasionally some animals such as nematodes and copepods.
Feeding habits	They feed throughout the year either at the surface or on the bottom of ponds.

[1]Based on Schuster, 1960.

MILKFISH

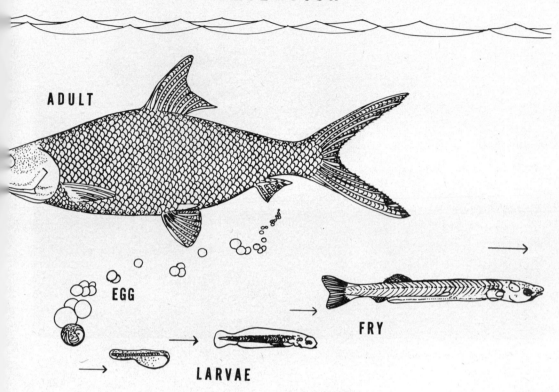

ADULT

EGG

LARVAE

FRY

Fig. 96. Milkfish spawn in near shore waters and the young drift into shallow water where fishermen catch them for stocking farms. *(J. Z. Iversen)*

History and Current Practice of Milkfish Culture

No one knows just when fish ponds were first constructed for rearing milkfish. The first "ponds" were simply fish traps—a dike across a bay or inlet. Later, gates were constructed which could be opened to allow the interchange of seawater and the entrance of young fish, then closed to prevent the fish from escaping. Predatory and competitor fish and numerous other species easily enter the ponds along with the milkfish. Primitive ponds of this sort still exist in Java, the Philippines, and the Hawaiian Islands.

From this haphazard start the pondfish industry, came into existence. Today young milkfish are caught close to shore and transferred to the ponds. This procedure has the advantage of allowing far fewer predators and competitors into the ponds than the older method of using tidal currents and gates. If the fry are not carefully sorted, large numbers of undesirable species still can be introduced into the ponds. Catching fry and transporting them to the ponds has the disadvantage that a supply of young must be sought, an expensive and time-consuming job which

Fig. 97. Milkfish ponds (tambaks) in Java.   (*W. H. Schuster*)

increases the price of fish for stocking. Added to this cost is that of transporting the young from the beaches to the fish ponds.

Milkfish farming in the Philippines now is a highly developed industry. Its production is encouraged by the prevailing monsoons and long periods of inclement weather during which no offshore fishing for marketable adult milkfish can be done, thus necessitating that the demand for fresh fish at these times be filled by the pond production of fresh milkfish (*Fig. 97*). This is further described later in the chapter.

Milkfish Fry Industry in the Philippines

Since milkfish have not been bred in captivity, all farming of this species depends upon fry caught by fishing along the shore. Men, women, and children fish for milkfish fry with a variety of gear, including fine-meshed dip-nets, seines, or traps. The fishermen depend on the tides to carry fry into their traps. Seines, 4·6 to 6 meters (15 to 20 feet) long, are drawn through shallow water by two persons. In some places, "lure-lines," made of weeds or cloth strung on long, thin ropes, accumulate fry so they can be netted when they seek shelter there. The fry are placed in white enamel basins where they are sorted from other species or debris, and are then placed in unglazed earthenware jars, which hold an estimated 2,000 to 3,500 each, for sale to the farmers.

Fig. 98. Milkfish ponds must be drawn down to concentrate and catch undesirable fish.   (*W. H. Schuster*)

Because of the small size of the fry, the catch is seldom counted. Men who handle fry regularly are able to estimate reliably how many are in each jar. The fry are hardy creatures—large numbers of them have been held for two weeks in jars with only the daily addition of sea-water. The fry are shipped to farmers and may be transported as far as 500 miles.

Some seventy-six fish species, including predatory fish, have been found in milkfish ponds. Some of those predators are accidentally planted in the ponds because of careless sorting of the milkfish fry in the jars sold to the farmers. Others enter the ponds when water is added from the sea. Also the predators often slip through the irregular mesh openings of the bamboo or cloth screens. *Fig. 98* shows one way of eliminating predators.

Milkfish rearing is specialized. Some farmers raise fry only to the fingerling stage, others raise fingerlings to marketable size. As was mentioned earlier in the chapter, because the yearly monsoons prevent offshore fishing, considerable interest develops in holding milkfish fry in brackish water for periods of up to a year, with minimum feeding. The fry, stunted by this technique, quickly resume growth when provided with ample food and can reach a marketable size during the monsoon season when demand for them is high, and the price is favorable.

Rates of Stocking, Growth, and Mortality

About 30–50 fry per meter square (10·8 square feet) are placed in nursery ponds (*Fig. 99*). When ample food exists in the pond, growth of fry is rapid, averaging about 1 millimeter (0·04 inch) per day, and at the end of one month, fingerlings may be 5–7·6 centimeters (2 to 3 inches) long. If there is plenty of filamentous algae for the fingerlings to eat in the rearing ponds, fingerlings can be stocked at a rate of about 1,500 per hectare (2·5 acres).

Mortality from the fry stage to marketable size may be as high as 70 per cent. Milkfish are harvested, usually at about 450 grams (1 pound) apiece, when they are between six and nine months old, although different sizes are harvested to meet different market conditions (*Fig. 100*).

After the milkfish are harvested, the ponds are refilled and a new growth of algae is set. When the algae is sufficiently dense, the ponds are restocked with fingerlings. This procedure permits three crops of fish to be reared to market size within two years. Two crops per year can be produced in well-managed ponds; in ponds where food is abundant and salinity and temperature ideal, three crops per year can be obtained.

Food and Feeding Habits

Milkfish are herbivores. They live mostly on algae or what Filipinos call *lab-lab* and *lamut*. *Lab-lab* is a plant and animal complex that supplies food to milkfish until they reach a length of about 7·6 to 10 centimeters (3 to 4 inches). It forms a dense mat over the entire pond and consists of unicellular filamentous algae, bacteria, protozoans, and diatoms. *Lamut* appears also as a dense mat, but it floats near the surface. It consists of about six species of algae which form a thick, green scum. The submerged leaves of a complex of higher plants, *Thalassia*, *Ruppia*, and others that Filipinos call collectively *digman*, may be eaten by the large milkfish. Characteristically, the higher plants begin to appear in the ponds after the algae becomes less abundant. The growth of the higher aquatic plants is a signal to the pond owner that the algae is greatly reduced and that his ponds are being overgrazed.

Usually farmers drain and dry milkfish ponds for varying periods between crops of fish before they refill them. The value of drying the ponds is controversial. Many milkfish farmers claim that drying is necessary to kill predatory fish and parasites and that it insures a good growth of *lab-lab* and *lamut*. Some studies suggest that drying the ponds also reduces the growth of higher aquatic plants, which is advantageous to the fish farmer. The addition of sea water with its nutrients fertilizes the ponds each time they are filled. In addition, in many areas of the Indo-Pacific, fresh water rivers which supply the water to keep the ponds brackish contain fertilizing elements from human and animal sewage collected upstream. Generally, no artificial fertilization of ponds is necessary in the Philippines.

Bottom type is one of the most important factors affecting algal growth in ponds. If the pond bottom has a high clay content and considerable

Fig. 99. A milkfish nursery pond for rearing fingerlings. Note the young mangroves round the edge of the large rearing pond to strengthen the dikes. (*W. H. Schuster*)

Fig. 100. Harvesting milkfish in a large farm in Indonesia. (*W. H. Schuster*)

CHAPTER 11

Mullet and Miscellaneous Pondfishes

The association between man and mullet is long-established. The Romans and Egyptians cultivated mullet for human food centuries ago. Today extensive fisheries for mullet have been developed in many countries of the world.

The mullet is a good-flavored fish, but shares the misfortune of the carp by being looked down upon in many countries with high living standards. However, it is considered desirable by many people, for it is heavily fished and farmed throughout its range. Some authors writing about mullet have described it as flavorful; Rachel Carson, the well-known writer, describes mullet in one of her earlier works as being oily, with a "nut-like" flavor.

Although mullet are abundant almost everywhere in tropical and subtropical waters, it has been suggested that no sea coast in the world is so bountifully populated with them as those of the southern Atlantic and Gulf States of the United States, with their broad margins of brackish water, numerous estuaries, and broad river mouths. One of the most abundant food fishes of the entire southern seaboard of the United States, they are caught principally by gillnets, trammel nets, beach seines, and stop-nets.

Description of Mullet and Life History

Mullet come from a large family which lives in the temperate and tropical waters of the world. In a particular region only a few species may occur, and even then one or perhaps two species are more abundant than the others (Table 12). The principal species in Florida is the black, or striped, mullet, *Mugil cephalus*, although *M. liza*, another dark-colored or "black" mullet, find the silvery or white mullets, *M. curema*, *M. trichodon*, and *M. gaimardiana* are also present. In each part of the world where mullet occur, they have special names. For instance, in southeastern United States such names as "jumping mullet," "sand mullet," "fat-backed," "big-eye mullet," and "lisa" are used.

Some species jump, occasionally clearing the sea surface by as much as a meter (3 feet). This has earned *M. cephalus* the title of "jumping mullet." These fish literally point themselves out to fishermen who are looking for them. The ability to jump is also to the mullets' advantage because they often obtain freedom by jumping over the corklines of nets the fishermen set around them. Why the mullet jumps is a question frequently asked, but the answers have no scientific basis.

It is surprising that in the light of the world-wide interest in this abundant fish, relatively little scientific information has been compiled on the

Table 12

SUMMARY OF INFORMATION ON STRIPED MULLET

Mugil cephalus

Identification	Body elongate; two dorsal fins. The first dorsal fin has four sharp spines. Lateral line absent. Eyes have gelatinous eyelids anterior and posterior to pupil. Body greyish above and silvery on sides and below.
Distribution	Nearly world-wide in temperate, tropical, and subtropical mainly marine and brackish waters, occasionally found in fresh water.
Age and growth	In Japan, black (striped) mullet grow to about 200 grams (6 ounces) between March–April and November-December. In India, black (striped) mullet reach about 45 centimeters (18 inches) in a year. In Florida, striped mullet reach 31 centimeters (12 inches) in three years.
Reproduction	In Philippines striped mullet spawn in the open sea during the dry season, and the fry appear in shallow coastal waters and around the mouths of rivers in April to July. Off southeastern United States, spawning occurs during October to February in offshore waters.
Food	Striped mullet eat algae growing on the substrate, decayed organic matter, and small crustaceans. When young, mullet eat plankton and algae near the surface.
Feeding habits	Omnivorous filter feeders, but to a considerable extent herbivorous.

important species. In 1875, the United States Fish Commission sent out requests for information on the habits of mullet to fishermen and fish dealers. The replies led the Commission to the conclusion that the mullet's habits are so peculiar that to understand them it would be necessary for naturalists to devote a considerable period to study them throughout their whole range. Since then out knowledge of mullet has increased very little.

Mullet feed in a head-down position, moving their heads from side to side so violently that at times their entire bodies vibrate. They appear to be surrounded by a cloud of mud during feeding, for they suck up mud from the bottom, sieve it in their mouths to remove food, then reject it. They also feed on surface scum, which contains diatoms. Mullet generally school when feeding near the surface.

Their intestines, over three to six times as long as the length of the fish, reflects their vegetable diet. Herbivorous fish characteristically possess long intestines which are required to be able to digest plant material.

Mullet occur in the sea, in estuaries, in brackish waters near river mouths, and some even migrate into fresh water. In some areas when mullet reach maturity they form large schools near shore and swim offshore to spawn. Spawning schools of striped mullet were discovered by U.S. Fish and Wildlife Service scientists off Florida's east coast along the 20 fathom curve. (This curve lies on the outer continental shelf, well inside the axis of the Gulf Stream.) In nature mullet release their eggs free in the sea to be fertilized externally (*Fig. 102*). Upon hatching, the larval mullet drift inshore, arriving there in large numbers when about 25 millimeters (1

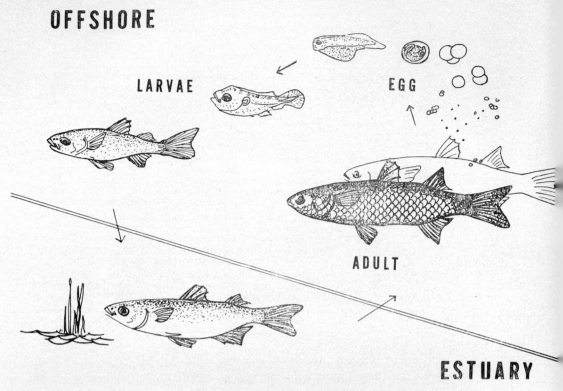

Fig. 102. Mullet spawn offshore and the young move into estuaries where they can be collected for confinement in ponds.   *(J. Z. Iversen)*

inch) in length. Once inshore they form small schools and move along the coast into estuaries. In Hawaii spawning schools occur near shore in very shallow water.

This species has been farmed successfully only by collecting the young when they first arrive inshore, or by attracting them into impoundments on tidal currents, and later placing them in large ponds to feed. No one has reared this species to adult size from the egg on a large-scale commercial basis. From Hawaii come reports of spawning adults in fish ponds, and in Japan it is reported that mullet have been raised from egg to juvenile in captivity.

In Korea the eggs of a mullet of uncertain species have been fertilized artificially by squeezing eggs from mature females and mixing them with milt. The greater the number of eggs placed together in containers, the greater the proportion of hatch obtained. The greatest survival occurred at salinities between 15 and 25 parts per thousand, but the young mullet lived only fourteen days. In the United States, running ripe male and female silver mullet were captured at sea, stripped, and the eggs fertilized. Hatching occurred after forty hours, and the larvae lived for thirty-two hours and grew only a fraction of an inch.

Fig. 103. Mullet thrive in shallow coastal lagoons with very high salinities.
(*Florida State News Bureau*)

Environment of the Mullet

Mullet apparently prefer warm water. The population of juvenile silver mullet seems to disappear from estuaries and beaches in North Carolina and Georgia in the late fall or early winter, so that young are scarce or absent during the winter. Absence of juveniles may be related to the cooling of the water during the fall, but water temperature is not the only factor governing this offshore movement. Mullet are occasionally killed by cold northern air masses moving into the shallow lagoons and bays of the inshore areas in Texas.

Although most mullet are found at salinities of 30 parts per thousand or below, they may thrive in areas of very high salinity. For instance in Laguna Madre, Texas, they occur in salinities that are seldom below 50 to 60 parts per thousand and may be as high as 80 parts per thousand. In some Bulgarian coastal lagoons with poor water exchange and high evaporation, mullet have been reported from waters with salinity as high as 83 parts per thousand.

Measurements of growth of striped mullet were obtained from four separate areas on the west coast of Florida and showed different average growth rates in each area (*Fig. 103*). Possible reasons for this growth–area relationship of mullet include the relative amounts of large shallow brackish areas, the availability and types of food and the stability of the temperature.

Mullet in Florida appear to be relatively non-migratory species, for they do not move any considerable distance along the coast. Over a period of several years, 90 per cent were recovered within 32 kilometers (20 miles) of where they were tagged.

Increasing Mullet Yields

Dr. G. R. Lunz, in South Carolina, impounded fish in earthen ponds to obtain estimates of yield, and without stocking them, fertilizing them, or applying any other management to these ponds, obtained about 114 kilograms (250 pounds) of marketable fish per acre annually. About 50 per cent of this total, by weight, was mullet. Total production was reduced by predatory fish such as trout (*Cynoscion nebulosus*), bass (*Sciaenops* sp.), and drum (*Pogonias* sp.), found when the ponds were drained. The ponds had an average salinity of 20 parts per thousand. The fresh water entered from a small stream, and when the tide level rose, saline water entered via an automatic flap valve and kept the ponds flooded to about 76 centimeters (2½ feet).

In later similar experiments in 1955, mullet again dominated the fish species trapped in his ponds, again being about 50 per cent of the total weight, or about 98 kilograms (216 pounds) of the 196 kilograms (430 pounds) produced per acre during the nine-month experiment. Dr. Lunz is confident that production could be increased with management.

Near St. Augustine, Florida, Malcolm Johnson stocked three ⅛-acre brackish water ponds with mullet and fertilized some of the ponds with 7–9–0 (7 parts available nitrogen to 9 parts phosphoric acid) inorganic commercial fertilizer. He attempted to clean out other species, yet numerous other predators rapidly replaced those removed. Total production over eleven months from his fertilized pond, placed on a per acre basis, was 125 kilograms (277 pounds), of which 53 kilograms (118 pounds) were mullet. None of the fish he raised approached marketable sizes. He found fertilizing ponds to be costly and it did not increase production sufficiently. Despite the advantages of rearing mullet, which feeds on the natural foods living in ponds, the poor market price in most of the United States of less than $0.10 per pound to the fishermen makes it, to use Johnson's words, "extremely doubtful that the fish could be produced as a major crop cheaply enough by this method to sell at a profit." The trend in production and value of mullet over a recent thirteen-year period in Florida showed production of mullet increasing while its value was decreasing.

In 1962 the Florida State Board of Conservation renamed black or striped mullet "lisa," a name used for mullet in Spanish-speaking countries, in an attempt to remove a stigma attached to the name "mullet," and hopefully to increase market demand.

Commercial Mullet Farms

In many areas throughout the world where mullet are farmed commercially, varying yields and varying degrees of care are involved.

In Israel, although most fish farming (carp) is done in fresh water, black mullet are raised in the large areas not arable because of salty soil and

Fig. 104. Sea water percolates through this dike made of coral and basalt that is used to enclose mullet and other pond fish in Hawaii. (*Bernice P. Bishop Museum*)

water. These mullet are caught in brackish rivers near the sea and transferred for cultivation to ponds.

Mullet are widely cultivated in the brackish water rice fields of India, especially in West Bengal. Several species of mullet are cultivated in the drainage canals and rice fields for part of their lives, together with other fishes and shrimps. In China, mullet fry are captured at low tide with dip nets and are stocked directly into the brackish water ponds, but are generally in less favor than milkfish, the mainstay of Philippines brackish-water fish farms.

Mullet and eels are cultured together in the same ponds in Japan. The young mullet migrating up rivers swim directly into brackish-water ponds and are held there through the warm growing season until autumn when they reach about 200 grams (0·4 pound) and are suitable for market.

Hawaii was at one time an important fish farming area, but its importance has dropped in recent years. Brackish and marine fish farms in Hawaii produce a variety of fish, in some cases as many as thirteen different species. The principal fish in the brackish ponds is *M. cephalus*, called "ama ama" by the Hawaiians. These impoundments in early times were owned by the king, or chief, and were constructed by the forced labor of the commoners (or the Menahunes, those legendary dwarfs who were supposed to have helped to construct them). Bay entrances were blocked off with loosely piled lava rock so that water could percolate through the 1·5 meter (5 foot) thick walls. Some mullet entered the ponds through sluice gates and others were captured in estuaries and placed into the ponds.

By 1900 only half the fish ponds in Hawaii that had existed thirty years earlier were still in use (*Fig. 104*). Transportation in those days was a serious problem, so when the natives moved inland sales of all species dropped sharply. Raising the profitable crops of taro and rice in shallow ponds also has contributed to the decrease in number of ponds available for fish farming. Some ponds became filled with water hyacinths and lava and were abandoned. John N. Cobb, in 1903, noted that real estate values were becoming so high that the land could not be kept in farms. Interestingly, he showed photographs of ponds in what is now Waikiki Beach! One of the oldest fish ponds, near Koko Head, is now a housing development.

At the turn of the century fish farms on the island of Oahu had seventy-two ponds which employed 142 persons. Of those employed throughout the archipelago at that time, one was American, 147 were Chinese, and about forty-three were Hawaiians. Production of pond-raised mullet there in 1900 was about 220,000 kilograms (485,000 pounds). By 1960 it was down to 15,440 kilograms (33,967 pounds).

In Arcachon, France, famous for its oyster and mussel production, mullet are grown in a system of many ponds with complicated sluice gates. In numerous areas along the Mediterranean Sea mullet are farmed.

Suitability for Farming

In many ways mullet are well suited for farming. Since they feed on algae, diatoms, small crustaceans, decayed organic matter, and mud, there is little need to feed them. An exchange of water in a properly located pond will bring in adequate food, and run-off from the land into the pond will carry nutrients which, in many areas, will produce the necessary fertilization for the plankton which mullet eat. With organic and inorganic fertilization one can increase the yields in mullet ponds, but not sufficiently to justify the expense of the fertilizer. Little care is required to produce these fish once they have been impounded. They are resistant to high temperatures and high salinities but are sensitive to low temperatures, apparently migrating offshore at the onset of cold weather.

Since mullet are herbivores and feed on small species of plankton, they can be raised in combination with other herbivorous fish and shrimp as is done in the Philippines.

The disadvantage of farming this species for profit is that in many areas, such as the southern United States and the Gulf of Mexico, there is an extremely low wholesale price for mullet. In most areas the price in the round is less than $0.10 per pound. In contrast to this, $0.80 to $0.90 (occasionally reaching $1.25) per pound to farmers is not uncommon for pond-raised mullet in Hawaii. In Florida commercially caught mullet are being canned and also processed into "fish sticks." Unless demand can be increased to raise the market value substantially, mullet have little future as a pondfish in the United States. Added to this is the high cost for the collection of young fish to supplement the stock of fish carried into the ponds by tide currents, and the sorting that must be done to exclude predators from the pond—expensive, but necessary. Despite this

Fig. 105. Experiments using hormones are underway at the Oceanic Institute in Hawaii to induce mullet to spawn in captivity. Some success in spawning mullet by this method has been achieved in Israel.

(*Oceanic Institute*)

disadvantage in the United States, in many areas of Europe, and in the Pacific islands where fresh fish is a substantial portion of the peoples' diet, mullet farming is important (*Fig. 105*).

Miscellaneous Pondfishes

Besides milkfish and mullet, other fish are farmed in brackish and marine waters in temperate and subtropical latitudes. These species have, for the most part, narrow geographical distributions and are farmed only to a limited extent. Some occur accidentally in brackish ponds where other species are being reared and are harvested and sold with the more desirable species.

One of these species, the pearl spot (*Etroplus suratensis*), is found in India, Pakistan, and Ceylon, where it reaches a maximum length of about 30 centimeters (12 inches). The name derives from the pearly spots found on the majority of scales on the dorsal portion of the fish. The pearl spot is farmed in either fresh or brackish water. During the second year they become sexually mature and breed in ponds without any special care or attention. During spawning the female cleans algae and other growth from a small area on submerged objects and attaches her 1,300 to 6,000 eggs, then the male fertilizes them. She guards the young which hatch from the eggs in about seven days. The young fish live almost exclusively on plants, and the older fish on fish larvae, aquatic insects, algae, and decaying plant remnants. The pearl spot attains a length of 10 to 12 centimeters (about 4 inches) by the end of the first year. As a rule, they occur with other fish which are reared in the brackish water ponds.

In Japan, China, Vietnam, and Taiwan, the eel (*Anguilla japonica*) breeds in the sea and moves into estuaries and rivers. In Japan eels are caught during February to April as they ascend rivers. After about a year in the ponds, they reach a saleable size of about 30 centimeters (12 inches) long, and weigh between 100 to 200 grams ($\frac{1}{4}$ to $\frac{1}{2}$ pound). Eels are voracious carnivores and are fed fresh or cooked fish, earthworms, or crushed clams. They are often raised together with carp and grey mullet which are too large for the eels to eat or on which they fatten. The surplus mullet or carp which survive the depredations by the eels are also marketed. Their production rate depends upon the amount of food supplied them; yields up to about 15,000 kilograms per hectare (13,200 pounds per acre) per year have been attained. Most are raised in fresh water.

The cock-up (*Lates calcarifer*) has a projecting jaw and a serrated gill cover, and reaches a length of about 170 centimeters ($5\frac{1}{2}$ feet). It is widespread in India, Thailand, Malaya, Vietnam, Philippines, Indonesia, Cambodia, and Australia. It occasionally occurs in ponds in association with other farmed fish. The adults do not breed in ponds, however; if a farmer wants to rear them he can collect fry in rivers, creeks, or brackish lagoons. They eat small valuable species such as shrimp so they are not suitable for farming together with them. The cock-up is carnivorous and feeds mainly on fish and crustaceans in the open sea. At the end of the first year they weigh about 500 grams (1 pound) and reach a length of about 38 centimeters (15 inches).

Tarpon (*Megalops cyprinoides*), found around the Indian and Pacific Oceans, is reared in India. (This fish is not the same as the popular sport fish found in the Caribbean and the Gulf of Mexico.) They are large fish and reach lengths in excess of 1 meter (39 inches). Like the cock-up, they breed in the sea but can be cultivated in ponds. The larvae and fry, which are found in estuarine waters, are hardy and can be transported long distances and even placed directly into fresh water. The young feed mainly on small crustaceans, diatoms, and algae. Since they are a predatory fish—the diet of the adults consisting of about 50 per cent fish—they are generally considered undesirable for fish ponds, although they have been found in such ponds under cultivation. In some brackish water ponds, they may attain a length of about 40 centimeters (16 inches) by the end of one year.

In Hawaii, the ten-pounder (*Elops machnata*) forms part of the brackish water pond crop. In 1964 over 1·7 metric tons (3,700 pounds) were harvested. The ten-pounder fry enter the ponds with tide water, and, once inside, feed mainly on crustaceans and small fish. This species may reach a length of over 700 millimeters (28 inches). The ten-pounder was once thought to be very predacious and hence undesirable as a fish for farming; however, now it appears they are not.

In the northern Adriatic Sea, eels (*Anguilla anguilla*), the sea bass, (*Morone labrax*), and *Sparus auratus* are all farmed in brackish ponds. These three species do not breed in ponds, but move up rivers from the sea where they are trapped in ponds, or the fry are purchased and placed in ponds. Both the bass and eels require large quantities of fish as food. These voracious feeders are fairly important in the fish ponds in the Po region.

Tilapia (*Tilapia mossambica*) is farmed in fresh and brackish waters in tropical areas. This fish, a prolific breeder in brackish ponds with potential in other areas, is discussed in Chapter 13.

Trout are usually raised only in fresh water; however, some species are able to live in fresh water when young and in the sea as adults. The rain-rainbow trout, also called steelhead, *Salmo gairdnerii*, when adult can be transferred to salinities of as high as full-strength sea water (about 35 parts per thousand). The Norwegians began raising trout in fresh water–salt water about 1910. Today it is still practiced there and also in Denmark and Australia.

In salt water, trout are less exposed to diseases such as viri and fungi which may plague them in fresh water. Faster growth may be obtained in salt water partly because more even temperatures exist in this environment than in fresh water. Sea water temperatures, for example, may be warmer in winter and cooler in summer than the fresh water supplying the ponds. The tempered waters cause the trout to feed for longer periods and, in turn, results in a more rapid growth and an earlier trip to market. Andrew W. Anderson, formerly United States Regional Fisheries Attache in Europe, reported that at one fresh water–brackish water trout farm in Norway, 4 kilograms (9 pounds) of food were required to produce 1 kilogram (2 pounds) of trout. In fresh water only, twice as much food was required.

Anyone who has compared the flesh of trout raised in fresh water only with that of trout raised in fresh and salt water, says that the latter have an improved taste and a darker, more appetizing color.

A farm located close to salt water is in a position to receive a substantial, inexpensive supply of marine industrial fishes to feed to the carnivorous trout. Trout farmers in Denmark, Norway, and Tasmania take advantage of their nearness to the sea to get industrial sea fish for trout feed.

Selecting a site for a fresh water–salt water farm is, of course, difficult. There must be an abundant supply of clean, fresh water, plus a nearby unpolluted brackish water source.

Frequently pumps are required to flood the fresh water ponds and to adjust the temperature and salinity.

If fresh water–salt water farms are suitably located, their advantages seem greater than the fresh-water only farm.

Other species of sea- and brackish-water fishes are also farmed, but in general they are not as important as those just described. Some can tolerate only very low salinities and are mostly farmed in fresh water or at the uppermost reaches of estuaries.

IV
POTENTIAL SPECIES

CHAPTER 12

Other Invertebrates for Farming

The species discussed so far are those presently farmed in temperate waters of the northern hemisphere. In this chapter and in the next, we cover mostly species that are not now being farmed but which have been considered for farming, and those that are farmed only on a small scale. These species possess characteristics which encourage interest in farming them. Important among these characteristics is their high market value. Too, they are species which either spawn or release eggs in captivity, and the adults can be held in captivity. Undetailed descriptions are given of the life histories of these species, mostly to permit judgment on the possibility of successfully farming them. Other species besides those discussed here may be farmed in the future as new information about the sea is obtained.

There are many cases on record of sea farming ventures which were far from being commercial, but these were developed into successful businesses by the ingenuity of a few people who found ways to shave expenses by employing new scientific and technical discoveries, thereby changing the entire market complexion of commodities.

Sponges

Sponges are simple animals consisting of several specialized types of cells. The different species of sponges vary greatly in color, shape, and size. When first removed from the sea, they are slimy and heavy and must be alternatively dried and pounded to remove the living tissue. It is the remaining skeleton that is marketed (*Fig. 106*). Commercial sponges sold principally for surgical purposes and for cleaning constitute only a small proportion of the thousands of different species living in the sea and fresh water. In the sea, sponges exist to depths of about 170 meters (560 feet). Commercial sponges tolerate temperatures of 10° to 35° Centigrade (50° to 95° Fahrenheit).

Sponges reproduce by regeneration, budding, and sexual means. In sexual reproduction a larval stage is produced which, after a short period of drifting, must find clean, hard objects to attach to or they will die.

In the United States in 1961 the total sponge landings sold by fishermen was valued at about $364,000.

Cultivation of sponges was carried out in the Mediterranean Sea during the eighteenth century. An early farm in the Adriatic Sea, near Trieste, was abandoned partially because of the hostility of sponge fishermen who feared that their livelihood would be threatened by low-priced, farm-raised sponges. Other more recent attempts, some in the Florida Keys,

Fig. 106. Sponges caught on public fishing grounds are made ready for market by drying and pounding them to remove living matter.   (*J. F. Storr*)

some near Miami, and some in the Bahamas, succeeded in producing marketable sponges in four to seven years. Early investigators concluded that farming attempts by fastening sponge cuttings to stones or cement

Fig. 107. Cutting sponges for cultivation. A two-year-old sponge has been cut from its base, bottom left, and the top part divided into quarters. One of the quarters has been attached to a rock, while another is being threaded on a string in preparation for tying to a rock. (*J. F. Storr*)

disks was the most practical way of starting their crop. Dr. F. G. Walton Smith, Director, Institute of Marine Sciences, University of Miami, in 1948 urged establishment of a government model sponge farm in the Bahamas to develop economically feasible methods to re-seed the commercial grounds (*Fig. 107*).

Two blows struck the sponge industry in the 1930s. Fungus disease literally wiped out the three principal commercial species, the wool, grass, and yellow sponges (*Fig. 108*). Subsequent diseases also hit this industry. Wool sponges were again attacked by fungus in 1947, and yellow and grass sponges in 1951. And the most disastrous effect on the fishery was the development of the cellulose sponge. Many other synthetic sponges have been produced since the first cellulose sponges were marketed, and although of different materials, they all decrease the demand for natural sponges by being cheaper and perhaps more attractive to the housewife than natural sponges. Any sponge fisherman will tell you, however, that

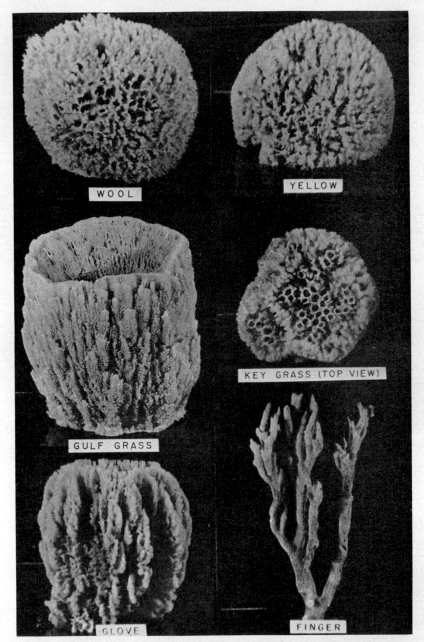

Fig. 108. Six species or subspecies of dried and cured American commercial sponges.   (*J. F. Storr*)

the sponges he fishes will outlast the synthetic ones, and, furthermore, he will tell you they do a better cleaning job.

The sponge farming operation is generally a simple one. Essentially large sponges are cut up, and the small cuttings are attached to disks.

Cuttings from sponges grow to market sizes more quickly than those reared from larvae. Concrete disks or bricks are placed in suitable water and the attached sponges are harvested when they reach marketable sizes.

Considering the popularity of synthetic sponges, the relatively high labor costs today, and the slow growth of natural sponges, sponge farming seems to have limited potential.

Conchs

One of the large snails, commonly called the queen conch (*Strombus gigas*), which in the shell may weigh more than 2·7 kilograms (6 pounds), has sea farming potential. This conch, characterized by a large, red, shell lip, is found throughout the Caribbean Sea and Atlantic Ocean east of Florida from shallow water to about 60 meters (200 feet) depths (*Fig. 109*). It is an important source of food in the Bahama Islands where the fishery at times exceeds $230,000 annually. Besides eating it fresh, the natives also preserve it by sun-drying. Dried conchs are said to keep for about five or six weeks in the shell.

Many aspects of the biology of this large snail favor it for farming. It lays egg masses on sandy areas of the sea bottom. These masses contain about 750,000 individual eggs in strings 50 to 75 millimeters (2 to 3 inches) long. Development is direct; small snails emerge from the eggs,

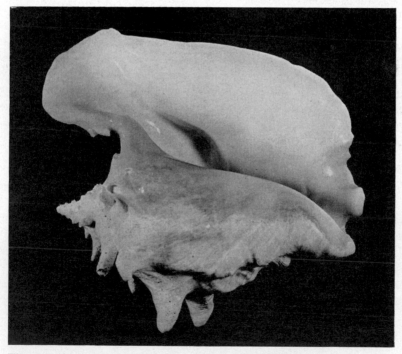

Fig. 109. A large conch from U.S. Virgin Islands—10 inches long, weighing 3 lb. 10 oz. In many areas of the Caribbean and the Bahamas, this species is important as food.
(*J. E. Randall*)

and there is no drifting larval stage. When the conch is young, spiny lobsters, logger-head turtles, octopuses, hermit crabs, and at least ten species of fish prey upon it. It is most vulnerable when it is small and has a thin shell. At this stage it buries itself in the sand during the day and emerges at night to eat. Conchs live on algae and vast sea grass pastures. Average growth is about 5 centimeters (2 inches) per year; and, based on old records, about four years are needed for it to grow to its largest size. But recently University of Pennsylvania scientists estimated that the large full-grown adult conch is only about two years old.

Dr. John E. Randall, who studied queen conchs in the Virgin Islands, found that they congregated along the sides of the wire pens he constructed for them. His first thought was that they were attempting to escape, but upon closer examination he discovered they were eating the algae from the lower portions of the fence. Abundant algae higher up on the fence where conchs could not reach it, was uneaten.

A few pearls have turned up in conchs, but these are generally of little value, only about $20 each because of their tendency to fade.

There is some expense to farming these snails. Conchs have to be fenced in since they move about in search of algae. In addition to holding the conchs in pens to prevent them from wandering away, fencing protects them from predators. Fortunately, most conch predators are large—they must be able to break or grind away the conch's heavy shell—so that the fencing need not be of fine mesh. Coarse mesh does not foul as easily as fine mesh and is generally more durable. Another advantage to farmers is the direct development in the conch's life; when the conch spawns in enclosures, the young do not drift but grow up on the pens. There is no need to go out and catch young to rear. Too, food need not be provided because they can graze on almost any of the smaller algae in the area.

Despite these suggestions that conch farming is practical, the relatively low price of about $0.21 per pound for whole conchs (in the Bahamas) is against it (*Fig. 110*).

Abalones

The abalone has favorable attributes for farming. Numerous eggs are laid; in some species it has been estimated at between one hundred thousand and 2·5 million, which, after one to two weeks, develop into free-swimming larvae. Once they settle to the bottom they become nearly sessile. The abalone is a herbivore. Its meat is described as delicious and is said to have the finest flavor of all mollusks. In 1960, in California, fresh-frozen meat of the red abalone brought between $1.50 and $2.75 per pound retail. The abalone has a conspicuous and attractive shell; some reach nearly 30 centimeters (1 foot) in length. Its powerful muscular foot, the edible portion, is cut into thin slices and pounded with a mallet to tenderize it.

Abalones grow rather slowly, however. In northern Japan a species which requires four years to reach commercial size will attain the same size in nine months in warmer southern waters. Because they can be raised from

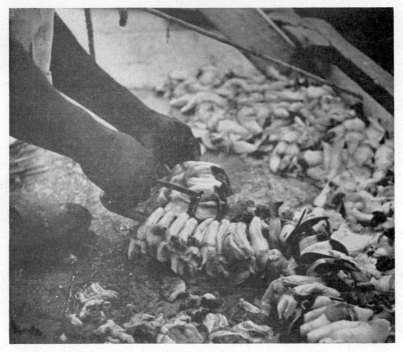

Fig. 110. Conch meats are placed on strings for sale in the Bahamas. (*J. E. Randall*)

eggs, the Japanese established a farm to determine if the abalone can be raised profitably.

Bait Worms

The number of sport fishermen all over the world has increased immensely in recent years. In the United States alone they have increased over two and a half times as fast as the population. A survey by the United States Bureau of Sport Fisheries and Wildlife estimates that by the year 2000 there will be over 62 million anglers in the United States.

With this increase in fishing effort goes the corresponding increase in the need for bait. Bloodworms (*Glycera bibranchiata*), and sandworms (*Neanthes virens*), earthworm-like dwellers of the intertidal zone from the Canadian Maritimes and New England, are very desirable as bait. They are now being harvested from wild populations by digging for them on tide flats (*Fig. 111*).

Diggers working during low tides with a short-handled rake, cull and throw back the smaller worms. About 250 large worms are placed in boxes with a few pounds of moist seaweed and shipped to buyers.

Valued at about 1 million dollars a year to United States fishermen, both bloodworm species are in considerable demand; some shipments are sent across the continent to California (*Fig. 112*).

Bloodworms are so-named because of the red-colored body fluid

Fig. 111. Bloodworm diggers work low tides on mud flats in Maine with short-handled rakes.   (*Ivan Flye*)

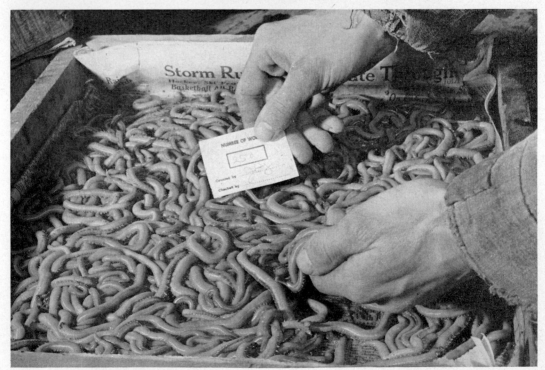

Fig. 112. Two hundred and fifty bloodworms (Count them!) ready for shipment.
(*Ivan Flye*)

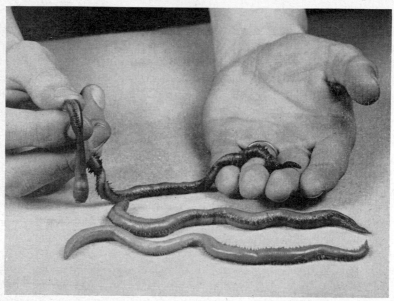

Fig. 113. The bloodworm, *Glycera dibranchiata*, is popular
with sportfishermen as bait. *(Ivan Flye)*

which contains a respiratory pigment similar to hemoglobin. These worms
thrive in areas where the sediments are stable enough to support their
burrows, where they spend most of the day. They emerge at night to feed.
Limited data are available on their biology. Females release about 1·2 to
3·0 million eggs during the summer which hatch into free-floating larvae.
After a brief drifting period, the young worms sink to the bottom and
burrow. They become 20 to 35 centimeters (8 to 14 inches) long by their
third year of life. The survival of young and hence the greatest production
takes place at water temperatures of 8° to 9° Centigrade (46° to 48°
Fahrenheit) during the spawning year (*Fig. 113*).

Bait worms could possibly be farmed because they produce many
young, grow rapidly, and require little feeding. Juvenile survival can be
increased by ensuring proper temperatures and supplying protection from
predators, and thus high production can be achieved.

Dr. Elizabeth C. Pope of the Australian Museum suggests the possibility of commercial bloodworm farming in Australia. Of the several
species present there, the bloodworm (*Marphysa sanguinea*) is probably
the most suitable for farming because it inhabits the dark, sandy mud or
ooze in or near beds of eel grass (*Zostera*) in inlets or estuaries in southern
Australia. Dr. Pope found a highly productive area where these worms
occurred and described it as an "accidental bloodworm farm." In this
situation, large ash beds had formed along the edge of the creek that was
being used to carry ash and cinders from below the grates of a power
house. Sea water was pumped from the inter-tidal creek and channeled
under the grate. The ashes fell into the creek and were carried to wide,

shallow ponds where a dense colony of bloodworms settled. This silty material, which seeped past the filter, was held together by a plant (glasswort), and kept moist and soggy by a continuous trickle of seawater on its way back to sea. Moreover, these bloodworms were easier to dig from the lightweight ash mud than from the heavy *Zostera* bed in the nearby stream. The conditions which were accidently produced in this power plant outflow could be reproduced in other suitable areas, therefore, it would seem that farms to raise *Marphysa* worms would be feasible.

The most important requirement for farming bloodworms would be to find natural beds of them adjacent to a suitable intertidal zone. Water from the area should be tested to be sure that it contains the larvae of the worms that will colonize the beds. Then artificial ash beds could be made and pumping operations started. Some type of fencing to keep predators off the tide flats would increase production.

American Lobsters

The female of the American lobster (*Homarus americanus*) intrigued early biologists, fishermen, and others in the fishing industry by displaying an abdomen covered with between 3,000 and 75,000 eggs. Since only a tiny fraction of the young that hatched from these eggs reached adulthood in nature, those interested in increasing fishery production decided they could improve on nature by supplementing natural production by artificial means (*Fig. 114*).

About 1905, large-scale lobster hatcheries were constructed in New England. Big live-cars (floating screened cages) with propellers to circulate the water were constructed in Rhode Island and were used to rear young larvae through about four stages (molts) after they hatched. (The lobster completes a drifting period of its early life after the fourth or fifth molt and takes up a bottom-dwelling existence.) Year after year, tiny lobsters were reared until they were about two weeks old then were released into the sea with the hope that they would settle to the bottom, survive, and grow to market size, thereby increasing the fishermen's catches.

These attempts at helping nature were unsuccessful because of the high cost of producing relatively few young lobsters, plus the high mortality the released lobsters suffered.

To get some idea of the problems involved in farming lobsters, let us briefly review their biology.

In Massachusetts the hatching peak of the American lobster occurs in late June or early July. As with many marine animals, the time required to pass through larval stages varies greatly with temperature. From about nine days to almost a month is required for the lobster larvae to pass from the egg into the fourth larval stage when they settle to the bottom for life. At this time, many lobsters are planted (*Fig. 115*).

Lobsters have lived in captivity for up to ten years. They can be fed finely ground hard clams, and as they grow larger they eat fresh fish, clams, and viscera of bay scallops. Daily feedings during the growing

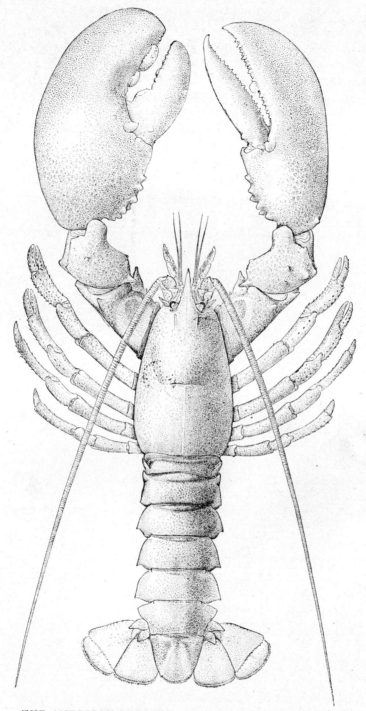

THE AMERICAN LOBSTER. (Male, much below natural size.)

Fig. 114. The American lobster is valued for its large claws.
(*United States Bureau of Commercial Fisheries*)

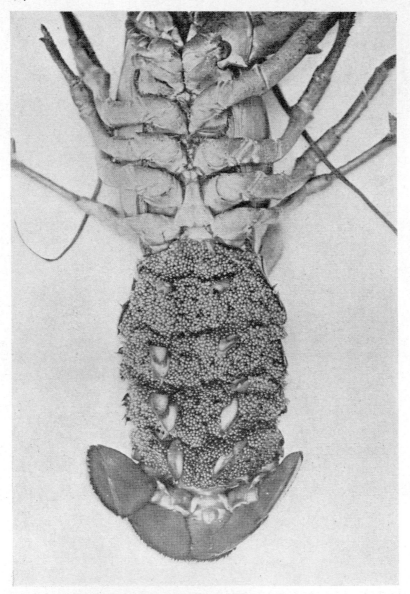

Fig. 115. A female lobster with eggs attached to the underside of her abdomen. The young are difficult to raise and the
adults grow too slowly for profitable farming.
          (*United States Bureau of Commercial Fisheries*)

season from spring through fall should be reduced to weekly during the
winter.

About five years is required for lobsters to reach a marketable size of 7·8
centimeters ($3\frac{3}{16}$ inch) carapace (head) length, the legal minimum catch-
able size in Massachusetts. It has been estimated that about 7 kilograms
(15 pounds) of food is required to raise a single lobster to this size.

Fishermen and others interested in farming these large-clawed lobsters suggest holding the adult animals, breaking off a single large claw from each one and marketing only the claw, leaving the lobster alive to regenerate the lost claw. The fault in this scheme is that as the lobster grows it molts less frequently than when it is young, hence it takes longer for a lost claw to be replaced. Another fault lies in the fact that generally the replacement claw is smaller than a normal claw. A further difficulty is that during regeneration, the growth of the rest of the animal is reduced. The average weight increase of about 18 per cent was found for lobsters with both claws intact, whereas the lobster regenerating one claw showed a growth increase of only 12 per cent in the same time period.

The American lobster, then, is another species which can be raised all the way from egg to adult, but farming them commercially at this stage of our knowledge seems to be impractical. The five years required for them to grow to a minimum legal size is a substantial deterrent.

European Lobsters

Other species of lobsters have been reared artificially elsewhere in the world in the hope of both supplementing natural production and of farming them. The European lobster (*Homarus vulgaris*) in England requires about six years to reach the minimum legal total length of 23 centimeters (9 inches). The problem of raising many lobsters cheaply has been studied there for about fifty years without a solution.

H. J. Thomas, Department of Agriculture and Fisheries for Scotland, in 1964 succinctly reviewed difficulties of artificial hatching and rearing of the European lobster. Although his article is intended for readers interested in this lobster in the United Kingdom, many points he makes can be applied profitably to rearing crustaceans elsewhere in the world. Of special value is his break-down of commercial rearing possibilities into three approaches.

1. *A short-term rearing in which lobsters are raised by natural hatcheries from egg to early stages for release into the sea.*

The objectives of this program, as in others throughout the world, is to augment the natural population and fishermen's catches. Thomas states that the running costs of the hatchery alone, disregarding the costs of hatchery construction, are far in excess of the value of the hatchery-raised lobsters taken in the commercial fishery.

2. *A long-term rearing in which mature female lobsters spawn and the young are raised to marketable sizes in captivity.*

Again Thomas is pessimistic about any hope of profit and points out that both larval and adult lobsters are cannibalistic. Any crowding, that occurs results in considerable destruction of animals. Of course, the long life of the European lobster, that is, some six years to rear it up to 23 centimeters (9 inches), is a considerable disadvantage to any attempt at farming. The costs to care for lobsters for six years make the chance for profit rather slim. In fact, he said that even if the British canned three-year-old lobsters 13 centimeters (5 inches) long, it is still doubtful whether the operation could be profitable.

3. *Short-term retention of lobsters.*

These animals are caught in the fishery and are not marketable either because they are slightly below minimum size, they have molted very recently and are soft, or they are carrying spawn. Such lobsters can be held until they reach market size, or until their shell hardens, when they can be marketed legally.

Thomas believes that of the three approaches, the latter is probably the closest to being profitable. However, he brings out that in this method problems result from conservation laws. It is presently illegal for anyone to possess undersized lobsters, or "berried" (carrying spawn attached to the fine hairs in the abdomen) lobsters. It would be difficult for the conservation officers to enforce laws if fishermen were allowed to catch and transport these illegal lobsters to holding ponds. Considering all approaches, he is pessimistic about any profitable enterprise stemming from the raising of lobsters in the United Kingdom.

Spiny Lobsters

Much confusion exists about the name of the spiny lobsters and their relatives, the northern lobsters. The American and European lobsters are cold-water species while the spiny lobster, found mostly in tropical waters, is also found in subtropical and temperate waters. The American lobster and its fresh-water cousin the crawfish have a pair or large crushing claws. The absence of these claws is the best way to distinguish a spiny lobster from a cold-water lobster. The claws and tail of the northern lobsters are eaten but only the tail of the spiny lobster is used. People from the midwestern United States, familiar with the crawfish in streams and marshes, call the spiny lobster a "salt-water crawfish" or "crawdad." "Rock lobster" is another name sometimes used for the spiny lobster. In the Caribbean region of South America, they are called "Angouste" and "langoste." In Florida, the name "spiny lobster" is preferred. The most important species in Florida is *Panulirus argus*.

The spiny lobster begins life as a fertilized egg attached to the outside of its mother's abdomen (*Fig. 116*). The young which hatch from the egg look like anything but lobsters. These tiny creatures eventually develop into leaf-like bodies with tiny hairs projecting from their legs which enable them to stay afloat and drift with the current or, alternatively, to hold onto something that is drifting. According to the best estimates, they may drift for approximately three to six months at the mercy of the currents and winds.

The young lobsters which survive the six months drifting stage have grown to a greatly increased size and superficially resemble the adult. Few of the eggs that hatches at the same time are still alive. At this point they must find a suitable rocky reef or rocky area on which to settle. They now take up a completely different type of existence, living in crevices or

Fig. 116. This spiny lobster is surrounded by many newly-hatched larvae.
(*Miami Seaquarium*)

holes into which they enter backwards with their long antennae sticking
out of the entrance. They apparently move very little during this stage
except to go out for night-time meals of snails, clams, and other lobsters.
Adult spiny lobsters can even eat heavy-shelled conchs. While they are
foraging for food, lobsters must be alert because sharks, grouper, jewfish,
and even larger lobsters which are also searching for food will eat them.

Crustaceans shed their skins as is necessary for growth and change of
body form. It is at these soft stages that they eat each other if they are
crowded and unable to find suitable cover.

Despite considerable attention to the problems of raising young spiny
lobsters from the eggs to even a juvenile stage, to date no one has been
successful. Because the requirements of the very young spiny lobsters are
not fully understood, biologists have not been able to duplicate them in an
artificial situation. The young adults can be held in impounded areas but
the costs of food and labor for an undetermined number of years prohibits farming them commercially. Tagging experiments to determine the
rate of growth produced such variable results that satisfactory growth
estimates could not be made.

The same general difficulty exists for spiny lobsters as for American
and European lobsters. The spiny lobster would seem to have even less
potential for farming because the larval life is considerably longer than that
for the cold-water lobster, and rearing them through these early stages
for so long a time, at this stage of our knowledge, seems to be a handicap
too formidable to overcome, at least on a profitable basis. It appears that

man will have to obtain naturally-raised, larger spiny lobsters from the sea, for a while at least.

Stone Crabs

The stone crab, or mud crab (*Menippe mercenaria*), has been considered for culture for the gourmet market because of the fine meat in its huge claws (*Fig. 117*). This crab ranges from about North Carolina around the southeastern United States to Mexico. It is found in Cuba and is abundant in the markets there where it is called "El Congrejo Noro."

The stone crab is an estuarine animal which hides under rocks and in crevices, and digs a burrow which may be 30 to 60 centimeters (1 to 2 feet) long and about 15 centimeters (6 inches) across. The young hatch at intervals throughout the spring and summer molt, next assume the adult crab form, then move to deeper channels. Considerable care should be taken in handling the stone crab—its large, powerful claws can crush a man's finger. Since the amount of meat in the body is too small to be sold, usually only the claws are sold for human food. Fishermen customarily remove the claws, then toss the animal back into the sea. A question frequently asked, to which we have no answer, is how long it takes the claws to regenerate.

Like northern lobsters, there are two possible ways of farming: one way is to raise the stone crabs from eggs to adults, and the other is to hold many adults and remove the claws periodically for sale.

Fig. 117. Although the large claws bring a good price, the stone crab is expensive to raise.   (*Miami Seaquarium*)

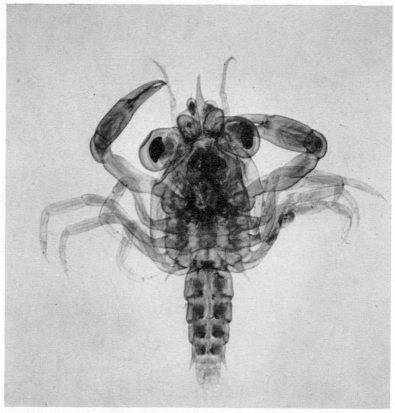

Fig. 118. One more molt and this young blue crab will resemble an adult. However, these delicate stages are difficult and costly to raise.

(*Virginia Institute of Marine Science*)

Larvae of the stone crab can be reared from egg to crab-stage in the laboratory in about twenty-seven days, using larvae of the brine shrimp as food. Normal zoeal development consists of five stages. Preliminary evidence indicates the need for warm water of high salinity for optimum survival of larvae.

Probably the rather long time required to reach adult stage prevents this species being of great value to farming. On the other hand, if the time required for regeneration of claws is short enough, or if growth can be increased by artificial means, such as by growth stimulants, then perhaps the holding procedure, wherein crabs will continually regenerate new claws, has some farming potential.

Blue Crabs

The blue crab (*Callinectes sapidus*) is a popular crustacean on the Atlantic coast and Gulf coast of the United States. It occurs also in the Mediterranean sea, and is thought to have been transported in the ballast tanks of ships from somewhere within the crab's range in the United States. A type

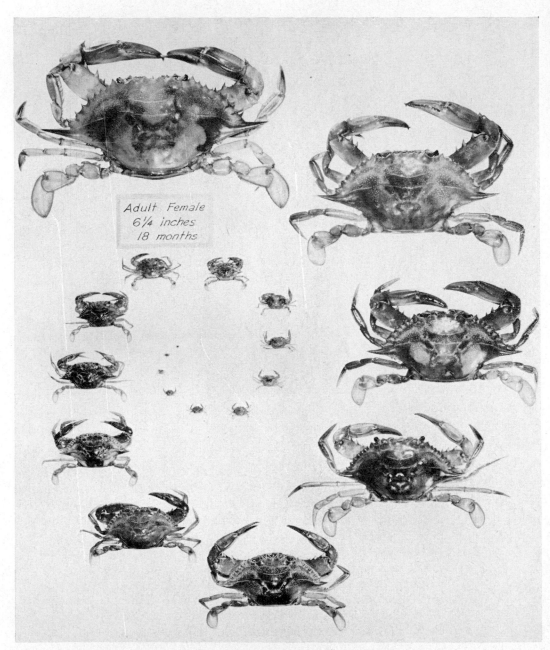

Fig. 119. Feeding blue crabs for a year or more prevents making a profit by farming this species.   (*Virginia Institute of Marine Science*)

of profitable, short-term farming is being carried out with blue crabs in the Middle Atlantic states which consists of holding the shedding or molting crab, sometimes called a "peeler." The crabs which are about to peel can be recognized because the color of the new shell can be seen under the old one. Farmers know that in just a week or two the crab will shed. Soft-shell crabs are more valuable than hard-shell crabs of the same size. Careful attention must be given to these soft crabs because their hard-shelled neighbors may eat them.

Farming blue crabs starting from eggs is not advisable just yet, nor has it a very bright prospect. It takes relatively long to raise the young. About fifteen days are required for the eggs, which the female carried around, to hatch, and the larval stages require about $1\frac{1}{2}$ months before they assume a crab-like form (*Fig. 118*). To obtain large crabs 15 centimeters (6 inches) across the back requires about a year and a half in both brackish water and sea water. It has been estimated that the maximum age of blue crabs is about three and a half years. They eat vegetation and fresh or decaying fish or meat. It is costly to provide them with the amount of meat required to equal the crab meat subsequently produced (*Fig. 119*).

Since in nature blue crabs move to different environments as they grow, it may be difficult to provide ideal situations for them in captivity to obtain maximum growth and survival.

All in all, their farming potential rates low at this time.

CHAPTER 13

Other Vertebrates for Farming

Various finfish other than those we have discussed so far have possible roles in the future of sea farming. These species have attributes which seem to make them suitable for farming; for instance, they will breed and mature in captivity and usually have a high market value. A few such species are given on the following pages to exemplify the many difficulties encountered in attempting to farm them (*Fig. 120*).

Sea farming does not include rearing and releasing of "homing" species into the sea to forage until they return to their birthplaces. One very important difference between land ranches and "sea ranches" is that the land rancher retains ownership of his animals by marking or branding them and keeps track of them, whereas the anadramous fishes which are released into the sea become part of the common property resource to be

Fig. 120. These plankton-eating mackerel recently reared from eggs by the United States Bureau of Commercial Fisheries at California hold promise of being farmed.   (*United States Bureau of Commercial Fisheries*)

harvested by anyone who has the tools and does not break any fishing laws. Despite this difference, the reader will find many references calling this technique "sea ranching" or "fish farming." These terms are sometimes used to gain public acceptance of research programs and government funds for management of fisheries. Artificial supplementing of commercial catches is mostly a fishery management technique because the government hatchery is rearing these fish for the entire fishery, not just for a farm. The necessary release of these anadramous species into public waters by the sea farmer is, in effect, "stocking the sea," and makes the crop available to any fisherman. He depends only on those fish which escape the fishery and the high natural mortality in the sea to return and earn him a profit. However, no matter how doubtful sea ranching may appear as a fishery management tool or "farming" technique at this time, it may eventually increase man's harvest of the sea and show a substantial profit between cost of released fish and value of returning adults. Hence some species which "home" are considered here.

Tilapia

Tilapia is a genus of warm water fishes related to the centrarchids which includes the common North American sun fish. The family to which it belongs, Cichlidae, includes many fresh water species popular with aquarium enthusiasts. *T. mossambica*, frequently called the Java tilapia because the first records of transplantation are from Java, is but one of the approximately one hundred species in this genus and is the only species of the genus important in brackish-water fish culture. Other *Tilapia* species are widely raised in fresh water. Many species of the family Cichlidae incubate their eggs and young, and protect them from predators, by holding them in their mouths (*Fig. 121*). Because of this behavior, this family of fishes has earned the commonly used, but incorrect, title of "mouth breeders." Actually "mouth brooders" would be more correct. Within the genus *Tilapia* there is considerable variation in the brooding habits. In some cases the eggs and young are incubated in the female's mouth, while in others, in the male's, and in some species both sexes brood the young.

Tilapia Transplantations

Man has transplanted marine fishes, mollusks, and crustaceans to virtually every conceivable place in the world. Most transplants for which we have records have been notably unsuccessful, but a few species like the striped bass, the Japanese oyster, and the Java tilapia have proved to be highly successful in their new environment.

The Java tilapia has been transplanted extensively since about 1939. It has spread to at least thirty countries and was most widely transplanted during 1949–51. In 1955 the United States Fish and Wildlife Service opposed the introduction of Java tilapia into the United States on the grounds that while prolific this species does not grow large and therefore has little market in the United States.

Fig. 121. Tilapia fry seek shelter in their mother's mouth when they are frightened.
(*FAO*)

The Java tilapia can tolerate a wide range of salinity and temperature and still grow and breed. It is therefore suited to salinity and temperature fluctuations normally found in brackish water, lagoons, and estuaries which might serve as ponds for this species.

Because Java tilapia are not predatory, milkfish, mullet, and shrimp can be raised in ponds with them. However, the additional fish placed in a pond should not compete for the available food which the tilapia uses, and vice versa. Feeding habits should determine the species placed together; the value realized from harvesting such a crop involving a combination of species should be greater than when there is only a single species alone. The growth of Java tilapia varies under different conditions of food, temperature, salinity and available space. On the average they grow to over 13 centimeters (5 inches) in three months. Males are larger than females, partly because during the period of incubation of the eggs and harboring of the young the female does not feed.

Feeding

The Java tilapia is generally classed as an omnivorous fish because it can live on a wide variety of plants and animals. They apparently prefer

Fig. 122. Spawning nests made by male tilapia in a pond in
Hawaii. (*United States Bureau of Commercial Fisheries*)

plants when they have a choice, but will eat small planktonic crustaceans if
they are plentiful. Most researchers who have studied their food habits
say that the tilapia prefer *Enteromorpha*, a genus of brackish water
algae.

Reproduction of Tilapia

The male Java tilapia digs a small depression in the sandy or muddy
bottom with its fins and clears the area of debris and algae (*Fig. 122*).
While guarding his nest against other male tilapia, he tries to attract
females to it. When a female enters the nest she releases her eggs into the
depression and almost immediately after he fertilizes the eggs, she takes
them into her mouth and swims away from the nest, or is chased away by
the male, who looks for another female and repeats the process. The female carries the fertilized eggs in her mouth for about sixty hours, at which
time the young hatch, then carries them for seven or eight days more.
When she releases the young, they form a small school near her, and if
frightened, they will dart back into her mouth for protection. A single
female at one spawning produces 75 to 250 eggs and may spawn as often
as six times per year. The young tilapia become sexually mature at three

Fig. 123. Redwood tanks for rearing tilapia at United States
Bureau of Commercial Fisheries Hawaii laboratory.
(*United States Bureau of Commercial Fisheries*)

months. Because of this high reproduction rate, ponds can become over-
crowded rapidly under suitable feeding and spawning conditions if no
predators are present in the ponds to reduce the size of the stock.

In some farms where it is impossible to drain the ponds and remove
predators, Java tilapia are planted. Although predatory fish will eat many
of them, because of the tilapia's high reproduction, predators do not
deplete their population as they would the population of, for instance,
milkfish which do not reproduce in ponds.

In brackish water the reproduction of Java tilapia is somewhat in-
hibited, but they reproduce year-around in fresh water. This tendency to
over-produce is a definite advantage to farming the species.

A number of factors can affect the production of tilapia fry (*Fig. 123*).
Since one male Java tilapia can mate with several females, it is advisable, if
not practical, to reduce the number of males in a brood area. If the
brood size is too large, it also affects the production of young by simply

Fig. 124. Newly-hatched tilapia fry being dip-netted from experimental pond in Hawaii.
(*United States Bureau of Commercial Fisheries*)

overcrowding and causing continual fighting for nest space and fighting to guard the nests. In Hawaii, an experiment placing various ratios of males and females, from 2 : 1 to 6 : 1 in favor of females with concentrations of from thirty to ninety fish in 3,140 liter (840 gallon) containers showed that three females to each male gave the highest fry production. The space available for each fish also affects fry production. Allowing each male about 3,600 square centimeters (4 square feet) of bottom area and 900 square centimeters (1 square foot) per individual yielded the highest production of almost 600 fry per female (*Fig. 124*).

Suitability of Tilapia for Farming

Of the fishes we consider in this chapter for culture, and of those that are now raised successfully, tilapia is interesting not only because it reproduces in captivity, but also because it tends to over-reproduce to the point where, without control, the farmer may get from his ponds many fish which are too small for market. The young begin to reproduce when only a few months old, and because they provide care for their young, high survival results.

Fig. 125. Harvesting tilapia in an experimental United States
Bureau of Commercial Fisheries pond in Hawaii.
(United States Bureau of Commercial Fisheries)

Two ways to prevent over-stocking of a pond where there is ample food
to insure rapid growth are by introducing predators into the pond and by
monosex (single sex) cultivation. In the first method of control, that of
introducing predators into the ponds with the Java tilapia, the surviving
tilapia grow to large sizes. In this method, the farmer can introduce
popular food fish as predators and can market both the tilapia and its
predator. Since the balance between the number of predators and the
number of tilapia cannot be well-maintained, determination of this ratio
may require frequent draining or seining of the ponds to obtain maximum
yield from both species. The drawback in this method is that counting the
fish is a time-consuming and costly procedure (*Fig. 125*).

But some ponds cannot be drained. In this case, the second method,
monosex culture, may apply. Male and female Java tilapia can be dis-
tinguished even when they are very young, making it possible to separate
the sexes and rear cultures of males and females in separate ponds.
Separate pond conditions give a greater yield of marketable fish from the
fewer, but larger, fish. A drawback in this method is the tedious examination of small fish to determine their sex.

Fig. 126. In Arizona and Alabama tilapia have been raised as sportfish. (*W. J. McConnell*)

In an effort to circumvent handling and sexing of the young fish, what was thought to be two subspecies of *T. mossambica* were crossed. Dr. C. F. Hickling, who first made these crosses, has been very successful in producing almost entirely male offspring (Chapter 5). Java tilapia raised in Java have been crossed with the same species raised in Zanzibar. This cross produces only male hybrids which grow to a size slightly larger than the parent and grow faster than either parent, reaching 450 grams (1 pound) in six months.

Java tilapia are raised in brackish-water ponds (Tambaks) in Indonesia and Malaya, alone or mixed with other species. Fishermen must seine ponds of pure stocks of Java tilapia with nets every two or three weeks to cut down the excess stock produced by the rapid reproduction characteristic of the species. For their labors, the fishermen usually receive no money but instead are paid with a portion of their catch.

The United States Bureau of Commercial Fisheries in Hawaii tried substituting Java tilapia for the natural bait (nehu) customarily used to chum skipjack close to vessels during hook-and-line tuna fishing. When the nehu is unavailable to the skipjack fishermen, they cannot fish. After some promising early trials, subsequent work unfortunately suggested that tilapia is too expensive. Although tilapia is a somewhat less attractive bait than nehu, it is hardier and will tolerate lower oxygen concentrations and a wider range of salinity than nehu so that there is yet hope for it to serve in this capacity.

In 1960, Java tilapia was suggested as a sportfish in southeastern United States. Dr. H. S. Swingle, who experimented with tilapia in Auburn, Alabama, stocked fresh water ponds with eighty brood tilapia per 0·4 hectare (per acre). About two weeks later, the young fish hatched and were fed pellets on a six-day-a-week schedule from April until October. After the first ninety days they had reached about 18 centimeters (7 inches) long. He opened the ponds to the public for sport fishing from August to October, and reported that fishermen, using mostly worms for bait, caught over 270 kilograms (590 pounds) of Java tilapia per 0·4 hectare (per acre) (*Fig. 126*). Perhaps brackish-water fish farms where anglers can catch all the fish they want, paying for them on a per-fish basis, may be successful. Trout farms in fresh water, operated on a similar basis, have become popular in the United States. However, Java tilapia will not winter over in most southern states.

The relatively small size that Java tilapia attains in temperate and subtropical waters is definitely a disadvantage to farming it. Since the species can breed in captivity, it is possible that through artificial selection large varieties which grow rapidly can be produced and make an important place for the species in brackish-water farming in temperate climates.

The hatching of *Anopheles* mosquitos is greatly reduced in brackish-water ponds by Java tilapia because the fish devour masses of the filamentous green algae which provides protection for mosquito larvae. Other top feeding fish such as *Gambusia* locate and prey on mosquito larvae after tilapia remove the algae.

Common Pompano

The common pompano (*Trichinotus carolinus*) which supports a moderate-sized fishery in Florida, extends along the south Atlantic and Gulf coasts of the United States. This species is being reared on a small scale in Florida, but its farming feasibility has yet to be established. Two conditions make this species costly to rear for market. First, since common pompano have not yet been raised from eggs in captivity, it is necessary to find and capture the young in their wild state to stock farm ponds. Second, the stock must be fed. Common pompano is so highly esteemed as a food fish that, with proper management, farming them could become a profitable venture (*Fig. 127*).

Biology of Pompano

Little is known on the biology of this valuable species. Mature common pompano move offshore and spawn in areas where currents will carry the young back to shore. Fish merchants in Florida who gut pompano caught near to shore say that they have never seen sexually mature

Fig. 127. The common pompano, a highly esteemed fish, is being reared in Florida on a commercial basis. *(Miami Seaquarium)*

pompano, which tends to confirm the hypothesis of the species' offshore spawning habit. Large schools of young pompano, measuring from about 13 to 25 millimeters ($\frac{1}{2}$ to 1 inch) appear on the north Florida beaches during April to November, where fish farmers can catch them for stocking their ponds to rear to market size.

The rate of growth, not yet known, must be determined before any concerted attempts to rear the species are made. One estimate gives about 25 centimeters (1 inch) per month. In one recorded experiment, scientists placed tiny common pompano, between 530 to 2,000 per half hectare (per acre) in fertilized ponds at St. Augustine, Florida, and fed them trash fish from shrimp trawlers. Daily production averaged about 4·0 kilograms per hectare (36 pounds per acre).

Farming

Other information required to help judge the value of the species for farming is how much food is required to produce a pound of pompano and how much it costs. We know what common pompano eats in nature—amphipods, bivalves, mollusks, crab larvae, copepods, and invertebrates' eggs—but since some of these foods are not available to feed to captive pompano, or perhaps not in sufficient quantities, an artificial feed must be found which will produce maximum growth.

Temperatures below 10 degrees Centigrade (50 degrees Fahrenheit)

Fig. 128. Young common pompano appear in large numbers
on beaches near St. Augustine, Florida during the summer.
(*E. S. Iversen*)

may be injurious or fatal to common pompano, hence limiting the area
where they can be farmed.

There are about eight pompano "farms" in Florida at present. Pompano
are being raised commercially at one of them, just south of Jacksonville.
The site is good, for there is a supply of young in the shallows of the ocean
next to the farm (*Fig. 128*). The farm consists of one large pond of about
1 hectare (2½ acres), about 4 meters (12 feet) deep. Sea water enters the
pond from the ocean nearby, and, even though the incoming water is
screened, the pond still becomes filled with numerous other species which
probably reduce the pompano's growth. No good records are available
on this operation as yet. Tankage (slaughterhouse waste), turkey pellets,
and antibiotics, plus trash fish from shrimp trawlers, have been fed to the

stock at different rates. The owners of the farm are confident that it will eventually be profitable. Of the other pompano farms in Florida, only vague accounts are available about their operations.

Plaice

A fish that might be farmed successfully in the future is being experimented upon in England and Scotland. The plaice (*Pleuronectes platessa*) is one of the flatfishes found around the British Isles, generally in water no deeper than 40 fathoms, although in some areas it has been recorded down to 100 fathoms. Plaice occur on sandy bottoms and, like many other flatfish, are able, by slow fin movements, to stir up sufficient sand from the bottom to bury themselves. In Holland, Belgium, Denmark, England, and Scotland, plaice is a popular fish because it is abundant, easy to fillet (they have a simple skeleton), and is flavorful. The plaice does not migrate far; the young are found near shore, but as they grow older, they move offshore into deeper water in the same general vicinity.

The females release from 10 to 700 thousand eggs during a single spawning which hatch after about two weeks into a drifting stage. After about $1\frac{1}{2}$ months, the small plaice, having drifted into an area suitable for their requirements, settle to the bottom and begin feeding on small worms, copepods, and mollusks, a diet they follow through adulthood.

Plaice Transplantations

The plaice was used in transplantation experiments in Denmark as long ago as 1892. In those early experiments it was thought that there must be overcrowding of fish in some areas which caused low production from grounds because of the shortage of natural foods. Plaice caught in areas of high density were taken from the North Sea and carried in tank trucks and planted on the east coast of Denmark. The growth of these transplanted fish (which had been tagged for later identification) in the areas of low density was twice that of the fish which grew up in the areas of high stock density.

Following other successful transplant experiments in 1920, it was advocated that large scale transplanting should be carried out. This was never done partly because questions such as which country or countries would bear the costs of transplanting, and, when the fish move into waters fished by many countries, who would be allowed to catch the transplants and realize the profit by the program. This plaice transplanting program, referred to as a type of sea farming, clearly reiterates the difficulties encountered when stock raised in government hatcheries, or by an individual, is released into the open sea for all fishermen or all countries to catch.

Plaice rearing

Even though large-scale transplantations have never been realized, interest in raising plaice is still active. Over the years young plaice have

Fig. 129. Interior view of hatchery at Port Erin, Isle of Man, where plaice and sole are raised.   (*Manx Press Pictures*)

been raised in government hatcheries and released into the sea with the hope that the fishermen's catches would be increased. Considering the time required for the released fish to grow to the sizes at which fishermen catch them, there is no strong relationship between the numbers of plaice released and the subsequent catches of the fishermen. This indicates that hatcheries are helping neither the fishermen nor Britain's economy. It is apparent that enormously large numbers of young plaice must be reared cheaply for release into the sea, and, in addition, they would require protection from their enemies if the scheme is to work. British hatcheries have changed their former methods to overcome these difficulties.

Plaice mass-rearing experiments have recently resumed on the Isle of Man, England, directed toward producing "postage-stamp" size plaice for release into closed-off inshore areas for subsequent catch by fishermen (*Fig. 129*). Substantial progress has been made in learning how to rear these fish, but the cost is extremely high and the problems of holding the fish in enclosed areas are still not solved (*Fig. 130*).

Although it has not become a commercial venture by any means, the

Fig. 130. Outdoor plaice-spawning ponds and sea fish hatchery, Port Erin, Isle of Man.   (*Manx Press Pictures*)

progress being made on their rearing, coupled with other new information on artificial breeding, cheaper food, and improved treatment of diseases, suggests plaice as a future possible farm fish of considerable value. But do not be misled; much work remains to be done before the scheme is economical, if ever. First, problems must be solved at the government hatcheries, then, perhaps, privately-owned plaice farms can become profitable (*Fig. 131*).

Salmon and Trout

The large adult chinook salmon (*Oncorhynchus tshawytscha*) cease feeding in the spring in the Pacific Ocean and return to fresh-water streams to spawn. Fighting for territory and mating begin shortly after spawning ripples are reached. The female selects the place for the nest, sometimes making many false starts before she finds a satisfactory location. Her choice apparently is largely determined by the type of water flow which occurs in the gravel streambed in which she begins digging. By instinct, she digs a nest only in gravel with a high flow; this in turn produced high survival of her eggs. She digs her nest by rolling onto her side and beating her broad, powerful tail, aided by the rapidly flowing currents which scour out a depression in the gravel. The male, meanwhile, guards the selected spot against other males, but gives little assistance to the female in her nest-making. As she deposits her eggs in the gravel nest, the male simultaneously released his milt onto them. The young salmon hatch with a large yolk sac some fifty days later (depending upon temperature). As they

Fig. 131. Sea fish (plaice) reared at Port Erin hatchery are released in this enclosed sea loch at Ardtoe, Scotland, to grow to market sizes.   (*White Fish Authority*)

wiggle their way up through as much as 30 centimeters (1 foot) of gravel into the stream above, the yolk sac is absorbed as food.

The early life of the six species of Pacific salmon differs greatly. Some forage for perhaps a year in the rivers of their birth, while some go to the sea soon after birth. Some salmon species live for up to three years in fresh water lakes which are connected to the streams. On reaching the sea, salmon grow rapidly. The pelagic phase is from three to eight years, but generally the adult chinook salmon return to their stream during their fourth or fifth year. In the open ocean they feed on herring, sand launce, and other small fish, crustacea, and squid. When they return to their fresh water home to spawn, they generally weigh between 4·5 to 22 kilograms (10 to 50 pounds); in Alaska some reach 45 kilograms (100 pounds)! (*Fig. 132*).

The great dream of hatchery-reared fish replenishing runs of over-fished salmon stocks further reduced by man's alteration of the natural habitat continues to fall, with a few special exceptions. A wealth of knowledge was gained about artificial spawning, feeding, and general care of these fishes during their early lives. Man can intercept the salmon on the spawning grounds, take their spawn and artificially breed them, and raise the young in the hatchery to a size at which they will move down to

Fig. 132. Salmon return from the sea to home stream to spawn.
(*International Pacific Salmon Fisheries Commission*)

the sea (up to about one year of age). Since salmon have a strong homing sense (they return to the home stream, and in many cases even to small streams within a large river system from whence they came many years earlier), it has been possible to establish runs of salmon in some barren streams. In the same manner of initiating a run in streams not previously supporting salmon, it is possible to start a run of salmon into a hatchery pond, or "fish farm."

Future Salmon Ranches

To start a run, salmon can be collected from streams near the fish farm, artificially spawned, and the fertilized eggs placed in troughs to hatch and grow. After periods varying from three months to a year, the young can be released to go downstream to the sea to spend their lives until the spawning urge awakens in them. Then they will make their way inshore, many moving as far as from the mid-Pacific Ocean, back into the stream and to the hatchery where they spent their early lives. This system has been used successfully in the United States Bureau of Commercial Fisheries Hatchery on the Columbia River, and at the University of Washington Experimental Hatchery in Seattle (*Fig. 133*).

Fig. 133. Adult salmon return from the sea to this federal hatchery via the fish ladder (narrow darker area leading into pond.)
(*United States Bureau of Sport, Fisheries and Wildlife, R. Glahn*)

It is possible to envision a future in this sort of sea-pasture arrangement. One obvious advantage is that the farmer or rancher can save the expense and labor of feeding the salmon during the period of their lives when they grow rapidly, by releasing fingerlings into the ocean to graze and grow. The survivors then later return to their home streams when they reach maturity.

Feasibility of Salmon Ranches

The release of fish at fingerling sizes means that they have passed some critical stage of their life cycle when large numbers of them die. But without protection, mortality is still high from then on, for in the open sea the chinook salmon (*Fig. 133a*) are eaten by salmon sharks, seals, sea lions, and other predators. For every salmon that escapes natural predators. there are other hazards. Waiting for them all along their route back to fresh water are fishing gears belonging to fishermen from several countries.

Fig. 133a. Runs of chinook salmon have been established which return to hatcheries earlier and have a higher survival than wild chinook salmon.
(*United States Bureau of Commercial Fisheries*)

Fig. 134. The steelhead trout (*Salmo gairdnerii*), like salmon, is anadromous. The small percentage of planted trout which returns from the sea, however, make sea ranching of this species expensive.

(*United States Bureau of Commercial Fisheries*)

On the high seas the Japanese and Russians may take them in large gill nets. If the salmon escape this gear, they may be taken off the coast of North America in purse seines or gill nets by American or Canadian fishermen.

Salmon Economics

Despite the existence of salmon hatcheries in the United States since before the turn of the century, few comprehensive analyses have been made of the cost required to produce salmon to the fishery. Liberations of large numbers of fish into the sea does not imply that hatcheries are efficient. The large fish must appear in the fishery to declare this fisheries management procedure to be successful.

At a hatchery in Washington State, survival figures of silver salmon (*O. kisutch*) were calculated based upon returns to the fishery from hatchery releases. The returns differed according to the length of the rearing periods; however, all survival figures were quite low. Rearing for only three months yielded less than 0·5 per cent returns; rearing for six months, 0·6 per cent returns; rearing for eight or nine months, 1·3 to 1·9 per cent returns; rearing for twelve months, 1·1 per cent returns; and rearing for fourteen months, over 0·8 per cent.

In a California hatchery, the average cost of rearing yearling steelhead trout in 1961 was $0.06 per fish, not including capital investment, capital improvement, or administrative costs. Only about 2 per cent of these sea-run trout weighing 1·3 kilogram (3 pounds) each returned to the river. The scientists calculated that the cost of each returning adult trout to the upper Sacramento River was about $3.00 (*Fig. 134*).

Ignore for the moment the extremely low rate of return from these stocking endeavors (frequently less than 1 per cent) and assume that mortality and expense can de reduced. Stocking the sea is clearly a govern-

Fig. 135. Hawksbill turtle, *Eretmochelys imbricata*, returns to sea after laying her eggs. Later she may be caught for the commercial value of her shell which is used in such products as jewelry and knife handles.   (*Florida State News Bureau*)

mental function because, in effect, it constitutes a subsidization of the fishing fleet. Any private individual engaged in stocking the sea with an anadramous species which must pass through public fisheries before it can home to his farm is analogous to a land farmer or rancher who allows the public to harvest what they want from his land, or his ranch, before he harvests the remainder.

Rearing steelhead trout and salmon commercially would be close to feasible if the costs could be greatly decreased. Many difficulties stand in the way of successful sea ranching.

Sea Turtles

The green turtle (*Chelonia mydas*) is a desirable gourmet food and has been so heavily exploited by man that it is no longer abundant. Tagging experiments have shown that some of the turtles which hatch on the beaches go to sea and return to spawn where they were born.

Here we have another species which has been suggested for a type of farming, or more exactly, sea-ranching. It is possible to raise the young turtles in hatcheries to about 23 centimeters (9 inches) in about six months, at which time they can be released. The sea farmer needs only to capture the females for harvest when they return to spawn on the beach. Some males could, presumably, be caught near the shores since they mate with females close to the beach.

Because breeding stock is available to sea farmers, and if it is demonstrated that a high proportion of the young return to the beach of their

Fig. 136. Newly-hatched turtles climb out of the nest and begin their dangerous journey to the sea.
(*Florida State News Bureau*)

birth, then artificial selection can be carried out for such attributes as faster growth and higher survival. Young turtles feed offshore on the vast sea grass (*Thalassia*) beds, so raising these animals could involve no feed bills. But, like the other examples of sea-ranching described earlier, only a small percentage survive, and while they are offshore they are fair game to anyone who can catch them. And, when they come ashore to spawn, they may be caught by poachers. A substantial market awaits this species throughout their circumtropical range if supply can be increased by farming techniques and suitable conservation measures (*Fig. 135* and *Fig. 136*).

Dr. John R. Hendrickson, Director, The Oceanic Foundation, Hawaii, points out that in Vietnam hawksbill turtles (*Eretmochelys imbricata*) have been reared. Highly skilled culturists could produce blonde or dark shell hawksbills by adjusting the turbidity of the water. The shells find a market because they can be easily worked into jewelry and ornamental objects.

V
PROBLEMS

CHAPTER 14

Disease, Predation, and Competition

To the fish farmer the effects of disease, predation, and competition upon fish stocks mean lower production. He should understand the extent of these losses and how they come about. With the proper information in hand, he can prevent and control them.

Disease

Disease is a deranged condition of an organism which may be inherited, but can also be caused by dietary deficiencies (Chapter 4), by physical and chemical factors in the environment (Chapter 15), or by parasites. In this chapter emphasis is placed on those disease-producing parasites of concern to fish farmers.

What is a parasite? It is any organism that lives part or all of its life in or on another organism (called a "host"), and is dependent on its host for metabolic requirements. Some parasites may do no more harm to the host than simply rob it of some of its food, but others can be pathogenic to the host. While some parasites do no harm to the hosts at certain times of the year, they cause considerable injury at other times. Sometimes a single parasite, or a species by itself, may do no substantial harm, but, in conjunction with other parasites of the same, or other, species, it may do great harm. It is difficult to determine whether or not a parasite is harmful.

The sea farmer need not be concerned about parasites that just obtain food from the host if the abundance of parasites is low, because usually the host can compensate by simply eating more food if it is available. But he must be knowledgeable about those parasites that cause diseases, and especially mortality, in fish held in impounded waters.

Parasites in Nature

Fish have become adapted to an environment of competition and encounters with large predators and diseases. While not all parasites are disease-producing and burden or hamper their hosts, any one that does so makes the host lethargic and contributes to its early death. And this arrangement serves the needs of the parasite, for many of them must pass through several hosts to complete their life cycle and reproduce (*Fig. 137*). When parasites are in the developmental stages requiring another host, it is to their advantage that the host fishes they are living in be hampered in some way in their struggle for existence so that they will be eaten by predatory fishes, birds, or mammals, and thereby pass into whichever is the normal host for the next stage of the parasite. In this way the parasites

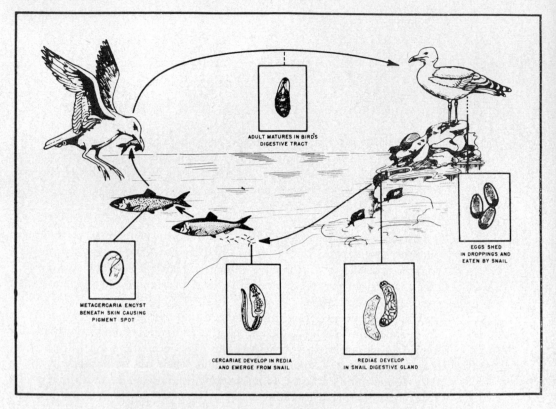

Fig. 137. Life cycle of a trematode, showing the several hosts these parasites must pass through to mature.   (*United States Bureau of Commercial Fisheries*)

find suitable requirements for growth and reproduction, and thus are able to continue their life cycle.

How widespread are diseases in the sea? From the tiniest one-cell animal up to giant whales, nearly every animal species has parasites of one kind or another. In some animals, parasites can be found inhabiting nearly every organ or surface area; some parasites are microscopic and can live within the animal's cells. It is virtually impossible to find a marine organism which does not harbor at least one parasite at some stage of its life history. The high degree of parasitism is illustrated by a species of oyster and salmon: approximately thirty diseases plague the American oyster someplace within its range, and a total of fifty different parasite species parasitize the sockeye salmon of the eastern Pacific Ocean (*Fig. 138*). The true importance of parasites in the economy of the sea cannot be appreciated because below the surface of the sea is a world strikingly inaccessable to direct observation by man. There, parasitism is a common way of life, and since predatory animals are known to more readily eat diseased animals, inroads by the combined effects of predators and parasites into wild populations are continuous.

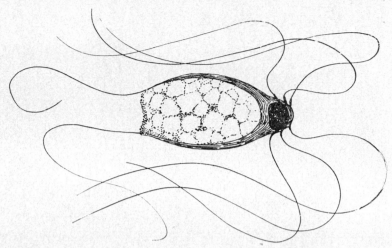

Fig. 138. A protozoan, one of the numerous parasites in-
fecting oysters.   (*After Mackin*, et al., *1952*)

Parasites and Impounded Stock

The sea farmer may rightly ask, "Why should I be concerned about loss
of fish in the sea due to disease? I will protect my stock from disease."
No matter how hard he tries, the fish farmer may still suffer some stock
loss because many of those diseases present in nature are also present in
farm ponds. And their effects in many cases, will be greater in the ponds
than in nature because of the condition that parasitologists call "super-
infection," meaning a reinfection by parasites in a host already harboring
these parasites (*Fig. 139*). In nature, the opportunity for disease organisms
to reinfect a host repeatedly is infrequent because infected fishes, un-
restricted by boundaries, may easily move out of an area where a disease is
present, or they may live widely distributed as opposed to concentrated in
ponds. If fishes are impounded in the presence of certain parasites, they
may become infected repeatedly until the intensity of the disease becomes
so heavy that it causes mass mortality.

In general, the main concern of the fish farmer is to produce the greatest
poundage of fish in the shortest time at the lowest cost. Increases in weight
of the total stock, minus losses including those due to disease, give the net
salable weight. The longer fish are held in captivity, the greater the chance
of them suffering diseases. In addition, as fish grow older they tend to
accumulate more parasites. Although the effect of the individual species of
parasites may be small, over the years the total effect of the accumulated
parasites on the host may be sufficient to cause death to the host and loss
to the fish farmer. Rapid-growing, disease-resistant species such as
shrimp are the most desirable to obtain high production in sea farms.

Many researchers point to the advantage of raising those animals which
feed low on the food web such as mussels, oysters, and mullet; in fact,
most of the animals suitable for brackish-water farming are in this category. Unfortunately these same finfish and shellfish are also heavily

Fig. 139. A protozoan parasite just under the skin of a trout. Heavy infection will probably kill the host.   (*M. Southward*)

parasitized (Appendix Table 1). Studies of the relationship between range of foods eaten and the number of parasites generally illustrates that fish with a wide variety of items in their diet are more heavily parasitized than those with a narrow diet.

Our knowledge of the parasites of fishes which can be farmed is, unfortunately, fragmentary at best. Rather complete lists of parasites of a few host species (oysters, for example), are available, and, for some of these parasites, the life cycles are known. For other species, even the identity of what parasites they harbor is unknown. Because salmon have been reared in hatcheries for over fifty years, many of the diseases that cause epidemics (epizootics) have been studied.

Parasites Important to the Fish Farmer

The parasite diseases that hatchery men and fish farmers must cope with can be divided into two large groups, ectoparasites or endoparasites, based on whether the parasites are found on the outside of the fish (gills, skin, and fins), or inside the fish (in the organs, muscles, or just beneath the epidermis) (*Fig. 140*). Ectoparasites include worms, crustacea, leaches, and one-celled animals. Ectoparasites are normally prevented from attaching to a host fish because the mucus on its epidermis bars their entrance. But if the host fish's mucus-secreting cells are lost through an abrasion or wound, its flesh is vulnerable to parasitic attack. Ectoparasites on fishes may be controlled by chemicals (*Fig. 141*).

Endoparasites spell trouble for a fish farmer. They are generally of three kinds: protozoans (single-celled animals), roundworms, and flatworms. Control is almost impossible because most of these parasites are deep inside the fish where chemicals will not reach them. Control by chemicals is feasible only for endoparasites of the gut, and great care must be taken so that the chemicals used are just strong enough to kill the parasites, yet do not seriously harm the host.

Because parasites are often located in the entrails and gills of fish, the farmer may not notice that his stock is diseased. Only a few parasite species are easily found. For example, a group of crab-like species (*Argulus*)

Fig. 140. These monogenetic trematodes parasitizing the lookdowns breed
rapidly and damage the skin and gills of fish.   (*Miami Seaquarium*)

known as "fish lice," which are not lice at all, may be seen as they skitter
about the skin of the fish. Occasionally, leaches (*Hirudinea*) or "blood
suckers," a sea-going relative of the earthworm, attach to the skin of the
fishes. They attach so loosely that they sometimes let go of the host when
it is caught. Fish lice and blood suckers can be easily removed when the
fish is skinned or scaled, so they generally present little problem for
marketing.

Some protozoans occur as small cysts scattered through the body
muscles of fishes. Each cyst, resembling tapioca, is nearly spherical and
contains infective spores (*Fig. 142*). No intermediate host is involved in
the transmission of these parasites. Other protozoans live in the blood of
fishes and may be carried from fish to fish by blood-sucking organisms. An
example of this type of protozoan are the Trypanosomes carried by leaches.
For many protozoans to infect another fish, they must be eaten by that
fish, or by a related species. These parasites are harmless to man.

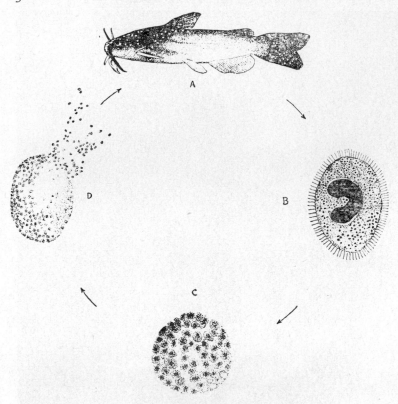

Fig. 141. Some parasites spend part of their lives swimming free in the water in search of a host. It is possible to control the parasite during its free-swimming stages. (*H. S. Davis*)

Fig. 142. Protozoan cysts in fish flesh are not harmful to man, but the parasite may kill the host.   (*W. M. Stephens*)

Roundworms may be found in the gut or encysted in the flesh of brackish-water and marine fishes. Usually only a few roundworms occur in each fish, but many members of any particular species of fish may be infected. When these infected fish are eaten by birds, or by mammals such as seals or porpoises, the young worms grow to adults in the gut and reproduce. The eggs passed into the sea are eaten by a suitable host which then becomes infected. The life cycle of roundworms cannot be completed unless a suitable intermediate host eats the infected fish. These worms will not infect man as a rule, so the farmer need not fear them, but when fish are filleted the worms can be seen by the consumer who might be repelled.

In the body muscles of some marine fishes are found "grubs," the young (larval) stages of flatworms. The life cycles of some of these flatworm parasites are extremely complicated. Each species passes through a number of stages during which it must live in certain organs of two or more host species to complete its life cycle. For example, the young stages may occur in certain snails or other shellfish, and the adult stages in fishes. In some fish the farmer may find these grubs entwined in the muscles.

Since some flatworms in fresh-water fishes are known to be harmful to man, and the flatworms in brackish-water mullet in the Philippines, Japan, and China are known to be a public health menace, these parasites require special attention. The flatworm which infects the mullet can seriously harm humans if the fish is eaten raw.

The lists in the Appendix Tables of diseases and parasites of some representative brackish-water finfish and shellfish show what groups of parasites may be found in or on hosts, and how heavily the host may be parasitized. Also, the number of diseases affecting oysters indicates to what extent clams and mussels, too, may be infected.

Since some milkfish, tilapia, and mullet farms located in the developing countries are often operated very casually, causes of epidemics, and even the epidemics themselves, frequently go undetected and the extent of disease-caused stock mortalities may not become widely known.

The difficulty in detecting fish parasites and diseases is illustrated by parasites of the American oyster. Shellfish parasitologists are uncertain of what the causative agents are of many oyster diseases. It is not known whether a single parasite, or two or more species acting together, cause certain diseases. Epidemics in recent years on the east coast of the United States were triggered by a parasite that experts for years were unable to identify. During this time the parasite was called MSX (Multinucleate Sphere Unknown). In 1966 it was identified as a protozoan.

Effect of Parasites on Hosts

If the incidence of infection in a pond is high, many of the farmer's fish may be lost before he can begin control measures. In addition to mortality, a reduction in growth of fish or shellfish can occur as a result of a heavy infection of parasites. In such situations, the parasites cause harm

Fig. 143. Protozoan cysts surrounding the brain cause loss of nerve control and eventually kill Florida mullet.   (*W. M. Stephens*)

to the host, which although insufficient to kill it, causes an unhealthy to poor condition. Ultimately, growth of a stock will be reduced by the large numbers of parasites that rob the hosts of sufficient nutrition (*Fig. 143*).

Another possible effect on a host is the formation of lesions (sores) on its skin and in its muscles while the parasites responsible for these lesions may not cause sufficient injury to the hosts to kill them, or even to noticeably slow down their growth. However, they are detrimental from the standpoint of the fish farmers because they affect the quality and appearance of the marketed product and reduce his yield. The meat weight of the oysters infected with the fungal disease *Dermocystidium marinum* is reduced when the infection is high. This disease is harmless to man, but if left to run its course is fatal to oysters.

Disease Prevention

Even though fish farming and raising of hatchery fish has gone on for decades (in the United States it started about seventy years ago), the disease problem in hatcheries still has not been solved. If anything, problems seem to have worsened. The late Dr. H. S. Davis pointed out that parasites and diseases of trout constitute one of the most important problems with which the fish culturist has to deal. Despite the best care taken of the hatchery facilities and parent stock, epidemics still flare up.

Some epidemics in the past have resulted from ignorance. On one occasion, in an effort to get inexpensive food to feed to young hatchery fish, carcasses of adult fish were ground up and fed to the young fish of the same species. Pathogenic parasites which do not require intermediate hosts to complete their life cycles are easily spread this way. One of the best examples of this type of error is the case of tuberculosis in a salmon hatchery in the U.S. Pacific Northwest. Unperceived by the hatchery workers, a species of tuberculosis bacterium occurred in the carcasses of adults that were fed to the young salmon. Prior to the release of the young for their journey to sea, certain fins were removed for identification purposes. When they returned to the hatchery years later, it was found that of the 288 returning fish *all* had tuberculosis. Over 350 wild salmon taken from nearby streams which had received no food from the hatchery were examined and none had tuberculosis.

Pondfish, too, can be inadvertently infected with any of a large number of diseases by feeding them raw fish of the same or closely related species. If the fish used as food is not closely related to the stock fish or is not an intermediate host of the adult to be fed, there is a good chance that the pondfish will not pick up diseases from this source. Because this diet involves high risk, it is advisable to find other cheap animal products to feed to the pondfish, such as slaughter-house wastes, fish wastes of species unrelated to those being farmed, or manufactured pelleted food. In Denmark, fresh water trout are fed marine fish with good results.

Nothing is more basic to the prevention of disease than sanitary conditions in impounded waters. This is obvious, but very important and should not be overlooked. The fish farmer should feed his stock just enough food so that little is left uneaten; preferably it should all be consumed. The accumulation of excrement on the bottom should also be avoided because it provides a breeding ground for disease-producing organisms, which, in turn, cause disease of the stock. Scraping or sweeping the bottom of the pond to remove this material should be avoided because of the deleterious effects on the pond and the stock. Such methods tend to remove desirable algae or other organisms that may keep the pond sanitary. There is also the risk of injuring the stock fish by mechanical means, thus affecting the protective mucus layer and epidermis of the fish, leaving them open for infection by bacteria and fungi. Instead, either a suction device of some kind should be used or the pond should be flushed. There is little chance for this type of pollution in ponds with good water exchange; the pond with little or no circulation is the one to be watched.

Before introducing new fish into ponds with existing stock they should be disinfected, placed in special ponds by themselves, and examined periodically for the presence of parasites.

Control of Parasites

From the standpoint of disease control, what is the lot of the fish farmer? He lacks the close contact and good visibility of his stock that the land farmer has. Only if he is able to observe individual fish and sees damaged

Fig. 144. Close-up of protozoan parasite under the skin of a
pin fish.   (*W. M. Stephens*)

skin caused by external parasites or notices any odd behavior among the
fish characterized by lethargy or by rubbing themselves on the bottom
or sides of the ponds, will he be warned of disease (*Fig. 144*). Unfortunately, when fishes reach this stage an epidemic may be well under way.
If the fish farmers can catch one of the infected fish, he might recognize
the general symptoms of the disease and can begin control measures.

Usually a microscopic examination of the diseased fish must be made to
identify which parasites are responsible for the disease. The average fish
farmer ordinarily does not have such equipment on hand, nor does he
usually have adequate training to identify the parasites. Identification of
the causative agent is necessary before any sort of treatment can begin.
Since he cannot call a veterinarian for help as a land farmer can, he must
rely on universities or government agencies to obtain identification of
parasites and suggestions as to treatment if any is known. It is advisable
to employ routine treatment even if diseases are only suspected.

There are several general procedures for treating diseased fish, especially those infected with ectoparasites. One method is to immerse or

Fig. 145. Occasionally stock must be netted and inspected for signs of disease.
(*Australian News and Information Bureau*)

dip the fish into a chemical solution for a fixed period of time. This allows
the operator to control closely both the strength of the chemicals and the
time the fish remains in them. Since each fish, or small group of fish, must
be removed from the ponds and handled separately, this method requires
expensive manpower (*Fig. 145*).

Another disease-control method is to add chemicals directly to the
ponds. By lowering the water level in the pond before adding the chemicals,
it is possible to reduce greatly the amount of chemicals needed for the
treatment. After a prescribed treatment time, adequate to kill the parasites, the water level in the pond can be raised, thus diluting the poison.
The drawback here is that it is impossible to quickly remove all the
chemicals from the pond. The concentration gradually loses strength, but
should be as diluted as rapidly as possible after the treatment so as not to
harm the host.

Using chemicals which will dissipate in water eliminates draining ponds
and prevents overexposure of fish to the chemicals. They become non-
poisonous to the host in a short time, yet remain in the pond long enough
to kill the parasites.

Many factors dictate the dosage of chemicals used to kill parasites. The temperature of the water will determine the effect the chemicals have on both the parasites and the hosts. Generally, a smaller dosage of chemicals is required in warm water than in cold water to kill parasites. The salinity of the water is also important because chain reactions may take place between the salt in the water and the poisons added to the water to kill the parasites. These reactions can become more important as the salinity increases, and perhaps less so when it decreases. Salinity and temperatures tend to act together to increase fish mortality, that is, if both factors are high, they would increase the effect of the chemicals on the parasites and hosts.

The quantity of organic matter in the pond is another factor to be considered when deciding the dosage of chemicals. The less the organic matter, the less dosage is required. Organic matter tends to bind some of the chemicals added to the water and prevents them from reaching the fish and the parasites. If all other conditions are similar when one treats parasites in dirt ponds (with their high organic material), higher concentrations of chemicals are required than in concrete ponds. The number of fish in the ponds, too, is an important factor. Generally, the more fish present, the higher the dosage of chemicals should be.

Each of these factors plays a part in determining desired dosage, and the interaction between them can greatly alter safe, sure dosage levels. One cannot say at what level chemicals should be added to insure a complete kill of the parasites yet will not harm host fish without first considering all of the above factors. For example, if temperature or salinity is high and organic matter is low, and the number of fish is low, then a low dosage level is required. The reason for low dosage lies in the combined effect of temperature and salinity and lack of any organic matter to dampen the effect on the few fish which receive the full effect of the poison.

No specific treatments are detailed here because, aside from the fact that this volume is not intended as a handbook, the many different hosts and the many different parasites, all or most of which have different levels of sensitivity to chemicals, require different treatment. To this can be added that there are many different treatments recommended for a particular parasite on a particular fish. For control of parasitic copepods, for example, as many as eight different chemicals have been suggested. The majority of work on control of fish parasites has been done for fresh water fish, and the efficiency of some of these treatments on saltwater fish is uncertain. Examples of some methods of treatment and control appear in the Appendix (Table 2).

After obtaining sound advice for disease treatment from universities or government laboratories, it is advisable to experiment with varying concentrations of chemicals on a few fish in small containers for varying periods of time. The fish farmer has far too much at stake to try experimental dosages on a large scale, especially where long-lived fish that are close to marketable size are involved. The successful fish farmer must arm himself with the best possible information known about the diseases of fish he is raising and the methods of preventing and controlling them.

Fig. 146. The English oyster borer destroys young oysters by boring through the shell and eating the flesh. *(P. J. Warren)*

Predators and Competitors

Diseases are clearly an important factor affecting losses of stock to fish farmers, but in some areas, under certain conditions, predators and competitors can be equally as important (*Fig. 146*).

Predators are generally (but not always) larger than the animal on which they feed. They usually do not remain as closely associated with the prey animal as parasites, but move about until they find prey animals to attack and eat (*Fig. 147*).

Competitors are organisms which may compete for space or food with another organism. They can be of the same or different species. Competition for space is keenest among sessile animals because they cannot move from an area it if becomes too crowded. In nature, animals with a high degree of mobility can spread out if space is available to them, but in impoundments this may be impossible (*Fig. 148*).

Examples of representative predators and competitors of farmed species are given in Appendix Table 3. This table like that on disease, indicates the number of different animals associated with farmed species. These lists are incomplete for any farmed species; just as with parasites, different predators and competitors may occur in different areas in the range of the farmed fish or shellfish. Others extend over their whole range. Examples of control methods for a few predators are given in Appendix Table 4.

Any species reared from eggs and subsequently transplanted into areas of controlled water supply can be kept relatively free from predators and competitors. On the other hand, placing animals in ponds connected to

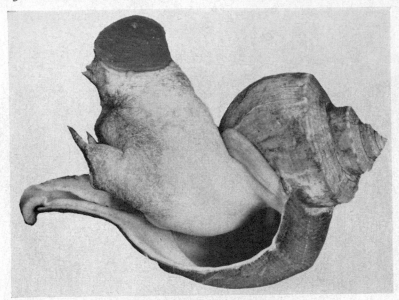

Fig. 147. This large conch destroys oysters.
(*United States Bureau of Commercial Fisheries*)

Fig. 148. Numerous plants and animals attach on and
around oysters and compete with them for food and dissolved
oyxgen.   (*U.S. Bureau of Commercial Fisheries*)

Fig. 149. Starfish, a serious pest on oyster beds, open
oysters and devour the meats. In some areas sea farmers
must exterminate them to prevent high losses.
(*Fisheries Research Board of Canada*)

the sea invites predatory and competitive animals to enter the ponds, and
thus the productivity of the stock is reduced (*Fig. 149*).

Cannibalism

Cannibalism, a special form of predation, is of no concern to fish farmers who raise oysters, clams, mussels, milkfish, or mullet. All of these
species feed low on the food web (plankton, algae, as well as on some
smaller animals). On the other hand, cannibalism occurs naturally in a
number of species that are farmed commercially, such as shrimps, crabs,
and tilapia. Shrimps and crabs become vulnerable to their fellows when
in the soft-shelled stage of their molting process. At this time other
shrimps or crabs of similar, or larger, size may very likely consume them.
Tilapia, as well as other cannibalistic fish, generally feed on substantially
smaller members of their own species. In Hawaii, it was found that the
maximum size of tilapia killed or consumed was about half or less the size
of the predatory tilapia. Since tilapia tend to over-reproduce, cannibalism
might not reduce the stock substantially in ponds with adequate food, but
in the case of shrimps, heavy cannibalism, unless checked, could have a
serious effect on the size of their population.

Sea farmers can use several methods to reduce the level of cannibalism
in their ponds. One way is to sort the animals then to place the various
sizes in different ponds. Besides reducing cannibalism, this procedure
allows the smaller fish to get enough to eat. Another way is to provide
adequate space for each fish. (What is adequate is difficult to determine.
The amount of space needed depends on a number of variables, such as
the size of the individuals in a stock and the volume of water available.)
Keeping the stock in the ponds well-fed is still another possible way to

reduce the level of cannibalism. In additional experiments in Hawaii it was found that fifty well-fed juvenile tilapia averaging about 37 millimeters ($1\frac{1}{2}$ inch) long, killed or consumed nine tilapia fry in fifteen minutes. But when this same group was not fed for three days, they killed and consumed seventeen fry in twelve minutes.

Aside from the biological problems discussed in this chapter, other snags and barriers confront a farmer in successfully establishing and operating a sea farm. Among these problems are pollution, theft, and conservation laws.

CHAPTER 15

Man-made Problems

Sea Farming and Conservation Laws

Nearly every fishery in developed countries, no matter what the size, whether sport or commercial, is regulated in one way or another. The intent of the laws is usually to prevent excessive fishing on stocks. The laws are implemented by limitation on sizes of individual fish (minimum size limits), or total weight of fish taken (quota), for seasons of the year during which fish cannot be caught (closed seasons), and by restrictions on the types of fishing gear used (gear restrictions). These limitations might not appear to concern the sea farmer since they are designed and intended to regulate fisheries, yet some do indeed. Many regulations governing fishing clearly state that fish farmers must abide by the laws applying to the fishery for the same species sought in the wild. Of the several regulations mentioned above, two stand out as being pertinent to the interests of fish farmers.

Minimum Size Limits

This type of law prevents fishermen from catching small fish, thereby allowing them to grow up and be caught when they are heavier, and thus increasing the total production from the fishing grounds. For this law to be effective, the mortality of the fish as they grow older cannot be excessive. Minimum size limits are imposed in some fisheries to allow fish to reach maturity and spawn to insure seeding of the grounds. The law is enforced by making it illegal to possess fish or shellfish below a certain size. Fish farmers in some areas have to follow the rules for the fishery, or they may be required to obtain special permits to allow them to fish for, or to possess, undersized fish. For example, pompano farmers in Florida must apply to the Florida State Board of Conservation for a permit to catch pompano under the legal minimum size of 25 centimeters (10 inches) as it is applied to the fishery. Law enforcement officers must be on guard to make certain that only those persons with permits to take undersized fish are actually engaged in fish farming.

Fishing for young of any species can cause animosity between sea farmers and fishermen. The fisherman who must wait to catch the adult fish may become single-minded in the belief that "his" fishery is being harmed by farmers who are removing the young fish. When we realize the extremely high rates of mortality between young fish and those of marketable sizes in nature, the sea farmer who collects his stock from the sea deprives the fishermen of at most, only a mere handful of fish. Some fishermen find this concept hard to believe.

Closed Seasons

The rationale behind closed seasons is to reduce the fishing effort on stocks of fish so that they will not be over-fished. Alternately, closed seasons may be used to protect fish during their breeding season. This fishery restriction may affect the sea farmers by prohibiting him from selling stock during periods closed to fishing. For example, oyster farmers in the State of Georgia can sell oysters only during the months when they can legally be caught on public grounds.

During closed seasons the sea farmer must feed and care for his stock until such time as the closed season ends and the law again permits him to sell his stock. This, in effect, works a hardship on the farmer by requiring him to hold his stock longer than necessary, and may reduce his profit. During closed seasons in the fishery the price paid to the farmer would be high, and the sea farmer would find it a good time to sell his stock.

Some fisheries administrators are aware of the fish farmer's position and understand that it is necessary for him to take advantage of closed seasons. In Hawaii, for instance, the law permits fish farmers, after purchasing a special license, to sell their pond-raised mullet even during the closed fishing season, January through March.

Other Laws

In some instances there are local laws against leasing of tidelands or other places suitable for farming. In Maine, New Hampshire, and Massachusetts laws based upon a Colonial tradition of free access to all waters and beaches often prevents the leasing of tidelands for farming. This tradition effectively hinders shellfish farming. On the other hand, the very successful private oyster farming in the State of Washington is due in part to the lack of tradition and precedents such as those on the Atlantic coast. There the fish farmer is unencumbered by laws applying to the fisheries.

Another law deterrent to fish farming existing in some countries is that the public shall have access to impoundments that are in excess of a certain number of acres, whether natural or man-made. While this law helps the sport fishermen to find places to fish, it virtually eliminates large-scale fish farming. Certainly the fish farmer cannot be expected to share his stock with the public, nor under such a law can he protect his farm from poachers.

Occasionally if pond construction protrudes into an estuary that is used for boat traffic, permission may have to be sought from navigation authorities. Aspiring fish farmers owning upland property (land which does not have water frontage) may need permission to dig water supply canals through land belonging to others. Canals dug in water frontage usually must be passable so that they will not conflict with the public interests or free access.

Before establishing a sea farm in any area, a prospective sea farmer should consult with local, state, and federal conservation agencies, development boards, and navigation authorities for accurate, up-to-date information on regulations affecting sea farming.

Preventing Theft

Theft is an important problem which fish farmers must contend with, and one which is difficult to prevent. It is not a new problem by any means because laws were established in Java in A.D. 1400 to protect brackish-water farmers from loss of their crops to thieves. More recently, advice on finding a location for a fish farm in fresh water is given by J. A. Slack in his book, *Practical Trout Culture* (1872):

On Selecting a Location for a Fish Farm. . . . It may here be suggested that the immediate vicinity of a large town is to be avoided, as the roughs, that class of population to be found in every city, have a fondness for trout; and a nocturnal visit from individuals of this stamp is generally attended by results far from pleasant. In fact, the stealing of trout from a private pond is too frequently regarded by even the so-called better classes as only a venial offense. In many of our States it is considered in law only as a trespass; and many have been deterred from engaging in fish-farming from want of proper protection for their crop; but unfortunately no distinction is made between fishes reared with much labor and expense and the wild denizens of the mountain brook, all, wherever found, being regarded as *ferae*, and their captors being liable only to a small fine and the market value of the fishes taken; in fact, Mr. Ward, of Mumford, N.Y., was obliged to suffer an imprisonment in the county jail, a few years, for peppering with shot the carcass of a scoundrel whom he detected in the act of stealing his fishes. . . . It is advisable that the ponds should be so located as to be in full view of the residence of the proprietor, and a good dog, or, better still, a pair, will generally give notice of the approach of a nocturnal visitor. We have no doubt but that the voices of our faithful bloodhounds Nero and Flora have frequently prevented the visits of poachers to our ponds.

Pollution

Pollution might be defined as adding anything to a body of water which it cannot assimilate and which has deleterious effects, such as adverse changes in the color and odor, or harms the aquatic plants and animals, or affects the health and well-being of humans.

Before 1900 most of the world's streams and rivers which fed into the estuaries, and the estuaries themselves, were unpolluted. The picture has since changed drastically (*Fig. 150*). It is difficult to find fresh water streams which are still able to support desirable fish. But even if some species of desirable fish can live in these streams, their flesh is often so tainted by pollution that they are unfit for human consumption. Over 160 million Americans live mostly in urban communities, many of which still do not have adequate sewage treatment facilities (*Fig. 151*).

Unfortunately, in some areas close to coastal waters and rivers leading to the sea, pollution by detergents and human wastes is increasing. This is occurring despite the construction of new sewage treatment plants, because areas using cesspools will connect to these plants which operate at

Fig. 150. In many cases, increased uses of brackish waters by man causes more pollution and prevents sea farming. Here, dredgers dig a channel for oil tankers at Long Island, New York.   (*R. A. Schmidt*)

Fig. 151. Intertidal areas with high biological productivity have been spoiled for wildlife by man.   (*R. A. Schmidt*)

somewhat less than 100 per cent efficiency and, therefore, increased amounts of sewage will reach the sea.

The severity of pollution depends on the types and amounts of wastes released and the size of the body of water. For example, pumping a few thousand gallons of sewage per hour into the Amazon River would cause very little harm because of the extremely large volume of water, while releasing sewage at the same rate into a very small river could have a drastic, even lethal, effect on plants and animals.

Types of Pollution

The most common organic pollutants include proteins (nitrogenous organic compounds), fats, soaps, coal, and oil, to name a few. The harmful effect, especially from the protein pollutants, is the amount of oxygen they remove from the water. Further, protein pollutants can carry disease organisms, and generally render the waters objectionable in odor and color. Color changes in a natural body of water reduce light penetration and kill aquatic plants. Detergents are becoming more of a problem, but largely to semi-aquatic birds and mammals because the chemicals cause these animals to lose their buoyancy. About 75 per cent of the detergents contain alkyl benzene sulfonate which is a chemically stable compound. Thus, the detergents containing this compound do not break down readily in nature. Oils and tars get into the water by many means, and since they usually float on the surface, they may do less damage to aquatic animals. However, in the case of oysters and clams which live in the intertidal zone, oils and tars which wash ashore from ships can cause high mortality or make these species unfit for human food.

Organic pollutants can taint the taste of fish and shellfish. They have also been known to cause abnormal growths or tumors on fish. Sewage pollution in San Francisco Bay caused some fish there to have large, unsightly growths on their bodies.

The mass losses ("fish kills") of fishes and shellfishes caused by the reduction of the amount of dissolved oxygen in the water is well-documented. In subtropical estuaries and canals such as those found in South Florida, fish kills occur naturally on occasion even though there is no pollution in the water. The high amount of dissolved organics require much oxygen. In the summer when the water does not hold much oxygen because of high temperatures, or during the night when the plants in the water cease photosynthesis and use oxygen, fish kills occur. Even small amounts of pollutants can increase mortality greatly in such habitats.

In some areas, limited pollution by organic waste or sewage is used to increase growth. In Indonesia, sewage drains into ponds causing milkfish and tilapia to grow rapidly (see Chapter 2).

Industrial Pollutants

Pollution of streams in the United States by industrial wastes is calculated to be about twice that caused by sewage from municipalities. These wastes generally consist of inorganic chemicals such as acids,

Fig. 152. Polluted waters pour from this large industrial area.
(*United States Department of the Interior*)

alkalies, soluble salts, or heavy metal salts. Such chemicals have direct lethal effects on aquatic organisms in contrast to the indirect effect which the organic materials have (*Fig. 152*). Another way in which these inorganic pollutants are harmful to organisms is that they change the acid–alkaline balance of the waters. The presence of inorganic pollutants is more difficult to determine than the organic ones, however, there may be evidence in the color, turbidity, or temperature of the stream the amount of suspended matter, detergents, and in some cases, even the radioactivity.

Industrial wastes kill large numbers of fishes and shellfishes in the United States (*Fig. 153*). These wastes occasionally damage the gills of fishes, especially if any amount of particulate matter is released into the water, and in heavy concentrations they will impart a cloudiness to the water which prevents aquatic plants from getting enough sunshine for growth. This latter effect is harmful since many animals depend on aquatic plants in one way or another, whether for food or because of the plant's capacity to reduce the level of dissolved carbon dioxide and increase the level of dissolved oxygen.

Fig. 153. Mass mortality of fish in this pond was caused by pollution.
(*United States Department of the Interior*)

Treating Polluted Water

Sewage is usually purified by two treatments. In the primary treatment, waste water passes through a screen or filter to catch any large objects, then through a chamber where heavy materials that pass through the screening, such as sand or gravel, settle out. The waste water moves next to a settling tank where it stands for an hour or more to complete the settling process. Here some of the heavier material drops to the bottom of the tank to form sludge, and other material rises to the surface to form a scum. It is possible at this stage to draw from between the surface and the bottom which is relatively free of pollution. About 35 per cent of the pollutants will be removed in this primary treatment. In the secondary stage of treatment, the waste water is carried into the filters and beds where bacteria break down any of the dissolved materials still being carried in the water. By this system it is possible to remove pollutants caused by sewage almost completely (*Fig. 154*).

Pollution by Pesticides

One of the most rapidly increasing threats to the fish and wildlife in many countries today is the increased pollution of natural waters by

Fig. 154. Domestic and industrial treatment plants could greatly reduce this noxious condition.   (*United States Department of the Interior*)

pesticides. Although DDT was first discovered in 1900, it was not until the 1940s that Dr. Paul Mueller showed the insecticidal value of this poison.

Today, the pesticide industry points to the rapid growth of the human population and emphasizes the need for pest control to make certain that foods for humans are not lost due to pests such as weeds, fungi, and insects. In addition, this industry points out that some 20 per cent of all foodstuffs planted by land farmers are lost before harvest due to pests, and, after the crops are harvested, insects, fungi, and rodents cause an additional estimated 10 per cent loss to occur during transportation and storage. Chemical companies credit the use of pesticides with keeping these losses at a relatively low level.

The pesticide industries seek chemicals which are most harmful to the plants (weeds or fungi), or animals (insects and rodents) they are attempting to control, but which will not harm the land farmer's crops. To be effective, the pests should be killed by very low concentrations of pesticides. Unfortunately these chemicals—specific for certain pests—may also do considerable harm to closely-related marine and brackish-water species which are desirable to man and which are farmed by man. A case in point is that extremely low concentrations of insecticides will also kill shrimp because both insects and shrimp are closely related. The insecticides may also kill or disable many other species of animals not so closely related; however, it may require larger concentrations to do this. For example, contamination can take place if a shrimp farm located in an estuary receives its water from a stream draining upland farms which have been treated with insecticides. Minute concentrations of the pesticide that is spread over the farm land can be carried downstream and into shrimp ponds and could result in a complete loss of stock to the farmer. These same concentrations entering ponds holding fish or oysters may do much less harm because these species are not closely related to the insects which the pesticide is designed to kill.

The lethal concentration of pesticides for various animals, determined by laboratory experiments, is shown in Table 13. In farm ponds, some chemicals would probably be adsorbed onto bottom materials such as mud and sand, and in time would disintegrate and become harmless to the animals in the pond. Nonetheless the lethal concentrations of pesticides clearly demonstrate the extremely minute quantities of pesticides required to kill or disable the species of fish and shellfish raised by fish farmers.

Chemical pollutants cause bivalves (clams, oysters, and mussels) to close their shells for periods up to two weeks. In very warm water the rate of metabolism of bivalves is high and they therefore must open their shells sooner than in cold water to get food and dissolved oxygen and to eliminate wastes. When they open their shells, if the concentration of insecticide in the water is high, they will be killed. In low concentrations of these poisons, oysters might not close their shells but they usually feed and grow at less than their usual rate.

All plants and animals are part of a food web. For example, in the sea tiny drifting plants are eaten by small copepods, which are eaten by small fish, which in turn are eaten by large fish. Anywhere along the web a species may begin to accumulated pesticides within its body. A large amount of the pesticide may be passed on to fish that eat them and may be fatal. In 1957 in California, a small, troublesome insect in Clear Lake was the focus of an extermination program. The lake was treated with an insecticide, DDD, at the rate of 0·02 parts per million. The plankton accumulated residues at 5 parts per million. Fish which ate the plankton concentrated the DDD in their fat to levels ranging from hundreds to toward 2,000 parts per million. Diving birds which fed on the fish died. The highest levels of DDD found in the birds was 1,600 parts per million.

Although small quantities of pesticides may enter a sea farmer's ponds from upstream plankton organisms can accumulate these poisons and his stock might die if they eat large amounts of the contaminated plankton.

Another effect of pesticides is that they destroy some links of the food web. For example, in a pond a massive kill of plankton could destroy the food for the fishes or shellfishes stocked in the pond (*Fig. 155*).

Environmental factors such as high temperature, low dissolved oxygen, will cause increased harm due to pesticides. In addition, if two or more pesticides are released into a pond a synergistic effect may cause increased mortality of the stock because the stock has a lower tolerance to two chemicals than it does to a single chemical.

Table 13

TOXICITY OF PESTICIDES TO SHRIMPS, OYSTERS, AND FINFISHES

Chemical	Dosage	Species	Size	Per cent mortality	Authority
81 per cent benzene hexachloride	50 ppb[1]	Penaeus setiferus, White shrimp	29—50 mm.	83 in 24 hours	Chin and Allen, 1957
	75 ppb	P. aztecus, Brown shrimp		50 in 24 hours	
Heptachlor endrin lindane	0·3—0·4 ppb	P. duorarum, Pink shrimp Brown shrimp	adults	50 killed or immobilized	Butler and Springer, 1963
DDT Chlordane Toxaphene Dieldrin	1·6 ppb	Pink shrimp Brown shrimp	adults	50 killed or immobilized	Butler and Springer, 1963
DDT	1 ppm[2]	Oysters	larvae	100 in 96 hours	Butler and Springer, 1963
Chlorinated hydrocarbons	0·0004—0·007 ppm	Striped mullet, Mugil cephalus	juvenile	50 in 48 hours	Butler and Springer, 1963
Mirex Kepone lindane Methoxychlor	10—100 times greater than chlorinated hydrocarbons	Striped mullet	juvenile	50 in 48 hours	Butler and Springer, 1963
Urea herbicides Monuron Diuron Neburon	0·5 ppb	Phytoplankton	—	100	Ukeles, 1960
DDT	91 grams per 0·45 hectare (0·2 lbs. per acre)	Striped mullet	small	100 in 9—14 hours	Croker and Wilson, 1965
Syndet	10 ppm	Striped mullet	large	15—44 in 23 days 50 in 96 hours	Eisler, 1965

[1] Parts per billion
[2] Parts per million

Nauplius: first larval stage occurring in many crustacean species (e.g. shrimps); characterized by an unsegmented body and three pairs of appendages.

Nematodes: roundworms which are both free-living, and parasitic in plants and animals. They occur in many species of aquatic animals.

Nori: Japanese name for the species of *Porphyra* seaweed which is farmed extensively.

Pathogenic: causes disease.

Parasite: an organism that lives part or all of its life in or on another organism called a "host" and is dependent on the host for its metabolism.

Pesticide: a chemical substance used to kill pests.

pH: a scale numbered from 0 to 14 which indicates the acidity and alkalinity of solutions. A value of 7 is neutral. Numbers less than 7 are acid; those above are alkaline.

Phytoplankton: tiny plants which drift with the currents.

Plankton: tiny plants and animals which drift with the currents.

Pollution: specific impairment of water quality by sewage, pesticides, and industrial waste; may create a hazard to public health.

Postlarvae: past the larval stages: stages which resemble the juvenile but are still lacking some characters.

Predation: the act of an animal eating another (prey) of a different, and usually smaller, species.

Prey: an animal that is hunted and eaten by predatory animals.

Propagation: to multiply plants and animals by any method from parent stock.

Protozoans: single-celled animals.

Protozoea: The larval stages between the nauplius and mysis in crustaceans. Usually with seven pairs of appendages.

Raft culture: growing oysters or mussels on shells or other materials suspended from rafts or floats. The term is sometimes used to describe any method of hanging culture.

Raising (rearing): to cause or promote the growth of crops (plants or animals).

Rearing: to care for and support up to maturity, as to raise shrimp to adults.

Re-lay: collecting oysters, clams, or mussels in one location and planting them in another to obtain better growth or better quality meats.

Resistant: able to withstand adverse environmental conditions or ward off diseases.

Riparian rights: rights, belonging to a person who owns land bordering on a watercourse or other body of water, concerning its bank, bed, or waters.

Sea farming: to promote or improve growth and hence production of marine and brackish water plants and animals by labor and attention, at least at some stage of the life cycle, on areas *leased or owned*. Usually intended as a profit-making venture.

Seed: young animals, generally oysters, clams, or mussels, used to stock ponds.

Sessile: stationary or attached animals such as mussels or sponges.

Sea water: water usually with salinity of 30 to 35 parts per thousand, as found in the open oceans. The salinity of estuarine waters usually varies around this value.

Shellfishes: aquatic invertebrates possessing a shell or exoskeleton, usually mollusks or crustaceans.

Shuck: to remove shells from oysters, clams, etc., for market, or in preparation for eating.

Spat: young oysters just past the veliger stage which have settled down and become attached to some hard object.

Spat-fall: the settling or attachment of young oysters which have completed their larval stages.

Specificity (of parasites): the range of hosts in or on which individual species of parasites will live.

Sidney Shapiro, "Fisheries of the World," U.S. Department of Agriculture, *Farmer's World, the Yearbook of Agriculture* (1964), 161–177.

Lionel A. Walford, *Living Resources of the Sea: Opportunities for Research and Expansion* (New York: The Ronald Press, 1958).

CHAPTER 2

SEA FARMING, PRESENT AND FUTURE

Umberto D'Ancona, "Fishing and Fish Culture in Brackish Water Lagoons," *FAO Fisheries Bulletin*, VII, 4 (1954), 147–172.

Anonymous, "History of Fish Farming," in *Fisheries, Fish Farming, Fish Management: Conservation-Propagation-Regulation*, I, Washington State Department of Fisheries (1960), 13–29.

John E. Bardach, "Marine Fisheries and Fish Culture in the Caribbean," *Proceedings of Gulf and Caribbean Fisheries Institute*, Tenth Annual Session, 1957 (1958), 132–138.

Robert Barton, "Britain's First Sea Fish Farm," *Australian Fisheries Newsletter*, XXIV (November 1965).

John G. Carlisle, Jr., "Housing Scheme for Fishes," *Sea Frontiers*, VIII (May 1962), 68–75.

John G. Carlisle, Jr., Charles H. Turner, and Earl E. Ebert, *Artificial Habitat in the Marine Environment*, The Resources Agency of California, Department of Fish and Game, Fish Bulletin 124 (1964).

Jacques-Yves Cousteau, "At Home in the Sea," *National Geographic Magazine*, CXXV (April 1964), 465–507.

A. Dannevig, "Propagation and Transplantation of Marine Fish in Europe," in *Proceedings of the United Nations Scientific Conference on the Conservation and Utilization of Resources* VII, Wildlife and Fish Resources (1951), 57–60.

C. H. Ellis, Richard T. Presey, and Wendell Smith, "Hatchery and Fish Farm Relationships," in *Fisheries, Fish Farming, Fish Management: Conservation-Propagation-Regulation*, I, Washington State Department of Fisheries (1960), 127–136.

David B. Greenberg, *Trout Farming* (Philadelphia: Chilton Company, 1960).

Joel W. Hedgpeth, "Founders of Fish Culture," *The Progressive Fish-Culturist*, 55 (November 1941), 11–14.

C. F. Hickling, "Fish Farming in the Middle and Far East," *Nature*, CLXI (1948), 748–751.

S. L. Hora and T. V. R. Pillay, *Handbook on Fish Culture in the Indo-Pacific Region*, FAO Fisheries Biology Technical Paper No. 14 (1962).

C. P. Idyll, "Contributions of Biology and Oceanography to Increased Harvest of Marine Fishes," *Transactions of the American Fisheries Society*, LXXXVII (1957), 282–292.

Shûzô Igarashi, "Studies on Air Screen in Water. I. Application for Fishing Gear. (2) On Intercepting Effect Upon Fishes," *Bulletin of the Faculty of Fisheries Hokkaido*, XIV (May 1963).

R. B. Iles, "Cultivating Fish for Food and Sport in Power-Station Water," *New Scientist*, XVII (January 31, 1963), 227–229.

Iversen, E. S., "Farming the Sea," *Oceanology International*, (May-June 1967), 28–30.

Philip Jackson, "Engineering and Economic Aspects of Marine Plankton Harvesting," Conseil Permanent International Pour l'Exploration de la Mer, Copenhagen, *Journal du Conseil*, XX, 2 (1954), 167–174.

Lord Kilbracken, "The Long, Deep Dive," *National Geographic Magazine*, CXXIII (May 1963), 718–731.

P. Korringa, "The Shellfish Industry in Holland," in *Proceedings of the United Nations Scientific Conference on the Conservation and Utilization of Resources VII*, Wildlife and Fish Resources (1951), 47–51.

M. Kurogi, "Recent Laver Cultivation in Japan," *Fishing News International*, II (July-September 1963), 273–274.

S. Y. Lin, "Fish Culture Project in Haiti," *Proceedings of Gulf and Caribbean Fisheries Institute*, Fourth Annual Session, 1951 (1952), 110–118.

Edwin A. Link and Bates Littlehales, "Outpost Under the Ocean," *National Geographic Magazine*, CXXVII (April 1965), 530–533.

C. E. Lucas and B. B. Rae, "Fish Farming in Temperate Waters," *Scottish Fisheries Bulletin*, 22 (December, 1964), 5–9.

Hans Mann, "Fish Cultivation in Europe," in *Fish As Food*, ed. G. Borgstrom, Vol. I (New York: Academic Press, 1961), 77–102.

C. H. Mortimer and C. F. Hickling, *Fertilizers in Fish Ponds: A Review and Bibliography*, Fishery Publications, Colonial Office, 5, London (1954).

J. H. Orton, *Oyster Biology and Oyster Culture*, being the Buckland Lecturee for 1935 (London: Edward Arnold & Co., 1937).

John Parvin and Marvin A. Smith, "Salmon and Steelhead Runs at the Eagle Creek National Fish Hatchery," *Progressive Fish-Culturist*: XXV, 2 (1963), 97–100.

T. Gottfried Pillai, "Fish Farming Methods in the Philippines, Indonesia, and Hong Kong," *FAO Fisheries Biology Technical Paper No. 18* (March 1962).

M. B. F. Ranken, "The Seas As a Solution to the World's Food Shortage," *Modern Refrigeration* LXV (October 1962), 959–962.

J. E. G. Raymont, "A Fish Farming Experiment in Scottish Sea Lochs," *Sears Foundation Journal of Marine Research*, VI, 3 (1947), 219–227.

——, "A Fish Cultivation Experiment in an Arm of a Sea Loch (Loch Craiglin). IV. The Bottom Fauna of Kyle Scotnish," *Proceedings of the Royal Society of Edinburgh*, LXIV, B (1948), 65.

Horacio Rosa, Jr., "Progress and Development in Fisheries Biology and Fish Culture," *FAO Fisheries Bulletin IV*, 4 (1951), 21–29.

E. O. Salo, "Possibility of Using Coastal Lagoons as Salmon and Steelhead Rearing Areas," in *Report of Second Governors' Conference on Pacific Salmon* (Olympia, Washington, 1963), 123–129.

F. G. Walton Smith, *"What is There for Industry in Oceanography?"* *Research Management*, IX, 3 (1966), 193–200.

—— and Henry Chapin, "Farming for Fishes," *The Sun, The Sea and Tomorrow* (New York: Chas. Scribner's Sons, 1954), Chapter 5, 81–105.

Keith A. Smith, "Development of An Air-Bubble Curtain for Catching Maine Sardines," *Proceedings of Gulf and Caribbean Fisheries Institute*, Twelfth Annual Session, 1959 (1960), 36.

——, "Air-Curtain Fishing for Maine Sardines, *Commercial Fisheries Review* XXIII, 3 (1961), 1–14.

——, "Air-Bubble and Electrical-Field Barriers as Aids to Fishing," *Proceedings of Gulf and Caribbean Fisheries Institute*, Thirteenth Annual Session, 1960 (1961), 73–86.

——, "The Use of Air-Bubble Curtains as an Aid to Fishing," in *Modern Fishing Gear of the World*, 2, (London: Fishing News (Books), Ltd., 1964), 540–544.

M. W. Smith, "Fish Ponds in Canada—A Preliminary Account," The Canadian Fish Culturist, Issue 29, (November 1961), 3–12.

Robet Sténuit, "The Deepest Days," *National Geographic Magazine*, CXXVII (April 1965), 534–547.

Catherine C. Summers, *Hawaiian Fishponds*, Special Publication 52, Bernice P. Bishop Museum, Honolulu (1964).

A. L. Sunier, "Contribution to the Knowledge of the Natural History of Marine Fish Ponds of Batavia," *Truebia*, II, 2–4 (1922), 157–400.

Edward M. Wood, "A Century of American Fish Culture, 1853–1953," *Progressive Fish-Culturist*, XV, 4 (1953), 147–162.

F. S. Russell and C. M. Yonge, *The Seas* (London: Frederick Warne & Co., Ltd., 1963).

C. M. Yonge, "Farming the Sea," *Discovery*, XXVII, 7 (1966), 8–12.

Part II—Procedures

CHAPTER 3

UTILIZING PRODUCTIVE AREAS

John S. Alabaster, "The Effect of Heated Effluents on Fish," in *International Conference on Water Pollution Research* (London), VII (1962), 541–563.

—— and A. L. Downing, *A Field and Laboratory Investigation of the Effect of Heated Effluents on Fish*, Ministry of Agriculture, Fish, and Food; Fisheries Investigations Series 1, VI, 4 (1966).

H. Blegvad, "Propagation and Transplantation of Marine Fish," *Proceedings of the United Nations Scientific Conference on the Conservation and Utilization of Resources*, VII. Wildlife and Fish Resources (1951), 51–57.

Philip A. Butler, "Oyster Growth as Affected by Latitudinal Temperature Gradients," U.S. Fish and Wildlife Service, *Commercial Fisheries Review*, XV, 6 (1953), 7–12.

Rachel Carson, *The Edge of the Sea* (Boston: Houghton Mifflin Company, 1955).

John R. Clark and Roberta L. Clark, Eds., *Sea-Water Systems for Experimental Aquariums, a Collection of Papers*, U.S. Fish and Wildlife Service, Research Report 63 (1964).

Donald P. deSylva, *The Live Bait Shrimp Fishery of the Northeast Coast of Florida*, Florida State Board of Conservation, Technical Series No. 11 (1954).

Lee M. Duncan, "Use of Bentonite for Stopping Seepage in Ponds," *Progressive Fish-Culturist*, IX, 1 (1947), 37–39.

Gordon E. Dunn, "Some Features of the Hurricane Problem," *Proceedings of the National Shellfisheries Association*, XLVII, August 1956 (1957), 104–108.

W. T. Edmondson, "Factors Affecting Productivity in Fertilized Sea Water," *Papers in Marine Biology and Oceanography*, *Deep Sea Research*, Supplement to Volume III (London & New York: Pergamon Press, 1955), 451–464.

—— Yvette H. Edmondson, "Measurements of Production in Fertilized Salt Water," *Sears Foundation Journal of Marine Research*, VI, 3 (1947), 228–246.

Henry T. Heg, "Hydraulic Control of Structures for Fish Farming Areas," in *Fisheries, Fish Farming, Fish Management: Conservation-Propagation-Regulation*, I, Washington State Department of Fisheries (1960), 113–120.

N. H. Holtan, "Sealing Farm Ponds," *Agricultural Engineering*, XXXI, 5 (1954), 64–68.

Robert M. Ingle, "The Life of An Estuary," *Scientific American*, CXC, 5 (1954), 64–68.

D. W. LeMare, "Application of the Principles of Fish Culture to Estuarine Conditions in Singapore," Indo-Pacific Fisheries Council, *Proceedings of the Second Meeting* (Cronulla, N.S.W., 1950), Sections 2 and 3, 180–183.

A. W. H. Needler, "Rearing Separate Oyster Spat on Trays," *Bulletin of the Biological Board of Canada*, B48 (1935), 1–12.

M. Nikolic and I. Stojnic, *A System of Oyster Culture on Floating Shellfish*

Parks, Studies and Reviews, General Fisheries Council for the Mediterranean, No. 18 (1962).

Eugene P. Odum, "The Role of Tidal Marshes in Estuarine Production," *The Conservationist*, XV, 6 (1961), 12–15.

W. Armstrong Price, "Oyster Reefs of the Gulf of Mexico," in *Gulf of Mexico: Its Origin, Waters, and Marine Life*, Paul S. Galtsoff, ed., U.S. Fish and Wildlife Service, Fishery Bulletin 89, LV (1954), 491.

G. A. Prowse, "Neglected Aspects of Fish Culture," *Current Affairs Bulletin of the Indo-Pacific Fisheries Council*, XXXVI (Bangkok, April 1963), 1–9.

D. B. Quale, "The Raft Culture of the Pacific Oysters in British Columbia," *Progress Reports (Pacific) of the Fisheries Research Board of Canada*, 107 (1956), 7–10.

John E. Randall, "An Analysis of the Fish Populations of Artificial and Natural Reefs in the Virgin Islands," *Caribbean Journal of Science*, III, 1 (1963).

George A. Rounsefell and W. Harry Everhart, *Fishery Science* (New York: John Wiley & Sons, 1953).

John H. Ryther, "Potential Productivity of the Sea," *Science*, CXXX (1959), 602–608.

Claire L. Schelske and Eugene P. Odum, "Mechanisms Maintaining High Productivity in Georgia Estuaries," *Proceedings of Gulf and Caribbean Fisheries Institute*, Fourteenth Annual Session, 1961 (1962), 75–80.

William N. Shaw, "A Fiberglass Raft for Growing Oysters Off the Bottom," *Progressive Fish-Culturist*, XXII, 4 (1960), 154.

——, *Raft Culture of Oysters in Massachusetts*, U.S. Fish and Wildlife Service Fishery Bulletin 197. LXI (1962), 481–495.

——, "Index of Condition and Per Cent Solids of Raft-Grown Oysters in Massachusetts," *Proceedings of the National Shellfisheries Association*, LII, August 1961 (1963), 47–52.

Harlan S. Spear and John B. Glude, *Effects of Environment and Heredity on Growth of the Soft Clam* (Mya arenaria), U.S. Fish and Wildlife Service, Fishery Bulletin 115, LVII (1957), 279–292.

Margaret Storey and E. W. Gudger, "Mortality of Fishes," *Ecology*, XVII, 4 (1936), 640–648.

Catherine C. Summers, *Hawaiian Fishponds*, Special Publication 52, Bernice P. Bishop Museum, Honolulu (1964).

J. M. Thomson, "Brackish Water Fish Farming," *Australian Fisheries Newsletter*, XIX, 11 (1960), 17–20.

Charles E. Wagner, "Fish Farm Engineering Research," in *Report of Second Governors' Conference on Pacific Salmon* (Olympia, Washington, 1963), 120–122.

Austin Williams, "Substrates as a Factor in Shrimp Distribution," *Limnology and Oceanography*, III, 3 (1958), 283–290.

R. S. Wimpenny, "The Productivity of Temperate and Tropical Waters," in *Proceedings of the Eighth Pacific Science Congress* (Quezon City, 1953), IIIA (1957), 1131–1137.

E. J. Ferguson Wood, "Some Considerations on Estuarine Productivity," in *Proceedings of the Eighth Pacific Science Congress* (Quezon City, 1953), IIIA (1957), 1107–1110.

Kenneth D. Woodburn, Bonnie Eldred, Eugenie Clark, Robert F. Hutton, and Robert M. Ingle, *The Live Bait Shrimp Industry of the West Coast of Florida (Cedar Key to Naples)*, Florida State Board of Conservation, Technical Series 21 (1957).

CHAPTER 4

FOODS, FEEDING, AND FERTILIZERS

Murray H. Amos, *Commercial Clams of the North American Pacific Coast*, U.S. Fish and Wildlife Service, Circular 237 (1966).

Alan D. Ansell, "An Approach to Sea Farming," *Australian Fisheries Newsletter*, XXI (September 1962), 17–18.

——, "Seafood From Industrial Waste," *Sea Frontiers*, IX, 3 (1963), 178–185.

Margaret E. Brown, "Experimental Studies on Growth," in *Physiology of Fishes*, I, ed. Margaret E. Brown (New York: Academic Press, Inc., 1957), Chapter IX, 361–400.

R. P. Casey, J. A. Lubitz, R. J. Benoit, B. J. Weissman, and H. Chau, "Mass Culture of Chlorella," *Food Technology*, XVII (August 1963), 85–89.

Bobby D. Combs, David D. Palmer, J. H. Finucane, and Roger E. Burrows, *Test of Hatchery Foods for Salmon*, 1953 and 1954, U.S. Fish and Wildlife Service, Special Scientific Report: Fisheries 160 (1955).

Harry C. Davis and Robert R. Guillard, *Relative Value of Ten Genera of Microorganisms as Foods for Oyster and Clam Larvae*, U.S. Fish and Wildlife Service, Fishery Bulletin 136, LXIII (1958), 293—304.

—— and R. Ukeles, "Mass Culture of Phytoplankton as Foods for Metazoans," *Science*, CXXXIV, 3478 (1961), 562–564.

W. T. Edmondson, "Factors Affecting Productivity in Fertilized Sea Water," *Papers in Marine Biology and Oceanography, Deep Sea Research*, Supplement to Volume III (London & New York: Pergamon Press, 1955), 451–464.

—— and Yvette H. Edmondson, "Measurements of Production in Fertilized Salt Water," *Sears Foundation Journal of Marine Research*, VI, 3 (1947), 228–246.

F. Gross, "An Experiment in Marine Fish Cultivation. I. Introduction," *Proceedings of the Royal Society of Edinburgh*, 63B (1947), 1–2.

——, "An Experiment in Marine Fish Cultivation. V. Fish Growth in a Fertilized Sea-Loch (Loch Craiglin)," *Proceedings of the Royal Society of Edinburgh*, 63B (1947), 56–95.

——, J. E. G. Raymont, S. R. Nutman, and D. T. Gauld, "Application of Fertilizers to an Open Sea Loch," *Nature*, CLXVIII (1946), 187.

John E. Halver, "Status of Salmon Nutrition Research," in *Report of Second Governors' Conference on Pacific Salmon* (Olympia, Washington, 1963), 94–97.

Shoichi Hashimoto, "Chemical Fertilization of Mullet Ponds," *Proceeding of Hawaiian Academy of Science*, Twenty-Ninth Annual Meeting 1953–1954, Honolulu (1954).

Robert W. Hiatt, "Food-Chains and Food Cycle in Hawaiian Fish Ponds. Part I. The Food and Feeding Habits of Mullet (*Mugil cephalus*), Milkfish (*Chanos chanos*), and the Ten-pounder (*Elops machnata*)," *Transactions of the American Fisheries Society*, LXXIV (1944), 250–261.

Herbert Hindu and Ravenna Ukeles, "Dried Unicellular Algae as Food for Larvae of the Hard Shell Clam, *Mercenaria mercenaria*," *Proceedings of the National Shellfisheries Association*, LIII, August 1962 (1964), 85–101.

Wallace F. Hublou, "Oregon Pellets," *Progressive Fish-Culturist*, XXV, 4 (1963), 175–180.

——, Joe Wallis, Thomas B. McKee, Duncan K. Law, Russell O. Sinnhuber, T. C. Yu, "Development of the Oregon Pellet Diet," in *Research Briefs, Fish Commission of Oregon*, VII, 1 (1959), 28–56.

M. C. Johnson, "A Suggested Inorganic Fertilizer for use in Brackish Water," *Proceedings of the Florida Academy of Science*, XVII, 2 (1954), 119–127.

——, "Preliminary Experiment on Fish Culture in Brackish-Water Ponds," *Progressive Fish-Culturist*, XVI, 3 (1954), 131–133.

Victor L. Loosanoff, Harry C. Davis, and Paul E. Chanley, "Behavior of Clam Larvae in Different Concentrations of Food Organisms," *Anatomical Record*, CXVII, 3 (1953), 586–587.

—— and J. B. Engle, "Use of Complete Fertilizers in Cultivation of Micro-organisms," *Science*, XCV (1942), 487–488.

G. M. Marshall and A. Orr, "Further Experiments on the Fertilization of a Sea Loch (Loch Craiglin). The Effect of Different Plant Nutrients on the Phyto-plankton," *Journal of the Marine Biological Association of the United Kingdom*, XXVII (1948), 360.

Ken McLeod, "Fertilization of Water," in *Fisheries, Fish Farming, Fish Management: Conservation-Propagation-Regulation*, I, Washington State Department of Fisheries (1960), 106–112.

C. H. Mortimer and C. F. Hickling, *Fertilizers in Fish Ponds: A Review and Bibliography*, Fishery Publications, Colonial Office, V (1954).

Herminio R. Rabanal, *The Culture of Lab-Lab, the Natural Food of the Milkfish Fry and Fingerlings Under Cultivation*, Department of Agriculture and Natural Resources, Manila, Technical Bulletin 18 (1949).

J. E. G. Raymont, "An Experiment in Marine Fish Cultivation. IV. The Bottom Fauna and the Food of Flat Fishes in a Fertilized Sea Loch," *Proceedings of the Royal Society of Edinburgh*, 63B (1947), 34–35.

I. A. Ronquillo and A deJesus, "Notes on Growing of Lab-Lab in Bangos Nursery Ponds," *Philippine Journal of Fisheries*, V, 2, 1957 (1959), 99–102.

—— and E. Villamater, "Observations on Artificial Feeding of Bangos Fry, *Chanos chanos* (Forskal)," *Philippine Journal of Fisheries*, V, 2, 1957 (1959), 103–112.

——, E. Villamater, and H. Angeles, "Observation on the Use of Terramycin and Vigofac-Enriched Diet on Bangos Fry, *Chanos chanos* (Forskal). *Philippine Journal of Fisheries*, V, 2, 1957 (1959), 113–124.

D. Z. Russell and A. S. Arguelles, "Soil Types and Growth of Algae in Bangos Fishponds," *Philippine Journal of Science*, LXI, 1 (1936), 1–7.

J. E. Shelbourne, "A Marine Fish-Rearing Experiment Using Antibiotics," *Nature*, CXCVIII, 4875 (1963), 74–75.

R. O. Sinnhuber, "How May Fish Hatchery Foods Needs Be Met?" *Oregon Fish Commission Research Briefs*, IV, 1 (1952), 9–11.

Jose I. Sulit, Ricardo S. Esguerra, and Herminio R. Rabanal, "Fertilization of Bangos Nursery Ponds With Commercial Chemical Fertilizer," *Philippine Journal of Fisheries*, V, 2, 1957 (1959), 125–133.

John W. Westgate, Thomas B. McKee, and Duncan K. Law, "Ranking of Wet Ingredients for Oregon Pellets," *Research Briefs, Fish Commission of Oregon*, X, 1 (1964), 35–40.

H. Wolf, "Colored Fish-Food Pellets," *Progressive Fish-Culturist*, XV, 5 (1953), 182.

Louis E. Wolf, *Fish Diet Disease of Trout. A Vitamin Deficiency Produced by Diets Containing Raw Fish*, Fisheries Research Bulletin No. 2, New York State Conservation Department, Bureau of Fish Culture (1942).

R. P. Wolff, *The Potential Use of Trash Fish Caught by Shrimp Trawlers*, mimeo-graphed, Institute of Marine Science, University of Miami, for Small Business Administration, Washington, D.C. (1963).

E. J. Ferguson Wood, "Some Considerations on Estuarine Productivity," *Proceedings of the Eighth Pacific Science Congress*, III, A (1956), 1107–1110.

James W. Wood and Joe Wallis, "Kidney Disease in Adult Chinook Salmon and Its Transmission by Feeding to Young Chinook Salmon," *Oregon Fish Commission Research Briefs*, VI, 2 (1955), 32–40.

Claude E. Zobell, "The Bacterial Flora of a Marine Flat as an Ecological Factor," *Ecology*, XXIII, 1 (1942), 69–78.

—— and C. B. Felthan, "Bacteria As Food for Certain Marine Invertebrates," *Journal of Marine Research*, IV (1938), 312–327.

CHAPTER 5

IMPROVEMENT THROUGH ARTIFICIAL SELECTION

Anonymous, "Hybrid Stocks and Selective Breeding," in *Fisheries, Fish Farming, Fish Management: Conservation-Propagation-Regulation*, I, Washington State Department of Fisheries (1960), 143–154.

James W. Avault, Jr. and E. W. Shell, *Preliminary Studies With the Hybrid Tilapia*, Tilapia nilotica *and* Tilapia mossambica, FAO World Symposium on Warm-Water Fish Culture, FR:IV/E-14, Rome (1966).

Paul E. Chanley, "Inheritance of Shell Markings and Growth in the Hard Clam, *Venus mercenaria*," *Proceedings of the National Shellfisheries Association*, L, 1959 (1961), 163–169.

A. F. Chestnut, W. E. Fahy, and H. J. Porter, "Growth of Young *Venus mercenaria, Venus campechiensis*, and Their Hybrids," *Proceedings of the National Shellfisheries Association*, XLVII, August 1956 (1957), 50–56.

J. A. Dalziel and K. G. Shillington, "Development of a Fast-Growing Strain of Atlantic Salmon (*Salmo salar*)," *The Canadian Fish Culturist*, 30, December 1961 (1962), 59.

H. C. Davis, "On Interspecific Hybridization in *Ostrea*," *Science*, CXI (1950), 522.

——, "The Influence of Heredity on the Spawning Season of Trout," *Transactions of the American Fisheries Society*, LXI (1931), 43–46.

A. H. Dinsmore, "Effect of Heredity on the Growth of Brook Trout," *Transactions of the American Fisheries Society*, LXIV (1934), 203–204.

Lauren R. Donaldson, "Can the Stocks of Anadromous Fish Be Improved in Quantity and Quality by Selective Breeding?" in *Report of Second Governors' Conference on Pacific Salmon* (Olympia, Washington, 1963), 102–104.

——, D. D. Hansler, and T. N. Buckridge, "Inter-Racial Hybridization of Cut-Throat Trout, *Salmo clarkii*, and Its Use in Fishery Management," *Transactions of the American Fisheries Society*, LXXXVI (1957), 350–360.

—— and Deb Menasveta, "Selective Breeding of Chinook Salmon," *Transactions of the American Fisheries Society*, XC, 2 (1961), 160–164.

—— and P. R. Olson, "Development of Rainbow Trout Brood Stock by Selective Breeding," *Transactions of the American Fisheries Society*, LXXXV (1956), 93–101.

G. C. Embody and C. O. Hayford, "The Advantage of Rearing Brook Trout Fingerlings from Selected Breeders," *Transactions of the American Fisheries Society*, LV (1925), 135–139.

H. B. Goodrich, "Mendelian Inheritance in Fish," *Quarterly Review of Biology*, IV, 1 (1929), 83–99.

Myron Gordon, "The Genetics of Fish Diseases," *Transactions of the American Fisheries Society*, LXXXIII, 1953 (1954), 229–240.

——, "Physiological Genetics," in *The Physiology of Fishes, Volume II: Behavior*, ed. Margaret E. Brown, (New York: Academic Press, Inc., 1957), 432–501.

Dexter Haven and Jay D. Andrews, "Survival and Growth of *Venus mercenaria, Venus campechiensis*, and Their Hybrids in Suspended Trays and on Natural Bottoms," *Proceedings of the National Shellfisheries Association*, XLVII, 1956 (1957), 43–49.

C. F. Hickling, "The Malacca Tilapia Hybrids," *Journal of Genetics*, LVII, 1 (1960), 1–10.

——, *Fish Culture* (London: Faber and Faber, 1962), Chapter 16, "Fish Genetics and Hybridization," 246–259.

——, *Fish Hybridization*, FAO World Symposium on Warm-Water Pond Fish Culture, FR:IV/R-1, Rome (1966).

R. C. Lewis, "Selective Breeding of Rainbow Trout at Hot Creek Hatchery," *California Fish and Game*, XXX, 2 (1941), 95–97.

Victor L. Loosanoff and Harry C. Davis, "Rearing of Bivalve Mollusks," in *Advances in Marine Biology, Volume 1*, ed. F. S. Russell (London and New York: Academic Press, 1963), 1–136.

R. Winston Menzel, "Seasonal Growth of Northern and Southern Quahogs, *Mercenaria mercenaria* and *M. campechiensis*, and Their Hybrids in Florida," *Proceedings of the National Shellfisheries Association*, LIII, August 1962 (1964), 111–119.

——, "Seasonal Growth of the Northern Quahog, *Mercenaria mercenaria* and the Southern Quahog, *M. campechiensis* in Alligator Harbor, Florida," *Proceedings of the National Shellfisheries Association*, LII, August 1961 (1963), 37–46.

C. Millenbach, "Rainbow Brood Stock Selection and Observations on Its Application to Fishery Management," *Progressive Fish-Culturist*, XII, 3 (1950), 151–152.

Richard B. Miller, "Have the Genetic Patterns of Fishes Been Altered by Introductions or by Selective Fishing?" *Journal, Fisheries Research Board of Canada*, XIV, 6 (1957), 779–806.

Carl D. Riggs and Kermit B. Sneed, "The Effects of Controlled Spawning and Genetic Selection on the Fish Culture of the Future," *Transactions of the American Fisheries Society*, LXXXVIII, 1 (1959), 53–57.

K. G. Shillington, "Selective Breeding of Speckled Trout," *Transactions of the American Fisheries Society*, LXIV (1934), 274–275.

Harlan S. Spear and John B. Glude, *Effects of Environment and Heredity on Growth of the Soft Clam* (Mya arenaria), U.S. Fish and Wildlife Service, Fishery Bulletin 115, LVII (1957), 279–292.

L. E. Wolf, "Development of Disease-Resistant Strains of Fish," *Transactions of the American Fisheries Society*, LXXXIII (1953), 342–349.

Kenneth D. Woodburn, "Survival and Growth of Laboratory-Reared Northern Clams (*Mercenaria mercenaria*) and Hybrids (*M. mercenaria* and *M. campechiensis*) in Florida Waters," *Proceedings of the National Shellfisheries Association*, LII, August 1961 (1953), 31–36.

Part III—Presently Farmed Species

Chapter 6

SEAWEEDS

Elmer Yale Dawson, *How to Know the Seaweeds* (Dubuque, Iowa: Wm. C. Brown Company, 1956).

——, *Marine Botany: an Introduction* (New York: Holt, Rinehart and Winston, Inc., 1966).

John B. Glude, *A Survey of Japanese Research on Shellfisheries and Seaweeds*, U.S. Fish and Wildlife Service, Circular 168 (1964).

M. Kurogi, "Recent Laver Cultivation in Japan," *Fishing News International*, II, 3 (1963), 273–274.

H. S. Olcott and M. B. Schaefer, "Food From the Sea," *Food Technology*, XXIX, (May 1965), 92–95.

W. L. Schofield, "History of Kelp Harvesting in California," *California Fish and Game*, XLV, 3 (1959), 135–137.

Hugh M. Smith, "The Seaweed Industries of Japan," *Bulletin of the Bureau of Fisheries*, XXIV, 1904 (1905), 133–165.

Donald K. Tressler and James McW. Lemon, *Marine Products of Commerce*, 2nd ed. (New York: Reinhold Publishing Corporation, 1951), Chapter 5, 47–106.

Lionel A. Walford, *Living Resources of the Sea: Opportunities for Research and Expansion* (New York: The Ronald Press Company, 1958), 121–132.

CHAPTER 7

OYSTERS

Jay D. Andrews and J. L. McHugh, "The Survival and Growth of South Carolina Seed Oysters in Virginia Waters," *Proceedings of the National Shellfisheries Association*, XLVII (1957), 3–17.

Anonymous, "Oyster Farming—Big Potential in New Zealand," *Commercial Fishing*, III (January 1965).

——, "Oyster Farming Interest Grows," *Commercial Fishing*, III (February 1965).

——, "Japanese Cultured Pearls," U.S. Fish and Wildlife Service, *Commercial Fisheries Review*, XXVII, 3, (1965), 129–130.

——, "Off the Bottom Oyster Culture Doubles Yields," *Fishing Gazette*, LXXXII (June 1965), 78–79.

——, "The Pacific Oyster," *Trade News*, XVIII, 10–11 (1966), 13–14.

Robert S. Bailey, *Let's Be Oyster Farmers*, Virginia Fisheries Laboratory, Educational Series No. 8 (1958).

Elinore M. Barrett, *The California Oyster Industry*, Fish Bulletin 123, The Resources Agency of California, Department of Fish and Game (1963).

Tom V. Binmore, "Oyster Spat Raised in Laboratory Has Exciting Commercial Outlook," *National Fisherman/Maine Coast Fisherman*, XLIV (February 1964).

Guillermo J. Blanco, "The Stake (Patusok) Method of Oyster Farming in the Dagat-Dagatan Lagoon, Rizal Province," *Philippine Journal of Fisheries*, IV, 1 (1956), 21–30.

Philip A. Butler, *An Investigation of Oyster Producing Areas in Louisiana and Mississippi Damaged by Flood Water in 1945*, U.S. Fish and Wildlife Service, Special Scientific Report: Fisheries No. 8 (1949).

——, "Growth and Mortality Rates in Sibling and Unrelated Oyster Populations," *Proceedings of Gulf and Caribbean Fisheries Institute*, Fourth Annual Session, 1951 (1952), 71.

——, *Effect of Floodwaters on Oysters in Mississippi Sound in 1950*, U.S. Fish and Wildlife Service Research Report 31 (1952).

——, "Seasonal Growth of Oysters (*C. virginica*) in Florida," *Proceedings of the National Shellfisheries Association*, XLIII (1952), 189–191.

——, "Importance of Local Environment on Oyster Growth," *Proceedings of Gulf and Caribbean Fisheries Institute*, Fifth Annual Session, 1952 (1953), 99–106.

——, "Summary of Our Knowledge of the Oyster in the Gulf of Mexico," in *Gulf of Mexico. Its Origin, Waters and Marine Life*, ed. Paul S. Galtsoff, U.S. Fish and Wildlife Service, Fishery Bulletin 89 (1954) 479–489.

A. R. Cahn, *Oyster Culture in Japan*, U.S. Fish and Wildlife Service, Fishery Leaflet 383 (1950).

Melbourne Romaine Carriker, *Critical Review of Biology and Control of Oyster Drills*, Urosalpinx and Eupleura, U.S. Fish and Wildlife Service, Special Scientific Report: Fisheries No. 148 (1955).

Walter A. Chipman and Paul E. Thompson, *Possibilities for Oyster Culture in Puerto Rico and the Virgin Islands*, U.S. Fish and Wildlife Service, Special Scientific Report: Fisheries No. 9 (1950).

Eleanor Clark, *The Oysters of Locmariaquer* (New York: Pantheon Books, 1964).

H. A. Cole, *Oyster Cultivation in Britain: A Manual of Current Practice* (London: Her Majesty's Stationery Office, 1956).

——, "Benthos and the Shellfish of Commerce," in *Sea Fisheries: Their Investigations in the United Kingdom*, ed. Michael Graham (London: Edward Arnold Ltd., 1956), 139–206.

Luis Costello, "Experiments in Oyster Culture," *Fisheries Research Board of Canada, Translation Series No. 367* (1961).

C. R. Elsey, "Oysters in British Columbia," *Bulletin of the Biological Board of Canada*, XXXIV, 17 (1933), 1–34.

James B. Engle, *Investigations of the Oyster Reefs of Mississippi, Louisiana and Alabama Following the Hurricane of September 19, 1947*, U.S. Fish and Wildlife Service, Special Scientific Report No. 59 (1948).

H. R. Found, "The Atlantic Oyster Industry," *Trade News*, X, 6 (1957), 3–7.

A. V. Friedrichs, Jr., "Oysters Through the Ages," *Louisiana Conservationist*, XIV, 11, 12 (1962), 21–23.

Torbjorn Gaarder and Paul Bjerkan, "Oysters and Oyster Culture in Norway," *Fisheries Research Board of Canada, Translation Series No. 217*, 1934 (1959).

Paul S. Galtsoff, *Introduction of Japanese Oysters into the United States*, Bureau of Fisheries, Fishery Circular No. 12 (August 1932).

——, *The American Oyster* Crassostrea virginica *Gmelin*, U.S. Fish and Wildlife Service, Fishery Bulletin LXIV (1964).

John B. Glude, "The Effect of Man on Shellfish Populations," *Transactions of the Sixteenth North American Wildlife and Natural Resources Conference* (1951), 397–403.

——, "Japanese Methods of Oyster Culture," U.S. Fish and Wildlife Service, *Commercial Fisheries Review*, XI, 8 (1949), 1–7.

——, *A Survey of Japanese Research on Shellfisheries and Seaweeds*, U.S. Fish and Wildlife Service, Circular 168 (1964).

J. L. Hart, *First Supplementary List of Useful Publications for Oyster Farmers of the Maritimes*, Fisheries Research Board of Canada, General Series Circular No. 41 (1963).

Dexter S. Haven, "Supplemental Feeding of Oysters with Starch," *Chesapeake Science*, VI, 1 (1965), 43–51.

C. P. Idyll, "The Pearls of Margarita," *Sea Frontiers*, XI, 5 (1965), 278–280.

Robert M. Ingle, *Oyster and Clam Culture in Florida*, Florida State Board of Conservation, Educational Series No. 5 (undated).

Susumo Ito and Takeo Imai, "Ecology of Oyster Beds. I. On the Decline of Productivity Due to Repeated Cultures," *Tohôku Journal of Agricultural Research* (Japan), V, 4 (1954), 251–268.

Trevor Kincaid, *The Oyster Industry of Willapa Bay, Washington* (Ilwaco, Washington: The Tribune, 1951).

P. Korringa, "The Shellfish Industry in Holland," *Proceedings of the United Nations Scientific Conference on the Conservation and Utilization of Resources*, VII (1951), 47–51.

——, "Recent Advances in Oyster Biology," *Quarterly Review of Biology*, XXVII, 3 (1952), 266–308 and 339–365.

Charles F. Lee and F. Bruce Sanford, "Oyster Industry of Chesapeake Bay, South Atlantic, and Gulf of Mexico," U.S. Fish and Wildlife Service, *Commercial Fisheries Review*, XXV, 3 (1963), 8–17.

Cedric E. Lindsay, *Oyster Culture in the State of Washington*, mimeograph of State of Washington Department of Fisheries Shellfish Laboratory, Brinnon, Washington (undated).

—— and Charles E. Woelke, "Production of Clam and Oyster Seed," in *Fisheries, Fish Farming, Fish Management: Conservation-Propagation-Regulation*, I, Washington State Department of Fisheries (1960), 81–85.

Victor L. Loosanoff, "Challenging Problems in Shellfish Biology," *Perspectives in Marine Biology, a Symposium*, ed. A. A. Buzzati-Traverso (Berkeley and Los Angeles: University of California Press, 1958), 483–495.

——, "New Shellfish Farming," *Transactions of the Twenty-Ninth North American Wildlife and Natural Resources Conference* (1964), 332–337.

——, *The American or Eastern Oyster*, U.S. Fish and Wildlife Service, Circular 205 (1965).

—— and Harry C. Davis, "Shellfish Hatcheries and Their Future," U.S. Fish and Wildlife Service, *Commercial Fisheries Review*, XXV, 1 (1963), 1–11.

—— and ——, "Rearing of Bivalve Mollusks," in *Advances of Marine Biology*, Volume 1, ed. F. S. Russell (London, New York: Academic Press, 1963), 1–136.

G. Robert Lunz, "Cultivation of Oysters in Ponds at Bears Bluff Laboratories," *Proceedings of the National Shellfisheries Association*, XLVI, 1955 (1956), 83–87.

J. G. Mackin, "Status of Researches on Oyster Diseases in North America," *Proceedings of Gulf and Caribbean Fisheries Institute*, Thirteenth Annual Session, 1960 (1961), 98–109.

J. S. MacPhail, "Use of the Escalator in Oyster Farming," *Trade News*, XIII, 3 (1960), 5–7.

Yoshiichi Matsui, "Aspects of the Environment of Pearl-Culture Grounds and the Problems of Hybridization of the Genus Pinctada," in *Perspective in Marine Biology, a Symposium*, ed. A. A. Buzzati-Traverso (Berkeley and Los Angeles: University of California Press, 1958), 519–531.

N. T. Mattox, "Report on the Attempted Introduction of the Virginia Oyster *Crassostrea virginica* Into the Waters of Puerto Rico," *Proceedings of Gulf and Caribbean Fisheries Institute*, Fourth Annual Session, 1951 (1952), 46–48.

Ken McLeod, "Oyster Farming," in *Fisheries, Fish Farming, Fish Management: Conservation-Propagation-Regulation*, I, Washington State Department of Fisheries (1960), 55–62.

Lynne G. McKee, *Planting and Marketing Oysters in the Pacific Northwest*, U.S. Fish and Wildlife Service, Leaflet 52 (1948).

—— and Richard W. Nelson, *Culture, Handling, and Processing of Pacific Coast Oysters*, U.S. Fish and Wildlife Service, Fishery Leaflet 498 (1960).

H. C. McMillin and Paul Bonnot, "Oyster Culture in California," *California Fish and Game*, XVII, 3 (1931), 246–251.

J. C. Medcof, "Oyster Farming in the Maritimes," *Fisheries Research Board of Canada, Bulletin No. 131* (1961).

R. W. Menzel, "Shellfish Mariculture," *Proceedings of Gulf and Caribbean Fisheries Institute*, Fourteenth Annual Session, 1961 (1962), 195–199.

Milo Moore, "Program for Cultivation of Oyster and Clam Areas," in *Fisheries, Fish Farming, Fish Management: Conservation-Propagation-Regulation*, I, Washington State Department of Fisheries (1960), 77–80.

——, Ken McLeod, and Don Reed, eds., *Fisheries, Fish Farming, Fisheries Management: Conservation-Propagation-Regulation* (Washington State Department of Fisheries, 1960).

A. W. H. Needler, "Oyster Farming in Eastern Canada," *Fisheries Research Board of Canada, Bulletin B59* (1941), 1–83.

J. H. Orton, *Oyster Biology and Oyster Culture*, being the Buckland Lectures for 1935 (London: Edward Arnold & Co., 1937).

William Reed, "Farming Under the Sea," *Current Affairs Bulletin of the Indo-Pacific Fisheries Council*, XXXVI (April 1963), 12–14.

— —, *Final Technical Report to Sudan Government on Marine Fisheries Develop-ment and Mother-of-Pearl Oyster Culture, 1958–1964, and Recommendations for Future Development*, Game and Fisheries Department, Ministry of Animal Resources (Sudan Government Printing Press, 1965).

F. S. Russell and C. M. Yonge, *The Seas: Our Knowledge of Life in the Sea and How It is Gained*, 2nd ed. (London and New York, Frederick Warne & Co. Ltd., 1936), Chapter 14, 293–318.

Manuel Sanchez y Sanchez, "The Culture of Oysters in North-Western Spain," Conseil Permanent International Pour l'Exploration de la Mer, Copenhagen, *Journal du Conseil*, XXII, 3 (1957), 197–199.

Clyde S. Sayce and Charles C. Larson, "Willapa Oyster Studies—Use of the Pasture Harrow for the Cultivation of Oysters," U.S. Fish and Wildlife Service, *Commercial Fisheries Review*, XXVIII, 10 (1966), 21–26.

N. B. Scofield, "Oyster Growing in California," *California Fish and Game*, XVIII, 1 (1932), 63–64.

William N. Shaw, "Pond Culture of Oysters—Past, Present, and Future," *Transactions of the Thirtieth North American Wildlife and Natural Resources Conference* (1965), 114–120.

— — and James A. McCann, *Comparison of Growth of Four Strains of Oysters Raised in Taylor's Pond, Chatham, Mass.*, U.S. Fish and Wildlife Service, Fishery Bulletin LXIII, 1 (1963), 11–17.

Hugh M. Smith, "Oysters: The World's Most Valuable Water Crop," *National Geographic Magazine*, XXIV, 3 (1913), 257–281.

R. O. Smith, *Summary of Oyster Farming Experiments in South Carolina, 1939–1940*, U.S. Fish and Wildlife Service, Special Scientific Report: Fisheries No. 63 (1949).

E. N. Steele, *The Immigrant Oyster* (Ostrea gigas), *Now Known as the Pacific Oyster*, (Olympia, Washington: Warren's Quick Print, 1964).

J. M. Thomson, "Oyster Farming," *Commercial Fishing* (New Zealand), I (August 1963), 34–38.

David H. Wallace, *Japanese Oyster Culture*, Oyster Institute of North America, Special Report No. 2 (1959).

— —, "Industry's Appraisal of the Future of the Oyster Industry," *Proceedings of Gulf and Caribbean Fisheries Institute*, Thirteenth Annual Session, 1960 (1961), 135–138.

— —, "Oysters in the Estuarine Environment," in *A Symposium on Estuarine Fisheries*, American Fisheries Society Special Publication No. 3, Supplement to XCV, 4 (1966), 68–73.

Charles E. Woelke, "Introduction of the Kumamoto Oyster, *Ostrea (Crasso-strea) gigas* to the Pacific Coast," in *Fisheries Research Papers*, Washington Department of Fisheries, I, 3 (1955), 41–50.

C. M. Yonge, *Oysters* (London: Collins, 1960).

CHAPTER 8

CLAMS AND MUSSELS

Alan D. Ansell, "Seafood from Industrial Waste," *Sea Frontiers*, IX, 3 (1963), 178–185.

— —, "The Clam and Industry in Britain," *Sea Frontiers*, X, 1 (1964), 48–55.

— —, "Experiments in Mollusc Husbandry," *Fishing News International*, III, 3 (1964), 216–219.

John P. Baptist, *Burrowing Ability of Juvenile Clams*, U.S. Fish and Wildlife Service, Special Scientific Report: Fisheries No. 140 (1955).

David L. Belding, *A Report Upon the Quahog and Oyster Fisheries of Massa-chusetts, Including the Life History, Growth, and Cultivation of the Quahog*

(Venus mercenaria), *and Observations on the Set of Oyster Spat in Wellfleet Bay*, Commonwealth of Massachusetts (Boston: Wright and Potter Printing Co., 1912).

——, "Conditions Regulating the Growth of the Clam (*Mya arenaria*)," *Transactions of the American Fisheries Society* (1913), 121–130.

A. R. Cahn, *Clam Culture in Japan*, U.S. Fish and Wildlife Service, Fishery Leaflet 399 (1951).

M. R. Carriker, "Biology and Propagation of Young Hard Clams *Mercenaria mercenaria*," *J. Elisha Mitchell Science Society*, LXXII, I (1956), 57–60.

A. F. Chestnut, "Growth Rates and Movement of Hard Clams *Venus mercenaria*," *Proceedings of Gulf and Caribbean Fisheries Institute*, Fourth Annual Session, 1951 (1952), 49–59.

——, W. E. Fahy, and H. J. Porter, "Growth of Young *Venus mercenaria, Venus campechiensis*, and Their Hybrids," *Proceedings of the National Shellfisheries Association*, XLVII, August 1956 (1957), 50–56.

H. C. Davis and P. E. Chanley, "Effects of Some Dissolved Substances on Bivalve Larvae," *Proceedings of the National Shellfisheries Association*, XLVI, 1955 (1956), 59–74.

Robert L. Dow and Dana E. Wallace, "A Method of Reducing Winter Mortalities of *Venus mercenaria* in Maine Waters," *Convention Addresses of the National Shellfisheries Association*, 1951 (1953), 15–21.

Irving A. Field, "Sea Mussels and Dogfish as Food," Bulletin of the Bureau of Fisheries, XXVIII, Part I (1908), 241–257.

——, "The Sea Mussel Industry," *Transactions of the American Fisheries Society* (1913), 131–142.

——, "Biology and Economic Role of the Sea Mussel, *Mytilus edulis*," *Bulletin of the U.S. Bureau of Fisheries*, XXXVIII, 1921–1922 (1923), 127–259.

John B. Glude, "Criteria of Success and Failure in the Management of Shellfisheries," *Transactions of the American Fisheries Society*, XCV, 3 (1966), 260–263.

A. H. Gustafson, "Growth studies on the Quahog, *Venus mercenaria*," *Proceedings of the National Shellfisheries Association*, XLV (1954), 140–150.

Robert W. Hanks, *The Soft-Shell Clam*, U.S. Fish and Wildlife Service, Circular 162 (1963).

Dexter Haven and Jay D. Andrews, "Survival and Growth of *Venus mercenaria, Venus campechiensis*, and Their Hybrids in Suspended Trays and on Natural Bottoms," *Proceedings of the National Shellfisheries Association*, XLVII, 1956 (1957), 43–49.

Edwin S. Iversen, "New Float Brings Hope to Mussel Farmers," *Fishing News International*, V, 10 (1966), 49.

B. H. Havinga, "Mussel Culture," *Sea Frontiers*, X, 3 (1964), 155–166.

James L. Kellogg, "The Clam Problem and Clam Culture," *Bulletin of the U.S. Fish Commission*, XIX, 1899–1900 (1901), 39–44.

——, "Observations on the Life History of the Common Clam, *Mya arenaria*," *Bulletin of the U.S. Fish Commission*, XIX, 1899–1900 (1901), 193–202.

——, "Conditions Governing Existence and Growth of the Soft-Shell Clam (*Mya arenaria*)," *Report of the Commissioner for the Year Ending June 30, 1903*, Part XXIX, U.S. Commission of Fish and Fisheries (1905), 195–224.

Cedric E. Lindsay and Charles E. Woelke, "Production of Clam and Oyster Seed," *Fisheries, Fish Farming, Fish Management: Conservation-Propagation-Regulation*, I; Washington State Department of Fisheries (1960), 81–85.

Victor L. Loosanoff, *Soft and Hard Clams of the Atlantic Coast of the United States*, U.S. Fish and Wildlife Service, Fishery Leaflet 13 (1943).

—— and Harry C. Davis, "Rearing of Bivalve Mollusks," in *Advances in Marine Biology*, I, ed. F. S. Russell (London and New York: Academic Press, 1963), 1–136.

Ken McLeod, "Clam Farming," in *Fisheries, Fish Farming, Fish Management: Conservation-Propagation-Regulation*, I, Washington State Department of Fisheries (1960), 63–72.

J. S. MacPhail and J. C. Medcof, "A New Digger for Soft-Shell Clams," *Trade News*, XV, 9 (1963), 3–5.

R. W. Menzel, "Shellfish Mariculture," *Proceedings of Gulf and Caribbean Fisheries Institute*, Fourteenth Annual Session, 1961 (1962), 195–199.

—— and H. W. Sims, "Experimental Farming of Hard Clams, *Mercenaria mercenaria*, in Florida," *Proceedings of the National Shellfisheries Association*, LIII (1962), 103–109.

Curtis L. Newcombe, "A Study of the Community Relationships of the Sea Mussel, *Mytilus edulis* L.," *Ecology*, XVI (1935), 234–243.

—— and Herman Kessler, "Variations in Growth Indices of *Mya arenaria* L. on the Atlantic Coast of North America," *Ecology*, XVII, 3 (1936), 429–443.

F. S. Russell and C. M. Yonge, *The Seas: Our Knowledge of Life in the Sea and How it is Gained*, (London and New York: Frederick Warne & Co. Ltd., 1963).

Osgood R. Smith, *Movements of Small-shell Clams*, (Mya arenaria), U.S. Fish and Wildlife Service, Special Scientific Report: Fisheries No. 159 (1955).

——, John P. Baptist, and Edward Chin, "Experimental Farming of the Soft-Shell Clam, *Mya arenaria*, in Massachusetts, 1949–1953," U.S. Fish and Wildlife Service, *Commercial Fisheries Review*, XVII, 6 (1955), 1–16.

H. S. Spear and John B. Glude, *Effects of Environment and Heredity on Growth of the Soft Clam*, U.S. Fish and Wildlife Service, Fishery Bulletin 115, LVII (1957), 279–292.

A. P. Stickney, "Feeding and Growth of Juvenile Soft-Shelled Clams, *Mya arenaria*," U.S. Fish and Wildlife Service, *Fishery Bulletin*, LXIII, 3 (1964), 635–642.

Donald K. Tressler and James McW. Lemon, *Marine Products of Commerce* (New York: Reinhold Publishing Corporation, 1951), Chapter 27, "The Clam Industry of the United States, 576–589.

Harry J. Turner, Jr., "Report on Investigations of the Propagation of the Soft-Shell Clam, *Mya arenaria*," in *Collected Reprints of Woods Hole Oceanographic Institution*, Contribution No. 462 (December 1948), 3–9.

——, "The Soft-Shell Clam Industry of the East Coast of the United States," in *Collected Reprints of Woods Hole Oceanographic Institution*, Contribution No. 462 (December 1948), 11–42.

——, John C. Ayres, and Charles L. Wheeler, "Further Observations on Predators of the Soft-Shell Clam," in *Collected Reprints of Woods Hole Oceanographic Institution*, Contribution No. 462 (December 1948), 47–49.

——, ——, and ——, "The Horseshoe Crab and Boring Snail as Factors Limiting the Abundance of the Soft-Shell Clam," in *Collected Reprints of Woods Hole Oceanographic Institution*, Contribution No. 462 (December 1948), 43–45.

Frank W. Weymouth, *The Edible Clams, Mussels, and Scallops of California*, Fish Bulletin No. 4, California Fish and Game Commission (1920).

Charles L. Wheeler, "The Soft Clam Fishery of Massachusetts," in *Collected Reprints of Woods Hole Oceanographic Institution*, Contribution No. 462 (December 1948), 51–61.

CHAPTER 9

SHRIMPS

Donald M. Allen, *Shrimp Farming*, U.S. Fish and Wildlife Service, Fishery Leaflet 551 (1863).

William W. Anderson, *The Shrimp and the Shrimp Fishery of the Southern United States*, U.S. Fish and Wildlife Service, Fishery Leaflet 589 (1966).

A. C. Broad, "Environmental Requirements of Shrimp," in *Biological Problems in Water Pollution, Third Seminar, 1962*, ed. Clarence M. Tarzwell, U.S. Department of Health, Education, and Welfare (1965), 86–91.

Edward Chin and Donald M. Allen, *A List of References on the Biology of Shrimp (Family Penaeidae)*, U.S. Fish and Wildlife Service, Special Scientific Report: Fisheries No. 276 (1959).

M. N. Delmendo and H. R. Rabanal, "Cultivation of 'Sugpo' (Jumbo Tiger Shrimp) *Penaeus monodon* Fabricius, in the Philippines," Indo-Pacific Fisheries Council, Proceedings of the Sixth Session (Tokyo, 1955), Sections 2 and 3, 424–431.

Sheldon Dobkin, *Early Developmental Stages of Pink Shrimp*, Penaeus duorarum, *from Florida Waters*, U.S. Fish and Wildlife Service, Fishery Bulletin 190, LXI (1961), 321–349.

Joseph Jay Ewald, "The Laboratory Rearing of Pink Shrimp, *Penaeus duorarum* Burkenroad," *Bulletin of Marine Science*, XV, 2 (1965), 436–449.

Motosaku Fujinaga, "Studies on the Development of *Penaeus japonicus* Bate," *Reports of Hayatoma Fisheries Institute*, I, 1 (1935), 1–51.

——, "Reproduction, Development and Rearing of *Penaeus japonicus* Bate," *Japanese Journal of Zoology*, X, 2 (1942), 305–393.

Clarence P. Idyll, "Shrimp Nursery: Science Explores New Ways to Farm the Sea," *National Geographic Magazine*, CXXVII (May 1965), 636–659.

Malcolm C. Johnson and J. R. Fielding, "Propagation of the White Shrimp *Penaeus setiferus* (Linn.) in Captivity," *Tulane Studies in Zoology*, IV, 6 (1956), 175–190.

G. L. Kesteven and T. J. Job, "Shrimp Culture in Asia and the Far East: a Preliminary Review: *Proceedings of Gulf and Caribbean Fisheries Institute*, Tenth Annual Session, 1957 (1958), 49–68.

Milton J. Lindner and William W. Anderson, *Growth, Migrations, Spawning and Size Distribution of Shrimp*, Penaeus setiferus, U.S. Fish and Wildlife Service, Fishery Bulletin 106, LVI (1956), 555–645.

G. Robert Lunz, "A Salt Water Fish Pond," *Contributions from Bears Bluff Laboratories* (*Wadmalaw Island, South Carolina*), No. *12* (June 1951).

——, "Harvest From an Experimental One Acre Salt-Water Pond at Bears Bluff Laboratories, South Carolina," *Progressive Fish-Culturist*, XVIII, 2 (1956), 92–94.

——, "Pond Cultivation of Shrimp in South Carolina," *Proceedings of Gulf and Caribbean Fisheries Institute*, Tenth Annual Session, 1957 (1958), 44–48.

S. F. Manning, "Trends in American Shrimp Cultivation," *World Fishing*, XIII, 12 (1964), 34–36.

Cecil Miles, "A World-Wide Approach to Fish Culture Improvement," *Proceedings of Gulf and Caribbean Fisheries Institute*, Thirteenth Annual Session, 1960 (1961), 156–162.

D. V. Villadolid and D. Villaluz, "The Cultivation of Sugpo (*Penaeus monodon* Fabricius) in the Philippines," *Philippine Journal of Fisheries*, I, 1 (1951), 55–66.

Gilbert L. Voss, *A Key to the Commercial and Potentially Commercial Shrimp of the Family Penaeidae of the Western North Atlantic and the Gulf of Mexico*, Florida State Board of Conservation, Technical Series 15 (1955).

Ray S. Wheeler, "Cultivation of Shrimp in Artificial Ponds," in *Annual Report of the Bureau of Commercial Fisheries Biological Laboratory, Galveston, Texas, Fiscal Year 1965*, Circular 246 (1966), 14–15.

Austin B. Williams, "A Contribution to the Life Histories of Commercial Shrimps (Penaeidae) in North Carolina," *Bulletin of Marine Science of the Gulf and Caribbean*, V, 2 (1955).

Z. P. Zein-Eldin and D. V. Aldrich, "Growth and Survival of Postlarval *Penaeus aztecus* Under Controlled Conditions of Temperature and Salinity," *The Biological Bulletin*, CXXIX (1965), 199–216.

—— and George W. Griffith, "The Effect of Temperature Upon the Growth of Laboratory-Held Postlarval *Penaeus aztecus*," *The Biological Bulletin*, CXXXI, 1 (1966), 186–196.

Motosaku Fujinaga, *Culture of Kuruma-Shrimp*, Penaeus japonicus, Indo-Pacific Fisheries Council, Technical Paper 59 (Seoul, 1963).

CHAPTER 10

MILKFISH

W. F. Carbine, "Bangos Culture in the Philippines," *Progressive Fish-Culturist*, X, 4 (1948), 187–198.

David G. Frey, "The Pond Fisheries of the Philippines," *Sears Foundation Journal of Marine Research*, VI, 3 (1947), 247–258.

Wallace E. McIntyre, "Philippine Fish Culture," *Scientific Monthly*, LXXVIII, 2 (1954), 86–93.

B. B. Pakrasi, P. R. Dos, and S. C. Thakurta, *Culture of Brackish Water Fishes in Impoundments in West Bengal, India*, Indo-Pacific Fisheries Council, Occasional Paper 66/5 (1964).

T. Gottfried Pillai, "Fish Farming in the Philippines, Indonesia, and Hong Kong," *FAO Fisheries Biology Technical Paper 18* (March 1962).

T. V. R. Pillay and B. Bose, "Observations on the Culture of Brackishwater Fishes in Paddy Fields in West Bengal (India)," Indo-Pacific Fisheries Council, *Proceedings of the Seventh Meeting* (Bandung, Indonesia), Sections 2 and 3, 187–206.

Herminio R. Rabanal, "Pond Culture of Warm Water Fishes, With Special Reference to Bangos or Milkfish Cultivation Under Philippine Conditions," *Proceedings of United Nations Scientific Conference on the Conservation and Utilization of Resources*, VII, Wildlife and Fish Resources (1951), 142–145.

——, "The Elevation of a Swampland Based on the Tidal Datum and Its Importance in Selecting Sites for *Chanos* Fish Pond Projects," Indo-Pacific Fisheries Council, *Proceedings of the Tenth Meeting* (Seoul, 1963), Section 2, 138–140.

——, R. S. Esguerra and M. N. Nepomuceno, "Studies on the Rate of Growth of Milkfish or 'Bangos,' *Chanos chanos* (Forskal), Under Cultivation," Indo-Pacific Fisheries Council, *Proceedings of the Fourth Meeting* (Quezon City, 1952), Section 2, 171–180.

W. H. Schuster, *An Annotated Bibliography on the Culture of Milkfish* Chanos chanos Forskal, Indo-Pacific Fisheries Council, Occasional Paper 52/3 (1952).

——, *Fish-Culture in Brackish Water Ponds in Java*, Indo-Pacific Fisheries Council, Special Publication No. 1 (Bangkok, 1952).

——, *Synopsis of Biological Data on Milkfish*, Chanos chanos (*Forskal*), *1775*, FAO Fisheries Biology Synopsis No. 4 (November 1960).

P. R. S. Tampi, "Utilization of Saline Mud Flats for Fish Culture, An Experiment in Marine Fish Farming," *Indian Journal of Fisheries*, VII (1960), 137–146.

Deogracias V. Villadolid and Herminio R. Rabanal, "Production Problems of Chanos Culture in the Philippines," *Proceedings of the Eighth Pacific Science Association*, Quezon City, November 1953 (1957), 873–885.

CHAPTER 11

MULLET AND MISCELLANEOUS PONDFISHES

H. Al-Hussaini, "On the Functional Morphology of the Alimentary Tract of Some Fish in Relation to Differences in Their Feeding Habits: Anatomy and Histology," *Quarterly Journal of Microscopical Science*, XC (1949), 109–139.

William W. Anderson, *Early Development, Spawning, Growth, and Occurrence of the Silver Mullet* (Mugil curema) *Along the South Atlantic Coast of the United States*, U.S. Fish and Wildlife Service, Fish Bulletin 119, LVII (1957), 397–414.

G. J. Blanco and Pascual A. Acosta, "The Propagation of the Grey Mullet in Northern Luzon Brackish-Water Fishponds," *Philippine Journal of Fisheries*, VI, 1 (1958), 1–5.

Frank T. Bell and Elmer Higgins, *A Plan for the Development of the Hawaiian Fisheries*, U.S. Bureau of Fisheries Investigations, Report No. 42 (1939).

C. M. Breder, Jr., "Interaction Between the Fishes *Mugil* and *Lagodon*," *Copeia*, 3 (1962), 662–663.

Gordon C. Broadhead, *Investigations of the Black Mullet*, Mugil cephalus, *in Northwest Florida*, Florida State Board of Conservation, Technical Bulletin No. 7 (1953).

——, *Growth of the Black Mullet*, Mugil cephalus L. *in West and Northwest Florida*, Florida State Board of Conservation, Technical Bulletin No. 25 (1958).

J. D. Bromhall, "A Note on the Reproduction of the Grey Mullet, *Mugil cephalus* Linnaeus," *Fisheries Journal of Hong Kong University*, I, 1 (1954), 19–34.

John N. Cobb, "The Commercial Fisheries of the Hawaiian Islands," *Bulletin of the U.S. Fish Commission* (1903), 717–765.

Alfred W. Ebeling, "The Dentition of Eastern Pacific Mullets, With Special Reference to Adaptation and Taxonomy," *Copeia*, 3 (1957), 173–185.

Malcolm C. Johnson, "Preliminary Experiment on Fish Culture in Brackish-Water Ponds," *Progressive Fish-Culturist*, XVI, 3 (1954), 131–133.

John D. Kilby, "A Preliminary Report on the Young Striped Mullet (*Mugil cephalus* Linnaeus) in the Gulf Coastal Areas of Florida," *Quarterly Journal of Florida Academy of Sciences*, XI, 2 (1949), 7–23.

G. Robert Lunz, "Harvest From an Experimental One Acre Salt-Water Pond at Bears Bluff Laboratories, S.C.," *Progressive Fish-Culturist*, XVIII, 2 (1956), 92–94.

K. K. Sarojini, "The Food and Feeding Habits of the Grey Mullets, *Mugil parsia* Hamilton and *M. speigleri* Bleeker," *Indian Journal of Fisheries*, I, 1, 2 (1954), 67–93.

J. M. Thompson, "Growth and Habits of the Sea Mullet *M. cephalus* in Western Australia," *Australian Journal of Marine and Freshwater Research*, II, 1 (1951), 193–235.

——, "The Organs of Feeding and the Food of Some Australian Mullet," *Australian Journal of Marine and Freshwater Research*, V, 3 (1954), 1–24.

Aristocle Vatova, "The Salt-Water Fish Farms of the North Adriatic and Their Fauna," Conseil Permanent International Pour l'Exploration de la Mer, Copenhagen, *Journal du Conseil*, XXVII, 1 (1962), 109–115.

Part IV—Potential Species

CHAPTER 12

OTHER INVERTEBRATES FOR FARMING

M. C. Cormier, "The Bloodworm Industry in the Maritimes," *Trade News* (August 1963), 3–5.

Keith W. Cox, "Review of the Abalone of California," *California Fish and Game*, XLVI, 4 (1960), 381–406.

——, *California Abalones, Family Haliotidae*, Fish Bulletin No. 18, The Resources Agency of California, Department of Fish and Game (1962).

D. R. Crawford and W. J. J. deSmidt, "The Spiny Lobster, *Panulirus argus*, of Southern Florida: Its Natural History and Utilization," *Bulletin of United States Bureau of Fisheries*, XXXVIII (1923), 281–310.

Charles E. Dawson, Jr. and Clarence P. Idyll, *Investigations on the Florida Spiny Lobster* (Panulirus argus Latreille), Florida State Board of Conservation, Technical Series No. 2 (1951).

Robert L. Dow, "Changes in Abundance of the Marine Worm, *Glycera dibranchiata*, Associated With Seawater Temperature Fluctuations," U.S. Fish and Wildlife Service, *Commercial Fisheries Review* (August 1964), 7–9.

——, and Dana E. Wallace, *Marine Worm Management and Conservation*, Bulletin of Maine Department of Sea and Shore Fisheries (1955).

Francis Hobart Herrick, "Natural History of the American Lobster," *Bulletin of the Bureau of Fisheries*, XXIX (1911), 149–408.

John T. Hughes and George C. Matthiessen, "Observations on the Biology of the American Lobster, *Homarus americanus*," *Limnology and Oceanography*, VII (July 1962), 414–421.

W. L. Klawe and L. M. Dickie, "Biology of the Bloodworm. *Glycera dibranchiata* Ehlers, and Its Relation to the Bloodworm Fishery of the Maritime Provinces," *Fisheries Research Board of Canada, Bulletin No. 115* (1957).

A. D. Mead, "A Method of Lobster Culture," *Bulletin of the Bureau of Fisheries*, XXVIII, Part 1 (1910), 219–240.

Elizabeth C. Pope, "Can Marine Worms be Farmed?" *Australian Fisheries Newsletter*, XXIV; 2 (1965), 13–15.

Hugh J. Porter, "Zoeal Stages of the Stone Crab, *Menippe mercenaria* Say," Chesapeake Science, I, 3–4 (1960), 168–177.

John E. Randall, "Monarch of the Grass Flats," *Sea Frontiers*, IX, 3 (1963), 160–167.

——, "The Habits of the Queen Conch," *Sea Frontiers*, X, 4 (1964), 230—239.

John D. Riley, "Marine Fish Culture in Britain. VII. Plaice (*Pleuronectes platessa* L.) Post-larval Feeding on *Artemia salina* L. Nauplii and the Effects of Varying Feeding Levels," Conseil Permanent International Pour l'Exploration de la Mer, Copenhagen, *Journal du Conseil*, XXX, 2 (1966), 204–221.

Leslie W. Scattergood, Ed., *Translations of Foreign Literature Concerning Lobster Culture and the Early Life History of the Lobster*, U.S. Fish and Wildlife Service, Special Scientific Report: Fisheries No. 6 (1949).

——, *A Bibliography of Lobster Culture*, U.S. Fish and Wildlife Service, Special Scientific Report 64 (1949).

F. G. Walton Smith, *The Spiny Lobster Industry of Florida*, Florida State Board of Conservation, Educational Series No. 11 (1958).

William M. Stephens, "A Remarkable Animal—The Sponge," *Sea Frontiers*, X, 1 (1964), 15–23.

John F. Storr, *Ecology of the Gulf of Mexico Commercial Sponges and Its Relation to the Fishery*, U.S. Fish and Wildlife Service, Special Scientific Report: Fisheries No. 466 (1964).

H. J. Thomas, "Artificial Hatching and Rearing of Lobsters—A Review," *Scottish Fisheries Bulletin*, 21 (June 1964), 6–9.

W. A. Van Engel, "The Blue Crab and Its Fishery in Chesapeake Bay, Part 1—Reproduction, Early Development, Growth, and Migration," U.S. Fish and Wildlife Service, *Commercial Fisheries Review*, XX, 6 (1958), 6–17.

D. G. Wilder, "The Growth Rate of the American Lobster (*Homarus americanus*)," *Journal of the Fisheries Research Board of Canada*, X, 7 (1953), 371–412.

CHAPTER 13

OTHER VERTEBRATES FOR FARMING

B. R. Allanson and R. B. Noble, "The Tolerance of *Tilapia mossambica* (Peters) to High Temperature," *Transactions of the American Fisheries Society*, XCIII, 4 (1964), 323–332.

Frederick Berry and Edwin S. Iversen, "Pompano: Ecology and Farming Potential," *Proceedings of Gulf and Caribbean Fisheries Institute*, Nineteenth Annual Session, 1966 (1967), 116–128.

A. B. Bowers, "Marine Fish Culture in Britain. VI. The Effect of the Acclimatization of Adult Plaice to Pond Conditions on the Viability of Eggs and Larvae," Conseil Permanent International Pour l'Exploration de la Mer, Copenhagen, *Journal du Conseil*, XXX, 2 (1966), 196–203.

——, "Farming Marine Fish," *Science Journal* (June 1966), 2–7.

E. L. Brannon, *The Influence of Physical Factors on the Development and Weight of Sockeye Salmon Embryos and Alevins*, Progress Report 12 of International Pacific Salmon Fisheries Commission (1965).

Vernon E. Brock, "A Note on Spawning of *Tilapia mossambica* in Sea Water," *Copeia*, 1 (1954), 72.

—— and Michio Takata, *Contribution to the Problems of Bait Fish Capture and Mortality Together With Experiments in the Use of Tilapia as Live Bait*, Final Report of Industrial Research Advisory Council Grant No. 49, to Division of Fish and Game, Territory of Hawaii, (January 1955).

H. J. Campbell, "The Rearing of Salmonids in Some Artificial Nursery Areas in Oregon," in *Report of Second Governors' Conference on Pacific Salmon* (Olympia, Washington, 1963), 136–140.

Pierre Chimits, "Tilapia and Its Culture," *FAO Fisheries Bulletin*, VIII, 1 (1955), 1–33.

——, "The Tilapias and Their Culture," *FAO Fisheries Bulletin*, X, 1 (1957), 1–24.

H. A. Cole, "Farming the Sea," *Geographical Magazine* (London), XXXVIII, (July 1965), 184–194.

Oliver B. Cope and Daniel W. Slater, *Role of Coleman Hatchery in Maintaining a King Salmon Run*, U.S. Fish and Wildlife Service, Research Report 47 (1957).

Umberto D'Ancona, "Fishing and Fish Culture in Brackish-Water Lagoons," *FAO Fisheries Bulletin*, VII, (1954), 147–172.

McFadden Duffy, "Pompano Parade," *Louisiana Conservationist* (February 1961), 2–4.

C. H. Ellis and R. E. Noble, "Calculated Minimum Contributions of Washington's Hatchery Releases to the Catch of Salmon on the Pacific Coast and the Costs Assessable to Hatchery Operations," Washington Department of Fisheries, *Fisheries Research Papers*, II (April 1959), 88–99.

Hugh M. Fields, *Pompanos (Trachinotus Spp.) of South Atlantic Coast of the*

United States, U.S. Fish and Wildlife Service, Fishery Bulletin 207, LXII (1962).

R. E. Foerster, "An Investigation of the Relative Efficiencies of Natural and Artificial Propagation of Sockeye Salmon (*Oncorhynchus nerka*) at Cultus Lake, British Columbia," *Journal of the Fisheries Research Board of Canada*, IV, 3 (1938), 151–161.

E. Ford, *Tha Nation's Sea-Fish Supply*, being the Buckland Lectures for 1936 (London: Edward Arnold & Co., 1937).

F. Gross, J. E. G. Raymont, G. M. Marshall, and D. T. Gauld, "Fish-Farming Experiment in a Sea Loch," *Nature*, CLIII (1944), 483–484.

William Hagen, Jr., *Pacific Salmon: Hatchery Propagation and Its Role in Fishery Management*, U.S. Fish and Wildlife Service, Circular 24 (1953).

Richard J. Hallock, William F. Van Woert, and Leo Shapavalov, *An Evaluation of Stocking Hatchery-Reared Steelhead Rainbow Trout* (Salmo gairdnerii gairdnerii) *in the Sacramento River System*, State of California Department of Fish and Game, Fish Bulletin 114 (1961).

Alister Hardy, *The Open Sea: Its Natural History (Part II) Fish & Fisheries: With Chapters on Whales, Turtles and Animals of the Sea Floor* (London: Collins, 1959).

Charles F. Hickling, "The Cultivation of Tilapia," *Scientific American*, CCVIII, 5 (May 1963), 143–152.

——, "The Malacca Tilapia Hybrids," *Journal of Genetics*, LVII, 1 (1960), 1–10.

——, *Fish Culture* (London: Faber and Faber, 1962).

Thomas S. Hida, Joseph R. Harada, and Joseph E. King, *Rearing Tilapia for Tuna Bait*, U.S. Fish and Wildlife Service, Fishery Bulletin 198, LXII (1962).

A. E. Hofstede, R. O. Ardiwinata, and F. Botke, Eds., *Fish-Culture in Indonesia*, Indo-Pacific Fisheries Council Special Publications No. 2 (Indonesia: Indo-Pacific Fisheries Council, 1953).

Charles O. Junge, Jr. and Lloyd A. Phinney, *Factors Influencing the Return of Fall Chinook Salmon* (Oncorhynchus tshawytscha) *to Spring Creek Hatchery*, U.S. Fish and Wildlife Service Special Scientific Report: Fisheries No. 445 (1963).

Joseph E. King and Peter T. Wilson, *Studies on Tilapia as Skipjack Bait*, U.S. Fish and Wildlife Service, Special Scientific Report: Fisheries No. 225 (1957).

S. Y. Lin, "Fish Culture Project in Haiti," *Proceedings of Gulf and Caribbean Fisheries Institute*, Fourth Annual Session, 1951 (1952), 110–118.

Murray Morgan, "College-Bred Fish for Man's Delight," *Harper's Magazine* (July 1965), 47–51.

A. L. Pritchard and Albert L. Tester, "Food of Spring and Coho Salmon in British Columbia," *Fisheries Research Board of Canada, Bulletin No. 65* (1944).

Gerald L. Paulik, "Are Adequate Techniques for the Evaluation of Artificial Propagation Available?" in *Report of Second Governors' Conference on Pacific Salmon* (Olympia, Washington, 1963), 133–135.

John D. Riley and Graham T. Thacker, "Marine Fish Culture in Britain: III. Plaice (*Pleuronectes platessa* L.) Rearing in Closed Circulation at Lowestoft," Conseil Permanent International Pour l'Exploration de la Mer, Copenhagen, *Journal du Conseil*, XXVII, 1 (1963), 80–90.

Ernest O. Salo and William H. Bayliff, *Artificial and Natural Production of Silver Salmon*, Oncorhynchus kisutch, *at Minter Creek, Washington*. Washington Department of Fisheries, Research Bulletin No. 4 (1958).

Robert E. Schroeder, "Buffalo of the Sea," *Sea Frontiers*, XII, 3 (1966), 176–183,

J. E. Shelbourne, "Marine Fish Culture in Britain: II. Plaice Rearing Experiment at Port Erin, Isle of Man, During 1960, in Open Sea Water Circulation",

Conseil Permanent International Pour l'Exploration de la Mer, Copenhagen, *Journal du Conseil*, XXVII, 1 (1963), 70–79.

——, "Marine Fish Culture in Britain: IV. High Survivals of Metamorphosed Plaice During Salinity Experiments in Open Circulation at Port Erin, Isle of Man, 1961," Conseil Permanent International Pour l'Exploration de la Mer, Copenhagen, *Journal du Conseil*, XXVIII, 2 (1963), 246–261.

——, "Artificial Propagation of Marine Fish," in *Advances in Marine Biology Volume 2*, ed. F. S. Russell, (London: Academic Press, Inc., 1965), 1–83.

——, J. D. Riley, and G. T. Thacker, "Marine Fish Culture in Britain: I. Plaice Rearing in Closed Circulation at Lowestoft, 1957–1960," Conseil Permanent International Pour l'Exploration de la Mer, Copenhagen, *Journal du Conseil*, XXVIII, 1 (1963), 50–69.

Richard S. Shomura, "Effectiveness of Tilapia as Live Bait for Skipjack Tuna Fishing," *Transactions of the American Fisheries Society*, XCIII, 3 (1964), 291–294.

H. S. Swingle, "Comparative Evaluation of Two Tilapias as Pondfishes in Alabama," *Transactions of the American Fisheries Society*, LXXXIX, 2 (1960), 142–149.

J. A. Tubb, "Introduction of Tilapia to Hong Kong," *Hong Kong University Fisheries Journal* (December 1954), 63–65.

Richard N. Uchida and Joseph E. King, *Tank Culture of Tilapia*, U.S. Fish and Wildlife Service, Fishery Bulletin 199, LXII (1962).

H. Van Pel, "Pond Culture of Tilapia," *South Pacific Commission Quarterly Bulletin*, V, 3 (1955), 30–31.

R. S. Wimpenny, *The Plaice*, being the Buckland Lectures for 1949 (London: Edward Arnold & Co., 1953).

Jacques S. Zaneveld, "Laboratory Experiments on Raising *Tilapia mossambica* in Salt Water," *Proceedings of Gulf and Caribbean Fisheries Institute*, Eleventh Annual Session, 1958 (1959), 132–133.

Part V—Problems

CHAPTER 14

DISEASE, PREDATION, AND COMPETITION

William P. Braker, "Controlling Salt Water Parasites," *The Aquarium*, XXX, 1 (1961), 12–15.

Philip A. Butler, "The Southern Oyster Drill," *Proceedings of the National Shellfisheries Association*, XLIV, 1953 (1954), 67–75.

H. C. Davis, V. L. Loosanoff, W. H. Weston, and C. Martin, "A Fungus Disease of Clam and Oyster Larvae," *Science*, CXX, 3105 (1954), 36–38.

Brian Earp, "Progress in Fish Disease Control," in *Fisheries, Fish Farming, Fish Management: Conservation-Propagation-Regulation*, I, Washington State Department of Fisheries (1960), 141–142.

James B. Engle and Charles R. Chapman, "Oyster Condition Affected by Attached Mussels," *Proceedings of the National Shellfisheries Association*, 1951 (1953), 70–78.

John B. Glude, "The Hydraulic Clam Rake, A New Method of Gathering Seed Clams," *Proceedings of the National Shellfisheries Association*, 1952, 163–166.

C. F. Hickling, *Fish Culture* (London: Faber and Faber, 1962), Chapter 17, 260–269.

G. L. Hoffman, *Recommended Treatment for Fish Parasite Diseases*, U.S. Fish and Wildlife Service, Fishery Leaflet 486 (1959).

——, "The Control of Fish Parasites," in *Biological Problems in Water Pollution, Third Seminar, 1962*, ed. Clarence M. Tarzwell, U.S. Department of Health, Education, and Welfare (1965), 283–287.

—— and C. J. Sindermann, *Common Parasites of Fishes*, U.S. Fish and Wildlife Service, Circular 144 (1962).

Andreas Holmsen and Joseph Stanislao, "Economics of Quahog Depuration," *Economics of Marine Resources*, No. 4, Department of Food and Resource Economics, University of Rhode Island, Bulletin 384 (no date).

Sewell H. Hopkins, "Parasitism," in *Treatise on Marine Ecology and Paleo-cology*, ed. Joel Hedgpeth, (Baltimore: Waverly Press, 1957), Chapter 15, Section B, 413–428.

Robert F. Hutton, Franklin Sogandares-Bernal, Bonnie Eldred, Robert M. Ingle, and Kenneth D. Woodburn, *Investigations on the Parasites and Diseases of Saltwater Shrimps (Penaeidae) of Sports and Commercial Importance in Florida*, Preliminary Report, Florida State Board of Conservation Marine Laboratory, Technical Series No. 29 (1959).

Dwayne Nathaniel Kruse, "Parasites of the Commercial Shrimps, *Penaeus aztecus* Ives, *P. duorarum* Burkenroad, and *P. setiferus* (Linn.)," *Tulane Studies in Zoology*, VII, 4 (1959), 123–144.

Victor L. Loosanoff, "Recent Advances in the Control of Shellfish Predators and Competitors," *Proceedings of Gulf and Caribbean Fisheries Institute*, Thirteenth Annual Session, 1960 (1961), 113–128.

——, "Pesticides in Sea Water and the Possibilities of their Use in Mari-culture," in *Conference on Research Needs and Approaches to the Use of Agri-cultural Chemicals from a Public Health Viewpoint*, ed. C. O. Chichester (New York and London: Academic Press, 1965).

——, C. L. MacKenzie, Jr. and L. W. Shearer, "Use of Chemicals to Control Shellfish Predators," *Science*, CXXXI, 3412 (1960), 1522–1523.

——, ——, and ——, "Use of Chemical Barriers to Protect Shellfish Beds from Predators," in *Fisheries, Fish Farming, Fish Management: Conservation-Propagation-Regulation*, I, Washington State Department of Fisheries (1960), 86–90.

G. Robert Lunz and Charles M. Bearden, "Control of Predaceous Fishes in Shrimp Farming," *Contribution No. 36 from Bears Bluff Laboratories* (Wad-malaw Island, South Carolina, 1963).

Ken McLeod, "Predator Control," in *Fisheries, Fish Farming, Fish Manage-ment: Conservation-Propagation-Regulation*, I, Washington State Department of Fisheries (1960), 163–182.

Clyde L. MacKenzie, Jr., "A Practical Chemical Method for Killing Mussels and Other Oyster Competitors," U.S. Fish and Wildlife Service, *Commercial Fisheries Review*, XXIII, 3 (1961), 15–19.

J. G. Mackin, "Diseases of Oysters and their Relation to the Gulf Coast Oyster," *Proceedings of Gulf and Caribbean Fisheries Institute*, Third Annual Session, 1950 (1951), 24.

Carl Oppenheimer, "Disease as a Factor in Natural Mortality of Marine Fish," *FAO Fisheries Bulletin*, VI, 6 (1953), 215–222.

——, "Why Study Marine Fish Diseases?" Conseil Permanent International Pour l'Exploration de la Mer, Copenhagen, *Journal du Conseil*, XIX, 1 (1953), 39–43.

——, "On Marine Fish Diseases," in *Fish As Food, Volume II, Nutrition, Sanitation, and Utilization*, ed. Georg Borgstrom (New York and London: Academic Press, 1962), 541–572.

M. Plehn, *Practicum der Fischkrankeiten* (Stuttgart: E. Schweizerbart'sche Verlagsbuchhandlung, Erwin Nagele, G.m.b.H., 1924).

Robert R. Rucker, "Some Problems of Private Trout Hatchery Operators," *Transactions of the American Fisheries Society*, LXXXVII, September 1957 (1958), 374–379.

——, "Status of Fish Diseases and Relation to Production," in *Report of Second Governors' Conference on Pacific Salmon* (Olympia, Washington, 1963), 98–101.

Wilhelm Schaperclaus, *Fisch-Krankheiten* (Berlin: Akademie-Verlag, 1954).

Carl J. Sindermann, "Diseases of Marine Fishes," in *Advances in Marine Biology*, Volume IV, ed. F. S. Russell (London and New York: Academic Press, 1966), 1–89.

Osgood R. Smith, *Movements of Small Soft-Shell Clams*, (Mya arenaria), U.S. Fish and Wildlife Service, Special Scientific Report: Fisheries No. 159 (1955).

——, John P. Baptist, and Edward Chin, "Experimental Farming of the Soft Clam, *Mya arenaria*, in Massachusetts, 1949–1953," U.S. Fish and Wildlife Service, *Commercial Fisheries Review*, XVII, 6 (1955), 1–16.

S. F. Snieszko, "Therapy of Bacterial Fish Diseases," *Transactions of the American Fisheries Society*, LXXXIII (1953), 313–330.

——, "Selected Topics on Bacterial Fish Diseases," *The Canadian Fish Culturist*, 32 (1964), 19–24.

——, "The Control of Bacterial and Virus Diseases of Fishes," in *Biological Problems in Water Pollution, Third Seminar, 1962*, ed. Clarence M. Tarzwell, U.S. Department of Health, Education, and Welfare (1965), 281–282.

—— and G. L. Hoffman, "Control of Fish Diseases," *Laboratory Animal Care*, XIII, 3 (1963), 197–206.

Yun-An Tang, "The Use of Saponin to Control Predaceous Fishes in Shrimp Ponds," *Progressive Fish-Culturist*, XXIII, 1 (1961), 43–45.

Harry J. Turner, Jr., *Report on Investigations of the Propagation of the Soft Clam*, Mya arenaria, Contribution No. 462 of Woods Hole Oceanographic Institution (1948), 1–61.

Lionel A. Walford, *Living Resources of the Sea: Opportunities for Research and Expansion* (New York: The Ronald Press, 1958).

Charles E. Woelke, "A Newly-Identified Oyster Predator," *Fisheries Research Papers*, Washington Department of Fisheries, I, 2 (1954), 50–51.

CHAPTER 15

MAN-MADE PROBLEMS

G. W. Allen, "Estuarine Destruction—A Monument to Progress," *Transactions of the Twenty-Ninth North American Wildlife and Natural Resources Conference* (1964), 324–331.

Anonymous, "Pollution of Water," in *Gulf of Mexico: Its Origin, Waters, and Marine Life*, ed. Paul S. Galtsoff, U.S. Fish and Wildlife Service, Fishery Bulletin LXXXIX (1954), 555–577.

D. D. Belcher, "Problems in Commercial Trout Production." *Transactions of the American Fisheries Society*, LXXXVII, (1958), 368–373.

C. M. Breder, Jr., "The Problems of Marine Fish Culture," *Transactions of the American Fisheries Society*, LII, (1922), 210–218.

Philip A. Butler, "Effects of Pesticides on Commercial Fisheries," *Proceedings of Gulf and Caribbean Fisheries Institute*, Thirteenth Annual Session, November 1960 (1961), 168–172.

——, "Reaction of Estuarine Mollusks to Some Environmental Factors," in *Biological Problems in Water Pollution, Third Seminar, 1962*, ed. Clarence M. Tarzwell, U.S. Department of Health, Education, and Welfare (1965), 92–104.

——, "Fixation of DDT in Estuaries," *Transactions of the Thirty-First North American Wildlife and Natural Resources Conference* (1966), 184–189.

——, "The Problems of Pesticides in Estuaries," in *A Symposium on Estuarine Fisheries*, American Fisheries Society Special Publication No. 3, Supplement to SCV, 4 (1966), 110–115.

—— and Paul F. Springer, "Pesticides—A New Factor in Coastal Environments," *Transactions of the Twenty-Eighth North American Wildlife and Natural Resources Conference* (1963), 378–390.

Edward Chin, and Donald M. Allen, "Toxicity of An Insecticide to Two Species of Shrimp, *Penaeus aztecus* and *Penaeus setiferus*," *Texas Journal of Science*, IX, 3 (1957), 270–278.

R. A. Croker and A. J. Wilson, Jr., "Kinetics and Effects of DDT in a Tidal Marsh Ditch, Santa Rosa Island, Florida," *Transactions of the American Fisheries Society*, XCIV (1965), 152–159.

H. C. Davis, "Effects of Some Pesticides on Eggs and Larvae of Oysters (*Crassostrea virginica*) and Clams (*Venus mercenaria*)," U.S. Fish and Wildlife Service, *Commercial Fisheries Review*, XXIII, 12 (1961), 8–23.

Ronald Eisler, "Some Effects of a Synthetic Detergent on Estuarine Fishes," *Transactions of the American Fisheries Society*, XCIV, 1 (1963), 26–31.

William R. Gould and Philip A. Butler, "Estuarine Pesticide Studies," *Proceedings of Gulf and Caribbean Fisheries Institute*, Sixteenth Annual Session, 1963 (1964), 78–79.

A. F. C. Greene, "Some State Problems Associated With the Commercial Trout Industry," *Transactions of the American Fisheries Society*, LXXXVII (1958), 365–367.

Robert M. Ingle, "Studies on the Effects of Dredging Operations Upon Fish and Shellfish, *Proceedings of Gulf and Caribbean Fisheries Institute*, Fifth Annual Session, 1952 (1953), 106.

S. F. Manning, "Problems of Sea Farming Aren't All Technical," *National Fisherman/Maine Coast Fisherman*, XLIV (April 1963), 22–23.

——, "Many Factors Figure in Building of Successful Shrimp Pond," *National Fisherman/Maine Coast Fisherman*, XLIV (May 1963), 38–39.

Ken McLeod, "Pollution Control," in *Fisheries, Fish Farming, Fish Management: Conservation-Propagation-Regulation*, I, Washington State Department of Fisheries (1960), 155–162.

N. Reynolds, "Further Experiments on Mussel Purification," Conseil Permanent International Pour l'Exploration de la Mer, Copenhagen, *Journal du Conseil*, XXIV, 3 (1959), 486–493.

Seton H. Thompson, "What is Happening to Our Estuaries?" *Transactions of the Twenty-Sixth North American Wildlife and Natural Resources Conference* (1961), 318–322.

Ravenna Ukeles, "Effects of Several Toxicants on Five Genera of Marine Phytoplankton," presented at 1960 Convention of National Shellfisheries Association. Data given in *Effects of Pesticides on Fish and Wildlife: A Review of Investigations During 1960*, U.S. Fish and Wildlife Service, Circular No. 143, page 21 and Table 10 (1962).

R. W. Williams, W. E. Eldridge, E. M. Mains, and J. E. Lasater, *Toxic Effects of Sulfite Waste Liquor on Young Salmon*, ed. G. A. Holland, Washington Department of Fisheries, Research Bulletin No. 1 (1953).

Charles E. Woelke, "Bioassays of Pulp Mill Wastes With Oysters," in *Biological Problems in Water Pollution, Third Seminar, 1962*, ed. Clarence M. Tarzwell, U.S. Department of Health, Education, and Welfare (1965), 66–77.

Parke H. Young, "Some Effects of Sewer Effluent on Marine Life," *California Fish and Game*, L, 1 (1964), 33–41.

Part VI—Evaluation

CHAPTER 16

SOME GUIDELINES

J. E. Bardach, "Marine Fisheries and Fish Culture in the Caribbean," *Proceedings of Gulf and Caribbean Fisheries Institute*, Tenth Annual Session, 1957 (1958), 132–138.

D. C. Haskell, "Labor to Produce Fifty Tons of Trout: A Time Study," *Progressive Fish-Culturist*, XIV, 3 (1952), 87–97.

O. R. Kingsbury, "Production Statistics and Costs in Relation to Fish Hatcheries," *Transaction of the American Fisheries Society*, LXXX (1951), 148–153.

H. A. Reiger, "A Cost Analysis of Farm Ponds in Tompkins County, N.Y.," *Progressive Fish-Culturist*, XXV, 3 (1963), 144–148.

M. W. Smith, "Fish Ponds in Canada—A Preliminary Account," *The Canadian Fish Culturist*, Issue 29, November, 1961 (1962), 3–12.

A. A. Woodham, Chairman, "Fish Farming—The Intensive Production of Fish for Human Food," in *Proceedings of the Nutrition Society*, XXV (1966), 120–144.

Check list

This check list, adapted from one prepared by the U.S. Bureau of Commercial Fisheries for fresh water fish farming, is presented to guide anyone interested in starting a sea farm. All the points for consideration are interrelated, and decisions on any one of them bears on the others. Unless *careful research is done on each pertinent item before* beginning sea farming, failure can easily result.

To be sure, many of the answers to these questions can only be estimates, but the future fish farmer should answer them as best he can. Also, he should estimate costs high and production low, then determine if the operation still seems to be a good business venture.

After all plans have been prepared and these questions answered to the best of his ability, we strongly advise the future fish farmer to discuss them with experts in fields such as biology, engineering, and real estate, and to observe established sea farms.

I. CAPITAL FINANCING

A. Have you sufficient capital to develop land into farms above the cost of the land? This could cost more than several thousand dollars per acre.
B. Are you financially able to pay a fixed monthly overhead per surface acre, i.e. repairing dikes, cleaning ponds?

II. PHYSICAL FEATURES

A. Impounded areas.

(1) Are adequate sites available for ponds?
(2) Can ponds be located so that they can be drained almost dry?
(3) Is the substrate suitable for water retention, or must some type of sealant be used?
(4) Is there danger of loss of stock due to storms, flooding, or erosion?

B. Open intertidal areas (beaches, tide flats) for shellfish.

(1) Can these areas be purchased outright or leased only?
(2) Are there natural populations of shellfish in this areas?

C. Open intertidal areas and impounded areas.

(1) What is the source of water coming into your pond or intertidal area?
(2) Can predator and competitor species be eliminated easily?
(3) Can you protect your farm from poachers at a reasonable cost?

D. Pollution.

(1) How can you detect pollutants entering your farm?
(2) How can you prevent pollutants from entering your ponds?
(3) What recourse will you have in case of loss due to pollution?
(4) Is a purification unit required for your shellfish farm?
(5) Can technical assistance be obtained for detection of pollution, and at what cost?

III. BIOLOGICAL ASPECTS

A. How much literature is available on the species you intend to farm?
B. What environmental conditions, such as salinity, temperature, and dissolved oxygen are required by the stock? Does your site provide these?
C. What is known of the growth rates of the species you intend to farm? How long will it take to produce stock of marketable size?
D. How much production per unit area can be expected?

E. Diseases.

    (1) Can you provide proper conditions such as adequate clean water and good flushing of ponds to prevent disease?

    (2) What facilities will you have available for detecting diseases as soon as they appear?

    (3) Are parasitologists available to assist in identifying diseases and suggesting proper control techniques? What costs may be involved?

IV. OPERATIONS

A. Source of stock.

    (1) Spawning and raising your own stock.

        (a) How can brood stock be obtained?

        (b) How many brood pairs should be stocked per unit area to produce young for your needs?

        (c) Compare costs of rearing the young to a size where they could be obtained from other producers or from nature.

    (2) Purchasing or fishing for young.

        (a) Are young available for sale or by fishing to stock your farm?

        (b) How much can you pay for young to stock your ponds and still realize a profit?

        (c) Can a reliable supply of young be obtained cheaply by fishing?

B. Feeding.

    (1) What feeds are required for the farmed species as young and as adults? Are these feeds readily available at a reasonable cost?

    (2) At what rate should feeding be done to obtain maximum production?

    (3) If stock will be feeding on natural food coming into the ponds, is the proper food available and abundant year around?

    (4) What method must be followed, and for how long prior to harvest, to eliminate "flavoring" (off-taste from type of food eaten) in your stock?

C. Equipment.

    (1) What equipment is required for your operation to facilitate economic farming?

    (2) Is this equipment available, or must it be custom manufactured?

    (3) Estimate the cost of repairing equipment.

D. Operating costs.

    (1) Calculate as best you can all production and processing costs.

    (2) What will be your costs for overhead and operating?

    (3) Can you compete in the market with the other fish farmers or with the product caught by domestic commercial fishing?

E. Processing market fish.

    (1) Harvesting.

        (a) What will be the most economical way to harvest your stock?

        (b) What is the most desirable time to harvest your stock?

    (2) Transportation.

        (a) What facilities do you have available for handling fish from the harvest to market or processing plant?

        (b) In what condition do you expect to sell your fish? Alive? Processed?

V. MARKETING.

A. Potential markets.

    (1) What markets are available for the species you intend to raise?

        (a) As human food delivered to market or by consumer fishing.

        (b) As bait for sale to sport fishermen.

        (c) As stock (fry and fingerlings) for other farmers.

B. Is processing and packaging a desirable part of your operation?

VI. MANAGEMENT.

A. Can you hire personnel at reasonable salaries to carry out all phases of your operation?

B. What safeguards can be built into your operation against emergencies? Can routine checks be made on chemical aspects of the water?

C. Will any conservation laws restrict your farming operation such as closed seasons when you cannot sell your stock, or minimum size laws?

D. What facilities are available and what costs would be involved to experiment on increasing production, e.g., different foods at various concentrations of stock?

E. What is the cost of maintaining biological and business records?

VII. FUTURE EXPANSION.

A. Is additional area available for enlarging your operations should expansion seem feasible?

B. Can you foresee future use of the land you intend to farm if at some time the operation should become unprofitable? Can the land be expected to increase in value?

APPENDIX

Appendix Table 1

EXAMPLES OF DISEASES AFFECTING MOLLUSKS, CRUSTACEANS, AND FISHES RAISED BY SEA FARMERS

Disease	Remarks
American oyster (*Crassostrea virginica*)	
Malpeque Bay disease	Pustules form, oysters become emaciated. In one epidemic mortality reached 90 per cent.
Haplosporidium sp. (Protozoa)	In one epidemic, 35 to 85 per cent of the oysters died.
Hexamitiasis, "Pit Disease" *Hexamita inflata* (Protozoa)	Occurs in the digestive tract of oysters. "Highly" pathogenic to oysters.
Dermocystidium marinum (fungus)	Parasite which causes oyster mortality in warm weather.
Shell Disease	Probably fungus. It apparently does not cause mortality in this oyster.
Foot Disease	Probably fungus. Not a serious disease.
Nematopsis (Protozoa)	Occurs in tissues. Probably not pathogenic.
Bucephalus haimeanus (Trematode)	Destroys ovaries.
Mytilicola intestinalis (Copepod)	Single specimen reported from Florida.
Pink shrimp (*Penaeus duorarum*)	
Gregarine, *Cephalolobus penaeus*	In stomach of shrimp.
Nematopsis penaeus	In intestine of shrimp.
"Cotton Shrimp" or "Milk Shrimp" microsporidian *Thelohania duorara* (Protozoa)	Found in organs and muscles. Causes softening of muscles, reduction in quality, and mortality.
Larval digenetic trematode *Opecoeloides fimbriatus*	Found in carapace, stomach, heart, and digestive gland.
Larval tapeworms, *Prochristianella penaei*, *P. monomegacantha*, and *P. dimegacantha*	Found in digestive gland (liver) and stomach.
Juvenile roundworm, *Contracaecum* sp.	Found in digestive gland (liver), and stomach.
Java tilapia (*Tilapia mossambica*)	
Trichodina spp. (Protozoa)	Destruction of epidermis and fraying of fins.
"Virus" (?) mortality	
Chilodon spp. (Protozoa)	Destruction of epidermis and fraying of fins.
Infectious pancreatic necrosis	Most serious disease of young *Tilapia*. High mortality of 2- to 3-week-old fry. It is thought to be caused by a virus. Fry show whirling motions, stop feeding, sink to bottom of tank. Body shrinks and head enlarges.
Ichthypthirius ("Ich")	Reported from Hawaii.
Milkfish (*Chanos chanos*)	
External flatworms (monogenetic trematodes)	Crustaceans, bacteria, viri, and fungi attach to milkfish. "Fin Rot epidemic" and "Milky epidemic" reported. No mortality caused by these diseases.

Appendix Table 2

EXAMPLES OF TREATMENT AND CONTROL METHODS FOR USE AGAINST SOME DISEASES CAUSED BY PARASITES[1]

Disease	Treatment	Control
Viri		
Lymphocystis (increase in epithelial cells)	—	Clean, dry ponds and tanks. Isolate diseased fish.
Infectious pancreatic necrosis	—	Clean, dry ponds and tanks. Isolate diseased fish.
Liver-kidney disease (syndrome)	—	Clean, dry ponds and tanks. Isolate diseased fish.
Bacteria		
Furunculosis	Chloramphenicol, tetracycline, and oxytetracycline, 50 to 100 mg/kg of food daily	
Gill disease (fusing and clubbing of the gills)	Roccal or Zephiran (quarternary ammonium compounds) about 2 parts/million of water	
Columnaris (external ulcers or lesions)	Chlortetracycline and oxytetracycline 20–60 parts/million of water	
Fin rot (disintegration of fins and tail)	1 part copper sulfate in 200 water for 1 to 2 minutes	
Fungi		
Dermocystidium marinum in oysters Saprolegnia spp.	Dip fish in malachite green of 1 part in 15,000 water	Avoid crowding of fish and high temperatures. Reduce salinity
Protozoans		
Ichthyophthirius ("Ich") white swellings on body	1 part formalin (40 per cent solution of formaldehyde) in 4,000 parts of water or 2 parts pyridylmercuric acetate (PMA) in one million of water—either treatment should be used daily, for 1 hour	Place fish in rapidly flowing water
Trematodes		
Monogenetic trematodes (external)	Same as for Ich disease	
Digenetic trematodes in intestine	Di-n-butyl tin oxide. Add to food 0·3 per cent	Kills snails (intermediate hosts) with copper sulfate—3 pounds/square foot
Cestodes		
Cestodes in intestine	Same as for digenetic trematodes. For one day	
Leeches		
	Dip of wettable powder of gamma isomer of benzene hexachloride at 0·5 parts/million of water	
Copepods		
Lernaea	Dip of wettable powder as for leeches. Give four treatments at 5 day intervals	

[1] Most of these treatments have been used successfully in fresh water. How useful they will be in salt water is not known. The concentration and action of the chemicals is determined by numerous variables (see Chapter 14).

Appendix Table 3

EXAMPLES OF PREDATORS AND COMPETITORS WHICH MAY OCCUR IN SEA FARMS AND AFFECT PRODUCTION

Soft clam (*Mya arenaria*)

Predators:
    Green Crab, *Carcinides maenas*
    Lady Crab, *Ovalipes ocellatus*
    Blue Crab, *Callinectes sapidus*
    Horseshoe Crab, *Limulus polyphemus*
    Starfish
    Drills
    Ducks
    Gulls
    Flounders and other bottom-feeding fish
Competitors:
    Other clams

American oyster (*Crassostrea virginica*)

Predators:
    Oyster drills
        Urosalpinx cinerea
        Eupleura caudata
        Thais lamellosa
        T. haemostoma
    Conchs
        Busycon contrarium
        B. canaliculatum
        Melongena corona
    Snails
        Odostomia bisuturalis
        O. impressa
        Murex pomum
    Starfish
        Asterias forbesi
    Flatworms
        Stylochus ellipticus
        S. inimicus
    Crabs
        Callinectes sapidus
        Cancer irroratus
        Carcinides maenas
        Menippe mercenaria
        Neopanopeus sp.
    Fishes
        Black drum, *Pogonias cromis*
Competitors:
    Boring sponges
        Cliona spp. (seven species)
    Boring clams
        Diplothyra smithii
    Mud worms
        Polydora websteri
        P. ligni
    Oyster crabs
        Pinnotheres ostreum
    Mussels
        Mytilus edulis
    Fouling organisms
        Slipper shell
        Crepidula spp.
    Tunicates
        Molgula manhattensis
    Sponges
    Hydroids
    Bryzoans
    Ascidians
    Algae

Pink shrimp (*Penaeus duorarum*)

Predators:
  Snook, *Centropomus undecimalis*
  Mangrove snapper, *Lutjanus griseus*
  Sea trout, *Cynoscion nebulosus*
  Red drum, *Sciaenops ocellatus*
  Pink shrimp, *Penaeus duorarum* (cannibalism)
  Plus numerous other carnivorous fish

Java tilapia (*Tilapia mossambica*)

Predators:
  Tilapia (cannibalism-fry on fry and adults on young)
  Pelican
  Purple heron
  Black crowned night herons
  Dragon fly nymphs

Milkfish (*Chanos chanos*)

Predators:
  Fish
  Water snakes
  Frogs
  Birds
Competitors:
  Mullet
  Clupeoids, *Pellona* sp.
  Perches (family Leiognathidae)

Appendix Table 4

EXAMPLES OF CONTROL METHODS FOR USE AGAINST PRE-DATORS WHICH DESTROY CLAMS, OYSTERS, SHRIMP, AND FISH[1]

Predator	*Control method*
Oyster drill *Eupleura* sp. *Urosalpinx* sp.	Chicken wire traps baited with small oysters successful in U.S.A. Trapping not successful in Britain where dredging is employed.
Starfish—on oyster beds *Asterias* spp.	"Mops" dragged over the bottom, oyster dredges, plowing bottom to bury starfish. Quicklime covering bottom at the rate of 570 to 800 kilograms per hectare (500 to 700 pounds per acre).
Crabs—on clam beds *Carcinides* sp. *Cancer* sp.	Baited traps—wire fences—pesticide soaked fish.
Predatory fish in shrimp ponds	Saponin (in tea seed cake). 6 parts per million—very expensive in U.S.A. Cube root powder (Rotenone) 1·5 parts per million (apparently not harmful to shrimp).

[1]Extreme caution should be exercised when attempting to control predators with chemicals. Approval should be sought from government health agencies if any chemicals are to be used for control.

TRADE JOURNALS AND PUBLICATIONS WITH OCCASIONAL ARTICLES ON SEA FARMING

The Fish Farmer, 1378 Livermore Avenue, Livermore, California 94550, U.S.A.

American Fishes and U.S. Trout News, 67 West 900 South, Sandy, Utah, U.S.A.

Feedstuffs, 2501 Wayzata Boulevard, Minneapolis, Minnesota, U.S.A.

National Fisherman, Camden, Maine 04843, U.S.A.

Sea Frontiers, International Oceanographic Foundation, 1 Rickenbacker Causeway, Miami, Florida 33149, U.S.A.

Gulf and Caribbean Fisheries Institute, 1 Rickenbacker Causeway, Miami, Florida 33149, U.S.A.

Oceanology International, Beverley Shores, Indiana 46301, U.S.A.

Commercial Fisheries Review, Superintendent of Documents, U.S. Government Printing Office, Washington, D.C. 20402, U.S.A.

The Progressive Fish-Culturist, Superintendent of Documents, U.S. Government Printing Office, Washington, D.C. 20402, U.S.A.

Fishery Bulletin, Superintendent of Documents, U.S. Government Printing Office, Washington, D.C. 20402, U.S.A.

Special Scientific Report: Fisheries, Superintendent of Documents, U.S. Government Printing Office, Washington, D.C. 20402, U.S.A.

Transactions of the American Fisheries Society, Washington Building, Suite 1040, 15th and New York Avenue, N.W., Washington, D.C., U.S.A.

Western Fisheries, Roy Wrigley Publication Ltd., 1104 Hornby Street, Vancouver 1, B.C., Canada.

Fisheries of Canada (formerly **Trade News**), Department of Fisheries, Ottawa, Canada.

Fishing News International, Ludgate House, 110 Fleet Street, London, E.C.4, England.

Ministry of Agriculture, Fisheries, and Food, Fisheries Experiment Station, Castle Bank, Conway, Caernarvonshire, United Kingdom.

World Fishing, Grampian Press Ltd., The Tower, 229–243 Shepherd's Bush Road, Hammersmith, London W.6, England.

Rivista Italiana di Piscicoltura e Ittiopatologia, Via Oberdan 8, Padova, Italia.

Australian Fisheries Newsletter, Fisheries Branch, Department of Primary Industry, Canberra, A.C.T., Australia.

The Fish Boat, 624 Gravier Street, New Orleans, Louisiana 70130, U.S.A.

In the United States, each coastal state has a Department of Conservation or Game and Fish Commission which can supply publications on sea farming.

ORGANIZATIONS DOING FISHERIES INVESTIGATIONS INCLUDING SEA FARMING

United States Fish and Wildlife Service, Department of the Interior, Washington, D.C., U.S.A.

Fisheries Research Board of Canada, Biological Station, St. Andrews, N.B., Canada.

Institute of Marine Research, Directorate of Fisheries, Bergen, Norway.

The White Fish Authority, Lincoln's Inn Chambers, 2/3 Cursitor Street, London E.C.4, England.

Ministry of Agriculture, Fisheries and Food, Fisheries Laboratory, Burnham-on-Crouch, Essex, United Kingdom.

Government Institute for Fisheries Investigation, Amsterdam, The Netherlands.

Confédération des Industries de Traitement de Produits des Pêches Maritimes, Paris, France.

Institut Scientifique et Technique des Pêches Maritimes, 6 rue Voltaire, Sète (Hérault), France.

Food and Agricultural Organization of the United Nations, Via delle Terme di Caracalla, Rome, Italy, (world-wide fish farming).

Instituto de Investigaciones Pesqueras, Paseo Nacional s/n, Barcelona (3), Spain.

Institute of Oceanography and Fisheries, Rt. Marjana, Split, Yugoslavia.

Sea Fisheries Research Station, P.O. Box 699, Habankim Str. 4, Haifa, Israel.

Fisheries Branch, Department of Primary Industry, Canberra, A.C.T., Australia.

Commonwealth Scientific and Industrial Research Organization, Marine Biological Laboratory, Cronulla, N.S.W., Australia.

Dagatdagatan Salt-Water Fishery Experimental Station, Malabon, Rizal Province, Philippines.

Tohoku Regional Fisheries Research Laboratory, Shiogama-shi, Miyagi Pref., Japan.

The Shrimp Co. Ltd., 418 Marunouchi Building, 2–2–1 Marunouchi, Chiyoda-ku, Tokyo, Japan.

Fisheries Research Section, Japan Fisheries Agency, Kasumegaseki, Ministry of Agriculture Building, Chiyoda-ku, Tokyo, Japan.

Hong Kong University Fish Research Unit, Hong Kong University, Hong Kong, China.

Indo-Pacific Fisheries Council, Regional Office for Asia and the Far East, Food and Agriculture Organization of the United Nations, Bangkok, Thailand.

Central Marine Fisheries Station, Mandapam Camp, Ramnad District, South India.